TUNNELS:
Planning, Design, Construction

Vol. 1

ELLIS HORWOOD SERIES IN ENGINEERING SCIENCE

TUNNELS:
Planning, Design, Construction

Vol. 1

T. M. MEGAW, M.Sc., Hon.D.Sc., F.I.C.E.
Consultant and Former Senior Partner

and

J. V. BARTLETT, C.B.E., M.A., F.Eng., F.I.C.E., F.I.E.Aust., F.A.S.C.E.
Director and Senior Partner
Mott, Hay & Anderson, Consulting Civil Engineers
Croydon, Surrey

ELLIS HORWOOD LIMITED
Publishers · Chichester

Halsted Press: a division of
JOHN WILEY & SONS
New York · Chichester · Brisbane · Toronto

ELLIS HORWOOD LIMITED
Market Cross House, Cooper Street, Chichester, West Sussex, PO19 1EB, England

The publisher's colophon is reproduced from James Gillison's drawing of the ancient Market Cross, Chichester.

Distributors:

Australia, New Zealand, South-east Asia:
Jacaranda-Wiley Ltd., Jacaranda Press,
JOHN WILEY & SONS INC.,
G.P.O. Box 859, Brisbane, Queensland 40001, Australia

Canada:
JOHN WILEY & SONS CANADA LIMITED
22 Worcester Road, Rexdale, Ontario, Canada.

Europe, Africa:
JOHN WILEY & SONS LIMITED
Baffins Lane, Chichester, West Sussex, England.

North and South America and the rest of the world:
Halsted Press: a division of
JOHN WILEY & SONS
605 Third Avenue, New York, N.Y. 10016, U.S.A.

© 1981 T. M. Megaw and J. V. Bartlett/Ellis Horwood Ltd.

British Library Cataloguing in Publication Data
Megaw, T. M.
   Tunnels. – (Ellis Horwood series in engineering science: mechanical and civil engineering)
   Vol. 1
   1. Tunnels
   I. Title   II. Bartlett, J. V.
   624.1'93   TA805

Library of Congress Card No. 81–4111   AACR2

ISBN 0–85312–223–7 (Ellis Horwood Ltd., Publishers)
ISBN 0–470–27151–5 (Halsted Press)

Typeset in Press Roman by Ellis Horwood Ltd.
Printed in Great Britain by R. J. Acford, Chichester.

Table of Contents

8   Table of Contents

Chapter 10 The Channel Tunnel and Seikan Tunnel

Authors' Preface

This book aims to explain the principles and practice of tunnelling, and to show the part which tunnels may play in solving some of the problems encountered by man, as his increasing numbers and activities cause congestion on the surface of the earth and a need for better communications. It is written in the hope that it will prove of use, not merely to those already involved in tunnelling but to engineers and others who may be drawn into a tunnelling project, or who should give consideration to tunnelling as contributing to the achievement of some desirable objective. It should also be of help to the tunnel specialist in its wide scope, and perhaps in giving him an insight into the problems of his colleagues and of the tunnel users.

The very question of what to include within the definition of a tunnel poses a problem. There are three aspects to be considered: form, function, and method of construction. In form it is characteristically an underground cavity, long in relation to its cross-section, and horizontal rather than vertical in alignment. In function a tunnel is typically for passage and conveyance of men and materials below ground. Method of construction might, in a narrow definition, be restricted to boring, by excavation and lining from within. In a wider sense, building or assembling the structure in a trench, under land or water, does produce a tunnel, and whether or not the operation can be called 'tunnelling' the means and the end are included and described in this book. Conversely, caverns or other underground storage may be tunnelled but the end product might not be categorised as a 'tunnel' and the particular features of such structures are not described in any detail. A formal definition of a tunnel might be thus: a passage constructed below ground, or water, of essentially cylindrical form and having its axial alignment not greatly differing from the horizontal; of dimensions sufficient for the passage of a man; excavated and lined from within, or by other means.

This book is not intended to be a catalogue of the latest tunnelling techniques or machines, nor does it contain any novel or advanced theoretical analysis; the extensive bibliography will enable readers to pursue such matters in books, periodicals and professional papers. There is no attempt to deal with costs, any figures for which become so quickly out of date.

In writing each chapter it was apparent that its subject could well fill a whole book by itself, but limitations of time and space had to be respected. It is to be hoped that a reasonable balance has been attained in providing two volumes. In the interests of readability, and usefulness to those seeking guidance on a particular subject, each chapter is largely self-contained. The authors are conscious that some overlapping and repetition has resulted, but believe that to be the lesser of two evils.

The plan of the book is to deal in the first volume with the history and scope of tunnelling and the techniques of bored tunnel construction, with a chapter describing and comparing two major undersea projects, the Channel Tunnel and the Japanese Seikan Tunnel.

The second volume describes other techniques — for tunnels in trench, under land and water — and the ancillary operations of shaft sinking and ground treatment. The relevance of geology is discussed, and there are chapters on the special requirements of tunnels for highways, metros and railways and their ventilation.

Each chapter has a brief bibliography dealing with its subject matter, while a more comprehensive and detailed bibliography is provided at the end of the book. In the text very few detailed references have been given because it is intended that it should be freely readable without interruption, to provide a general grasp of the subject.

Acknowledgements

In collecting material for the book and in writing it we have had invaluable assistance from some London Transport engineers and from many colleagues in Mott, Hay & Anderson. We are most grateful for all the help we have received and in particular thank the following for their very substantial contributions to specialist sections:

> Peter Bishop, Arthur Cairncross, Harry Chanter, Steve Gunn, Harry Hadaway, Ken Henderson, David Henson, Ian Hill, Terry Hulme, Jeff Marshall, Frank Turner.

Over a period of several years John Finch, as librarian, has given invaluable help as have Sue Mill and her willing colleagues in typing and retyping the manuscripts.

Illustrations used in the text have been derived from many sources, named where possible in the captions, and we acknowledge with thanks the assistance of those contributing.

1

History

1.1 FUNDAMENTAL OPERATIONS

The fundamental operations of tunnelling are:
(1)   Survey
(2)   Excavation of ground
(3)   Immediate support of ground
(4)   Permanent support of ground
(5)   Management of water
    Where all conditions are favourable, construction becomes relatively simple, but the history of tunnelling shows how often unexpected physical conditions have made a project impossible as originally conceived, and ultimately only achievable, after years of immense effort, by virtue of new methods.

1.1.1 Relationship to mining

Tunnelling as an art has its origins in the mists of the past. Its relationship to mining is very close, but there are important distinctions to be made. The primary objective in mining is to dig out valuable minerals: after they are worked out the access passages and other voids are no longer of use, and in that sense all mining is temporary. The time may be very long—salt is still mined at Hallstatt where the deposits were worked as early as 2500 B.C. In contrast, the primary objective in tunnelling is to provide a passage or other space for permanent use, which must remain safely available for its purpose indefinitely. In addition to provision of passages for men or materials tunnels are constructed for storage, for installation of plant and, throughout the ages, for attack and defence. In size, transport tunnels must be as large as necessary for traffic, whereas mining passages will rarely exceed dimensions of about 3 m.
    Another distinction to be drawn is that the organisation for tunnel construction is usually temporary; there is no settled community, and no continuity of construction. A team is built up, changing as the phases of construction develop, and is finally dispersed. Achievement of the objective is the end;

operation of the tunnel calls for entirely different men and skills. In mining, by contrast, a permanent community is established for the life of the mine, which may extend over several generations.

Most of the technology is the same for tunnelling and for mining and much is to be gained by interchange of information and ideas, but the differences are important. Attempts to employ coal miners in constructing London's underground in London Clay in the 1930's were said to be unsatisfactory because the coal mining tradition was to put in props but let the weight of the ground come down on to them, whereas the tunnelling technique was to wedge up to take the maximum possible weight immediately so as to minimise settlement and disturbances of the overlying strata.

It is also relevant that in tunnel construction the geometry and in particular the line must be pre-determined and followed closely from portal to portal, whereas in some types of mining the whole area of a stratum is to be excavated leaving only the necessary support to control subsidence, and in others an ore-bearing lode is followed wherever it may lead, excavating no more barren rock than essential for access. In all cases accurate survey is important.

The difference may be summarised paradoxically as permanent work by a temporary organisation contrasted with evanescent work by a permanent community.

1.2 ANCIENT MINES AND TUNNELS

1.2.1 Prehistoric mining

Despite the attempt to discriminate between tunnelling and mining, the earliest history must be traced through mining operations, first in extension of surface working for flint and later in the search for copper and other metals. The first tunnels in the narrower sense, excluding mining, may have been for supply of water to towns and other communities. Flint mines, such as Grimes Graves in Norfolk, were developed also in Belgium, northern France, Portugal, and elsewhere, dating back beyond 2000 B.C.; picks made from deer antlers were used, with flint axes and bone shovels. Salt mining at Halstatt from 2500 B.C. has already been mentioned and about 1000 B.C. those mines supported a very prosperous Bronze Age and early Iron Age community. Bronze picks and wooden mallets and shovels were initially used, but the use of iron was developed.

Copper, not merely native, but reduced by smelting from oxides was used by the Sumerians in the 4th millennium B.C., the ores being mined in the mountains of Armenia. Some time in that era adits were driven to follow the outcrops into the mountain-sides. Egypt of the Pharaohs obtained copper from Sinai and adjacent areas in the 3rd millennium B.C. Stone tools and wooden wedges expanded by wetting were used to drive up to 50 metres into the rock. Later, Egypt obtained its copper from Cyprus, named after its copper, and Armenia, and mined gold from deep shafts by slave and prisoner labour, mainly in the Nubian desert. 'Fire setting' seems to have been employed to mine hard rock.

Tin was essential for the production of bronze, which is an alloy of copper and tin and which is so much harder than natural copper that it competed with flint for tools and weapons and superseded it for many purposes. Phoenician sailors and traders produced supplies from Cadiz and from Cornwall before 1000 B.C. Cartagena was an important centre for silver mining.

Iron working seems to have originated about 1400 B.C. in Armenia, under Hittite domination, but it was not until about 1000 B.C. that knowledge spread over a wide area, effecting the transformation of the Bronze Age into the Iron Age.

1.2.2 Ancient tunnels

Water supplies provide further early examples of tunnels, and perhaps may be considered to mark the beginning of tunnelling as distinct from mining. Rock hewn temples and underground burial chambers in many parts of the world also exemplify methods and uses of underground excavation.

Extensive canal building was carried out in the 'Fertile Crescent' (Egypt, Palestine, Syria, Iraq) in ancient times for water supply and irrigation. A canal must follow a level course, and the need to pass a ridge entails either a long diversion round the end of the ridge, or a deep cutting, or a tunnel through the ridge. Sometimes the tunnel is the only possible solution if water from a mountain is to be conducted to a city in the plains. Where the supply of pure water is limited there are added advantages in carrying it underground which reduces evaporation and preserves it from surface contamination. Another reason for water tunnels was defensive: to preserve the water supply to a walled city under siege.

An early example from Greece of tunnelling through a ridge is the work of Eupalinus of Megara in 687 B.C. on the island of Samos. The tunnel, which was lined, was about 1000 m long and carried water through clay pipes laid in a trench cut in the floor.

The 'qanaats' of Iran and surrounding areas are small tunnels carrying water underground from hillside springs to towns or villages. Excavated normally from shafts at centres of about 50 m, their course across the desert is marked by the mounds of spoil at the shafts. Some of the shafts are gently inclined to provide easy access and the qanaats may terminate in deep wells.

Ancient strategic aqueducts are typified by the Siloam tunnel of Jerusalem excavated about 700 B.C. by King Hezekiah when an Assyrian siege was in prospect. The bible record in II Kings 20.20 reads, 'And the rest of the acts of Hezekiah, and all his might, and how he made a pool, and a conduit, and brought water into the city, are they not written in the book of the chronicles of the kings of Judah'.

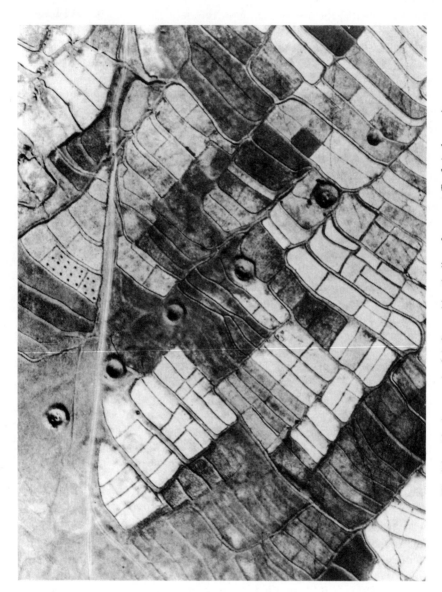

Fig. 1.1 – Air photograph of shafts marking the line of a qanaat (Prof. Ambraseys)

Examples of tunnelling from the classical periods of Greece and Rome are numerous, perhaps mostly for aqueducts. In Rome, water supplies were brought into the city from springs in the surrounding hills; over the period from 312 B.C. until about A.D. 52 aqueducts totalling some 350 km were built, almost wholly in tunnel, the system being based on gravity flow.

The Romans also used tunnelling for drainage and reclamation of marshes, and occasionally for roads, of which an outstanding example was the Pausilippo tunnel built in 36 B.C. between Naples and Pozzuoli which was about 8 m wide x 10 m high x 1740 m in length.

After the collapse of Roman power few major works were undertaken for many centuries. Tunnelling in mediaeval times became largely the art of the sappers in attacking walled fortresses, used also perhaps for the romantic underground passages reported to exist in many castles and monasteries. Civil engineering was very much in abeyance until stimulated by the needs of the canal builders.

1.3 CANALS

Except in very flat alluvial plains, canal engineers always face two problems to which tunnelling is relevant: changes of level and sufficient supply of water. Canal locks, by which barges can be transferred from one level to another, were the usual, though not the only solution of the first problem, but at the expense of demanding a supply of water for their operation. If a canal has to pass across a ridge of high ground water supply at the summit is likely to be scarce or non-existent unless pumps are used, while a flight of locks on each side becomes necessary if the canal is to follow the ground surface.

This is the situation where tunnelling may offer a solution which at once saves construction of locks with their demand for water and delays in transport and makes water supply much easier; by tunnelling, the 'summit level' may be lowered within reach of streams, and indeed the tunnel itself may tap underground streams. Passage through the tunnel, although it may be slow, is still likely to save much time and water compared with passage up and down again through flights of locks.

The pioneer tunnel of the Canal Age was constructed on the Canal du Midi, built in the years 1666-81 to connect the Atlantic to the Mediterranean and to save long, costly, and hazardous journeys round the Iberian peninsula and through the Straits of Gibraltar. It was a vast enterprise comprising 240 km of canal with over one hundred locks and with a summit level at nearly 200 m above sea level. Water was supplied from reservoirs built in the Montagnes Noires 20 km away. The project was promoted and executed by Pierre-Paul Riquet with the support of Louis XIV and his Minister of Finance, Colbert. The tunnel was not on the summit level but under a ridge over 100 km further east, near Béziers. The tunnel, 6.5 m x 8 m x 157 m long, was constructed in the years 1679-81. It was left unlined until 1691. Gunpowder was used in its construction, the first recorded use in tunnelling, although it seems probable that sappers, in their military capacity, had experimented earlier.

Before the days of gunpowder the nearest thing to explosives was fire setting, where the rock was heated up by burning quantities of wood and was then quenched with cold water, which opened up cracks and split off lumps. This method seems to have been used in ancient Egypt.

In England water transport became of increasing importance in the 16th century and was developed, first by way of improvement of navigable rivers, and then in the 18th century by canal construction, which indeed largely created civil engineering as a profession. Transport of coal and all heavy cargoes was almost entirely by water and the value of the river systems of the Severn, Thames, Mersey, Trent and others was enormously enhanced by construction of connecting canals, which of course had the typical summit problems, frequently resolved by tunnelling.

The first canal tunnels were on the Worsley—Manchester canal built by Brindley for the Duke of Bridgewater to carry coal direct from the mines at Worsley, some six miles west of Manchester, to the city. The canal was tunnelled into the sandstone at the colliery for about a mile, where later some forty miles of tunnels on various levels were developed. It was carried across the river Irwell on an aqueduct 12 m above the river and terminated again in a tunnel and vertical shaft under Castle Hill in Manchester. The canal, on a level throughout, and without locks, was opened in 1761 and resulted in the price of coal in Manchester being halved.

Brindley also built the Trent—Mersey, or Grand Trunk, canal 146 km long, which linked these rivers, and the Staffordshire—Worcestershire canal, 75 km long, connecting to the Severn at Stourport. This Grand Trunk canal was sponsored and strongly supported by Josiah Wedgewood of pottery fame. The Harecastle tunnel, 2090 m in length, carrying the canal at its summit through the ridge north of Stoke-upon-Trent, was a major undertaking. There were four other tunnels on the route including one of 1135 m at Preston-on-the-Hill, near Runcorn; there the canal joined the Duke of Bridgewater's canal leading down to the Mersey by a flight of locks. The Harecastle tunnel proved difficult. It was driven, with the use of gunpowder, from a number of shafts; springs were struck which flooded the works, and a drainage heading in advance of the work proved necessary. In contrast to the other four tunnels, which were 4.1 m wide x 5.3 m high, this tunnel was only 2.2 m x 3.6 m, and in operation a one way system had to be worked, the barges being 'legged' through, which took two hours. In legging, men lay on their backs on the barge deck and pushed the barge through by their feet against the tunnel roof. The canal took eleven years to build, largely because of this tunnel, and was not completed until 1777, five years after Brindley's death. The canal was a great success in reducing transport costs between Liverpool and the Potteries, but this 'single lane' tunnel remained a bottleneck and was not duplicated until 50 years later, when Telford engineered a new tunnel, also as a one way tunnel, but 4.3 m x 4.9 m, including a 1.5 m towpath. Fifteen shafts were sunk for the construction and sixteen cross headings to the old tunnel. Difficulties were again encountered with running sand and with extremely hard Millstone Grit, but the work was completed in three years, including brick lining, and without any loss of life. The tunnel is still open, but principally for recreational use; extensive repair work including concrete lining and roof bolting has been necessary in 1974.

Following Brindley's example, canals proliferated throughout England with their quota of tunnels. There was a boom in promotion of schemes with its peak in the years 1793-4. Development continued until the Railway Age. A notable tunnel was at Standedge about five miles south west of Huddersfield where the Pennine ridge was pierced by a tunnel 5000 m in length and at a height of 194 m above sea level. Work started in 1794 under Outram by sinking shafts, one of which was 70 m deep; the tunnel was 3.0 m wide x 5.5 m high and had four 'wides' within its length to provide passing places. Much of the excavation was through hard Millstone Grit and it took seventeen years to complete, being opened in 1811. Many lives were lost.

Mention may also be made of the Sapperton tunnel (1789), 3 km long, which was the summit level of the Thames–Severn canal, driven through the Oolite limestone strata into which it lost water. Telford's work on the second Harecastle tunnel has already been described. He had earlier been responsible for the Chirk and Whitehouses tunnels on the Ellesmere canal, in the vicinity of his famous Pont Cysyllte aqueduct—'the stream in the sky'. Late in his life, in 1830, the Cowley tunnel, driven under his direction on the Birmingham–Liverpool Junction canal, ran into such trouble that most of its length had to be opened out into a deep cutting and the tunnel finished up 74 m in length instead of the planned 630 m.

On the continent of Europe canal construction also demanded tunnels. Napoleon's St. Quentin canal had three major tunnels in its 100 km length. The Tronquoy tunnel, 1075 m long and 8 m wide, was driven through sandy gravel in 1803 by construction of the brick arch in a sequence of headings working upwards prior to removal of the 'dumpling'. This technique later developed into the 'German System'. The Riqueval tunnel, 5550 m long, was constructed simultaneously, in less difficult ground. A section of the canal was opened in 1810 and it was extended in 1822 by driving of the Noirieu tunnel, 12000 m long. The Canal de Bourgogne, started in 1775 and completed in 1825, is 245 km long and includes a 3 km tunnel. The Canal de la Marne au Rhin, 300 km long, built 1838-53, includes the 4 km Mauvages tunnel and four others.

In Belgium in 1828 the Charleroi Canal had to be tunnelled through a hill with quicksand, for which was developed the 'Belgian System', in which a small top heading is driven first and then enlarged progressively to allow the top half to be timbered and the arched lining built in brick or masonry, followed by underpinning of the sides in trench and final excavation of the 'dumpling' and construction of the invert. The canal has been modernised and the tunnel opened out and an inclined plane with a rise of 70 m has been provided.

American canal building also developed at the end of the 18th century. The first tunnel was driven in 1818 on the Schuylkill canal, its dimensions being 6 m x 5.5 m x 137 m long. It was opened out in 1855. The second American canal tunnel was the Lebanon tunnel at the summit of the Union canal, excavated in 1824–26 to dimensions 5.5 m x 4.6 m x 220 m.

After the coming of the railways few canal tunnels were built, but the latest and largest is the Rove canal tunnel providing a connection between Marseilles and the Rhone. It is one of the largest of all bores being 22 m x 15 m x 7.3 km through limestone. It was started in 1911 but delayed by the First World War and it was not completed and opened until 1928.

1.4 BRUNEL'S THAMES TUNNEL

Between the Canal Age and the Railway Age came the construction of Brunel's great Thames Tunnel, the first to pass under a tidal river and the first shield driven tunnel. It was in some respects far ahead of its time and its successful completion demanded so much time and effort and personal supervision that no similar enterprise was undertaken for nearly half a century.

Brunel's concept of a shield, in certain aspects inspired by the boring methods of the shipworm, *Teredo Navalis*, was covered by two patents in 1818 and was applied to the proposed dual carriage-way Thames crossing between Rotherhithe and Wapping, started in 1825 by the Thames Tunnel Company. An earlier attempt in this vicinity, first by Vazie and then by Trevithick in 1807 to drive a heading, or drift, as a preliminary to enlargement to a 5 m diameter tunnel had failed in the soft ground.

The fundamental problems of excavation and temporary support outlined at the beginning of this chapter were described by Brunel in his patent specification: 'I shall premise by observing that the chief difficulties to be overcome in the extension of tunnels under the beds of great rivers lie in the insufficiency of the means of forming the excavation. The great desideratum, therefore, consists of finding efficacious means of opening the ground in such a manner that no more earth shall be displaced than is to be filled by the shell or body of the tunnel, and that the work shall be effected with certainty'. . . . 'In the formation of a drift under the bed of a river, too much attention cannot be paid to the mode of securing the excavation against the breaking down of the earth . . . I propose to resort to the use of a casing or a cell, intended to be forced forward . . .'.

Brunel's shield was designed to provide:

(1) A skin, covering the ground on all sides. This was done by means of iron staves sliding forward as the excavation was advanced, and supported by iron frames.

(2) Means to support the face and yet provide access for excavation. The iron frames carried horizontal oak poling boards 150 mm x 75 mm in section, supported by screw jacks which could be moved forward one at a time as the small area of face open was excavated.

(3) Means to move the shield forward into the excavated space and then to build the permanent lining at the rear. The framework of the shield consisted of twelve 3-tier frames, supporting the staves at sides and top and providing working cells, each occupied by one miner; these frames were propelled forward one at a time by jacking from the completed arch brickwork.

The whole shield was 11.4 m wide x 6.8 m high x 2.7 m long. It was first assembled at the bottom of a 15 m diameter shaft, and then its somewhat complex mechanisms had to be operated by initially unskilled labour, in dirty, wet and dangerous conditions. As well as troubles in ensuring proper use of the various devices there were difficulties in keeping the shield on line, but in good clay it functioned satisfactorily. The hope of at least a roof of sound clay was not realised, and management of water became the main tunnelling problem. This is of course the fifth fundamental operation noted at the beginning of this chapter. The water softened the silt and clay and came in ever increasing volume: it was accompanied by methane causing minor explosions and by sulphureted hydrogen and other pollutants causing illness and death to the

Fig. 1.2(a) – Brunel's Shield. Longitudinal section of Brunel's Thames Tunnel showing: (i) excavation in progress in the shield at the face, (ii) brick lining built close behind shield, (iii) screw jacks at top and bottom thrusting the shield forward from the brickwork.

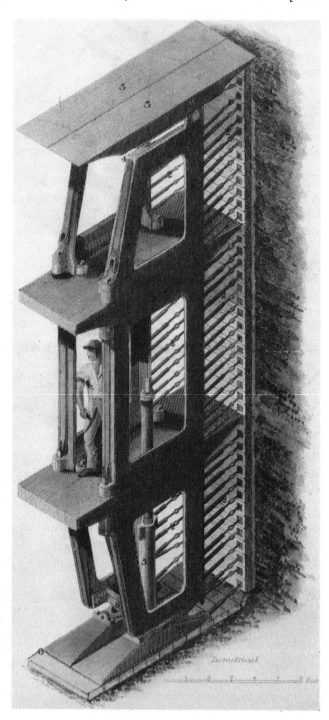

Fig. 1.2(b) – Brunel's Shield
One of the twelve divisions
of the shield, showing: (i)
the poling boards at the
face supported by screw
jacks, (ii) the top staves,
providing roof support,
(iii) the bottom shoes, resting on timbers.

face workers. Five times the whole tunnel was inundated from the river above and five times was reclaimed by dumping clay and gravel in the river bed and pumping out the water and digging out the debris. Tunnelling had started at the end of 1825, but after the second inundation, which was in January 1828 when 184 m out of 366 m had been completed, work was stopped for lack of capital and was not resumed until a government loan was granted at the end of 1834. A year was spent in replacing the shield with an improved structure and another five and a half years from March 1836 until November 1841 was required to finish the tunnelling. The tunnel was opened in 1842 but only to pedestrians as no money was available for carriageway access. It was ultimately sold in 1865 to the East London Railway Company who constructed the necessary approaches to make it a railway link through which London Transport trains still run regularly.

Sir Marc Isambard Brunel himself took a day-to-day part in the construction and controlled every detail. His even more famous son, Isambard Kingdom Brunel, was Resident Engineer in the first half up to the stoppage in 1828, but when work was resumed in 1835 he was no longer available as he had other interests, including the Box tunnel on the Great Western Railway.

1.5 RAILWAYS

Modern railway construction started with the Liverpool and Manchester Railway, opened in 1830, and involved tunnelling from the very beginning. Loco haulage terminated at Edge Hill in Liverpool where the railway faced a formidable barrier of high ground, and from that point two tunnels were driven: (1) a short tunnel of 265 m rising to Crown Street, up which passenger coaches were rope hauled to the surface, and (2) the long Wapping tunnel for goods traffic descending for 1930 m down a gradient of 1 in 48 to the docks. The tunnel was 6.7 m x 4.9 m in section. Shortly after opening, the railway was extended in tunnel from Edge Hill to its present terminus at Lime Street. This tunnel was 1852 m long and ran down a gradient of 1 in 97. It was worked by rope haulage until 1870 when loco working combined with artificial ventilation by an extract fan was introduced. About 1866 the tunnel was opened out into a cutting and widened to take four tracks. These tunnels were mainly in Triassic sandstone which stood up well, only requiring to be supported over parts of their length.

The enormous spread of railway construction in Great Britain by competing lines for much of the 19th century brought its quota of tunnels, mostly to minimise gradients and to obtain direct routes. Between 1830 and 1890 over fifty railway tunnels exceeding one mile (1.61 km) in length were completed, 25 of them between 1838 and 1850. Most were through hills, and in many water was the greatest enemy, inundating shafts, washing out sand, or softening shale. Exceptionally, the Mersey Railway Tunnel (1879–88) and the Severn Tunnel (1873–86) were beneath tidal rivers.

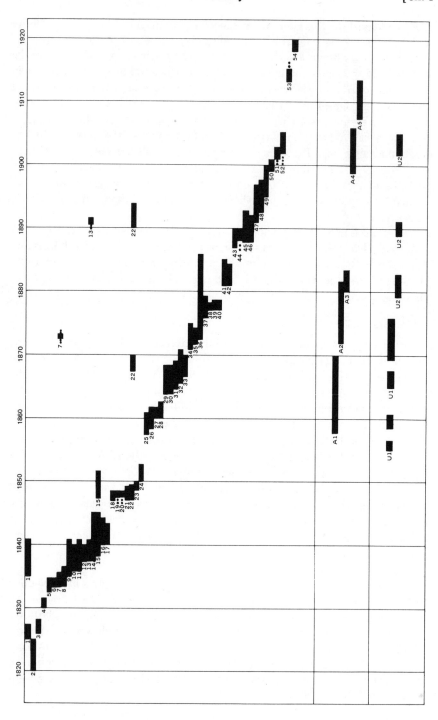

Dates	Name	L'gth m.	Notes
1 1825–43	Thames Tunnel	459	Brunel's tunnel. Converted to rail
2 1820–24	Strood	2130	Canal tunnel converted to rail
3 1826–29	Wapping	2057	Liverpool terminus. Rope haul
4 1830–32	Glenfield	1633	Leicester. Robert Stephenson
5 1833–36	Lime Street	1852	Liverpool terminus. Later opened out
6 1834–36	Primrose Hill	1081	London to Birmingham. George Stephenson
7 1834–37	Watford	1660	Watford duplicated about 1873
8 1834–38	Kilsby	2218	London to Bristol. I. K. Brunel. Up to 4000 men, 300 horses
9 1836–41	Box	2937	
10 1837–40	Summit	2638	Manchester to Leeds
11 1837–41	Clayton	2066	London to Brighton
12 1838–40	Clay Cross	1631	Derby to Leeds
13 1838–41	Merstham	1674	London to Brighton. Up to 6000 men, 500 horses. Adjacent Quarry tunnel 1892
14 1838–45	Sapperton	1701	London to Bristol. I. K. Brunel
15 1839–45	Woodhead	4848	Trans Pennine. Followed by down line 1847–52. Replacement 1949–53.
16 1840–44	Abbotscliff	1776	Near Dover. Also Shakespear Cliff. 1273 m and Martello 485 m
17 1840–43	Morley	3080	Leeds
18 1846–48	Sough	1843	Blackburn
19 1846?–48	Harecastle	1615	Midlands. Near Brindley's canal tunnel
20 1846?–48	Victoria	2474	Liverpool, to docks
21 1846–49	Bramhope	3439	Airedale – Wharfedale
22 1846–49	Standedge	4885	Also canal tunnel. Rail duplicated 1868–70. Double track duplication 1890–94
23 1848–50	Halton	1770	Birkenhead line
24 1850?–53	Merthyr	2283	Great Western

Dates	Name	L'gth m.	Notes
25 1857–61	Penge	1951	South London
26 1858–61	Lydden	2166	Near Dover
27 1860–62	Greenock	1930	Scotland
28 1860–63	Dove Holes	2729	Derby to Manchester
29 1864–68	Sevenoaks	3157	} London to south coast
30 1864–68	Polhill	2387	
31 1865–69	Oxted	2067	
32 1866–71	Caerphilly	1767	Wales
33 1867–70	Bradway	1853	Sheffield
34 1871–75	Blea Moor	2404	Settle to Carlisle
35 1872–74	Combe Down	1672	Bath to Templecombe. 6 tunnels in 26 miles
36 1873–86	Severn	7012	Subaqueous. T.H. Walker, contractor
37 1876–79	Ffestiniog	3528	Wales
38 1877–78	Queensbury	2287	Bradford – Halifax. 14 tunnels in 19 miles
39 1877–79	Corby	1761	} Kettering to Nottingham
40 1877–79	Glaston	1684	10 tunnels in 48 miles
41 1881–86	Mersey Railway	–	Subaqueous. Sir Francis Fox
42 1881–85	Drewton	1933	Hull – Barnsely. Closed 1959
43 1887–90	Rhondda Valley	3148	Wales
44 1887?–90	Sharnbrook	1701	Leicester – Bradford
45 1888–93	Totley	5697	} Sheffield – Manchester
46 1888–92	Cowburn	3385	
47 1891–96	Wenvoe	1707	Pontypridd
48 1893–97	Catesby	2743	South of Rugby
49 1895–00	Gildersome	2131	Leeds
50 1899–01	Disley	3535	Midlands
51 1900–03	Chipping Sodbury	4063	Near Bristol
52 1901?–05	Bolsover	2400	Chesterfield – Lincoln
53 1913–?	Llangyfelach	1785	Wales
54 1918–20	Ponsbourne	2454	North of London

ALPINE RAILWAY TUNNELS

Dates	Name	L'gth m.
A1 1857–70	Frejus	12.2 km
A2 1872–82	St. Gotthard	14.9 km
A3 1879–84	Arlberg	10.5 km
A4 1899–06	Simplon	19.5 km
A5 1907–13	Lotschberg	14.6 km

CLASSIC U.S. RAILWAY TUNNELS

Dates	Name	L'gth m.
U1 1855–76	Hoosac	7.4 km
U2 1879–05	Hudson River	–

The table shows construction dates of British railway tunnels, generally exceeding one mile (1609 m) in length, and also of the major Alpine railway tunnels and the American Hoosac and Hudson River tunnels. These are also displayed in the figure above, from which can be appreciated the relationship in time, and the periods of intense activity and relative inactivity.

Fig. 1.3 – A century of Railway tunnels.

Stephenson's Liverpool to Manchester line was quickly followed by his London to Birmingham line, and in the pursuit of good alignment and easy gradients five tunnels were necessary, the most difficult being those at Primrose Hill, Watford and Kilsby. Primrose Hill tunnel (1081 m) was driven in London Clay, which swelled and developed heavy pressures, cracking the brickwork lining in places. The contractor abandoned the work, which was completed by direct labour. Watford Tunnel (1660 m) was driven through the Chalk ridge which forms the north rim of the London Basin, but fissures in the chalk, filled with gravel, sand and clay and penetrated by water, caused much trouble and many lives were lost. Kilsby tunnel (2218 m) proved the most difficult, through a ridge of Liassic age south of Rugby. The ridge had already been pierced by a canal tunnel which had been routed to avoid quicksands shown by borings. The railway route was chosen in expectation of missing the quick-sands, but failed to do so. The work was done from eighteen shafts, and ever-increasing demands on pumps forced the contractor to abandon his con-tract, the tunnel being successfully completed by direct labour in 1838.

I. K. Brunel was appointed Engineer to the newly formed Great Western Railway in 1833, at the age of 26, and surveyed and planned the route from London to Bristol and designed and supervised the construction. Its major tunnel is Box tunnel (2937 m), 8 km north east of Bath, where the line pierces a ridge of Jurassic rocks, including the Great Oolite limestone, the Fullers Earth, and the Inferior Oolite. Water entering through fissures flooded sections of the tunnel twice during construction, but it was completed success-fully and opened, a year late, in 1841. Opponents had expressed alarm at its length, although not greatly in excess of Kilsby, and its gradient of 1 in 100, the whole proposal having been described as 'monstrous and extraordinary, most dangerous and impracticable'.

Another major early railway tunnel was Woodhead (4828 m) through the Pennine ridge at the summit of the Manchester line. The first single track tunnel was built in 1838-45, and the duplicate in 1847-52. These were high on the bleak moors and were built by tough gangs of railway navvies ('navigators' from the canal construction days), living in their own community in the roughest conditions and sometimes terrorising the neighbourhood. Both tunnels gave trouble from lack of ventilation and general maintenance and were replaced in 1954 by a new Woodhead tunnel taking both tracks and incorporating overhead electrification. The new tunnel took over four years to build, also suffering from falls of rock; nature's obstacles remained very real.

1.5.1 Mersey and Severn Railway Tunnels

Two subaqueous railway tunnels were built almost at the same time; first opened was the Mersey Railway tunnel, 1879-86, followed by the longer and more difficult Severn tunnel, which took 13 years, from 1873 to 1886. The Mersey tunnel, engineered by Sir Francis Fox, was through the Bunter Sandstone of the Triassic period, under the tidal River Mersey. It was driven from shafts 1618 m apart and 52 m deep on each side of the river, which allowed drainage headings to be driven on a rising gradient to mid-river. Colonel Beaumont's Tunnelling Machine, also used at this time in Channel Tunnel experiments, was used for much of the heading excavation, cutting a circular bore of 2.2 m diameter. It was also used for ventilation headings on the Liverpool shore. The main tunnel was 8 m x 7 m, lined with 0.7 m thick brickwork. The provision of forced ventilation to the stations, at the rate of 109 m^3/s, calculated to dilute engine fumes 500 times, is of interest. Much water was and still is pumped from this tunnel.

The Severn tunnel crosses the tidal river a little south of the modern suspension bridge. Its purpose was to replace the ferrying of passengers and shorten the journey from London or Bristol to Newport and Cardiff in South Wales. Parliamentary authority was obtained in 1872 and work started in 1873 with shaft sinking and a 2 m x 2 m pilot heading under the river. In July 1877, after 1500 m of pilot had been successfully completed, tenders for the main tunnel were invited, but rejected as too high; the Railway Company proceeded with the work themselves. Progress was satisfactory, almost to the meeting of the headings under the river; until in October 1879 the landward drive on the Welsh side struck the 'Great Spring' at the junction of the Millstone Grit and Carboniferous Limestone. The tunnel was flooded and work was held up for over a year while new arrangements were made. With Hawkshaw as Engineer and Walker as contractor work was resumed and the world's largest pump was installed. The junction was effected in 1881 and 3600 m of the bore had been enlarged and lined when in 1883 the Great Spring again broke in and flooded the tunnel, followed by breakdown of the largest pump and then by flooding of the working shafts and boiler plant by an abnormal tidal flood. The tidal range on the Severn is 15 m at maximum spring tides and its onset as the 'Severn Bore' is famous, but this tide was something quite exceptional. The tunnel was soon reclaimed, however, and in 1885 a train was passed through, but water pressure dangers appeared at the Great Spring and a new drainage shaft had to be sunk before the tunnel could be opened to traffic in 1886. The tunnel continues to carry main line traffic. Pumping from the Sudbrook shaft to which the flow of the 'Great Spring' was directed continues at a rate of 9-20 million gallons per day. In the years 1929-31 extensive and effective grouting was carried out where the tunnel runs through marl near the English side, and also round the adjacent shaft and the vent shaft on the Welsh side, because leakage through the brickwork had become excessive and cavities were being formed by erosion under and round the brick lining.

Another Severn tunnel has been driven in recent years to carry 400 kV power cables. It crosses at the site of the suspension bridge. The tunnel was lined with concrete segments. Part of the excavation was by drilling and blasting and part by machine, but some of the rock was too hard for economical machine cutting. Water was again troublesome but not catastrophic.

1.5.2 Alpine tunnels

The barrier interposed by the Alps between northern Europe and Italy was a
challenge to the railway builders of the 19th century which could only be met
by tunnelling. The major tunnels started in that century were the Frejus (Mont
Cenis), St. Gotthard, Arlberg, Simplon, followed in 1907 by the Lötschberg.
Across the Atlantic, in Massachussetts, the Hoosac tunnel, whose construction
was spread over twenty-one years, was the proving ground for valuable developments in compressed air rock drills.

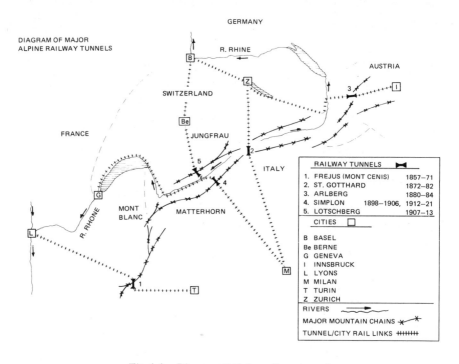

Fig. 1.4 – Diagram of Alpine railway tunnels

For each tunnel a choice had to be made between a short tunnel at high
level approached by severe gradients and sharp curves and vulnerable to winter
snow, and a much longer tunnel at a lower level. The operating advantages of
the lower and longer tunnel were generally decisive, and the long tunnels deep
below the mountain surface were chosen.

These tunnels involved new developments in drilling equipment and explosives and the builders faced almost insoluble problems of ventilation of the
works, enhanced by high temperatures of the rock, and hot springs up to 60°C.
Very severe pressures from rock deteriorating after exposure demanded quite
exceptional methods of construction. All the tunnels were eventually completed.

The col de Frejus, or Mont Cenis, tunnel to carry the railway from France to Turin was the first great Alpine tunnel, 1340 m above sea level. Its bored length appears to have been 12.23 km but it is now recorded as 13.7 km. Mountain streams were utilised to compress air to operate drills and provide ventilation. Housing with schools, hospitals, etc., was provided to accommodate a work force of 2000 men on each side. Work started in 1857 and the tunnel was opened fourteen years later in 1871, shortly after the death of its builder, Germain Sommeiler.

During the same period the Hoosac tunnel, connecting Boston to the Hudson Valley, was being built in America, but its construction was so protracted, from 1855 to 1876, that it became known as 'the Great Bore'. Contractor after contractor took it on and abandoned it. After various periods of direct labour under a State Commission a fifth contractor effected completion. The tunnel was 7.44 km long, mainly through schist and gneiss. Even in 1865 progress was only at the rate of 0.32 m per day, improved the following year to 0.46 m when machine drills were introduced, but by 1873 the rate had improved to about 1.65 m.

In the Alps, completion of the Frejus tunnel was followed by construction of the St. Gotthard tunnel over the years 1872-82. It provided the railway link from the Rhineland through Zurich to Milan. It is 14.9 km long and at a height of 1164 m. Louis Favre accepted an eight year contract, but died in 1879 when struggling to overcome appalling conditions of water, high temperatures and bad ventilation. The worst rock was decomposed felspar and gypsum which became plastic in moist air and developed pressures which were eventually held by a granite lining comprising arch, walls and invert with respective thicknesses of 0.6 m, 2.5 m, 1.4m. The bad conditions and accidents resulted in many deaths —about 25 a year—and much sickness and injury. Nearly 4000 men were employed at the peak of the work.

The Arlberg tunnel, 10.5 km long, linking the Austrian railways to Switzerland, was built during the period 1880-84 without any major setbacks. It was marked by competition between hydraulic and compressed air drills without showing any very clear balance of advantage in either system.

The Simplon tunnel between Berne and Milan is 19.8 km long, the longest of its kind, and was started in 1898 after geological forecasts of good rock. Great emphasis was laid on safety and welfare precautions, and as a result, despite some very difficult conditions, particularly from springs of water as hot as 60°C, the tunnel was completed and opened in 1906 with a far better record of health and safety than St. Gotthard: nevertheless, 39 lives were lost. The design was for twin single-track tunnels, both headings being driven concurrently from both ends, which produced great advantages in ventilation and also in drainage and escape routes. In addition to the high rock temperatures and hot water, major trouble was experienced with a zone of micaceous limestone and gypsum which softened when exposed and developed very high pressures in the 3.5 m x 3.2 m heading. Over a 42 m length no timber was strong enough to withstand the squeeze, and what was virtually a box heading of 74 steel frames built of joists 356 mm deep was constructed. Enlargement to full size had to be executed by excavating under and round the frames in short lengths, filling in with heavy masonry as quickly as possible. As so often in those enterprises the man carrying the greatest responsibility, Alfred Brandt, died in the course of the work in 1898. Enlargement and completion of the duplicate heading to provide the second track was not done until the years 1912-21.

The Lötschberg tunnel which is 14.6 km in length at a height of 1245 m is complementary on the north side of the Rhone valley to the Simplon tunnel on the south side, and its construction followed accordingly in the years 1907-13. The whole rail link was 58 km long including the summit tunnel and thirty-three other tunnels. The special tunnelling hazard of this work was that the heading unexpectedly ran out of rock and into alluvial filling more than 186 m deep below the Gastern valley. The tunnel filled with waterborne sand and gravel, burying 25 men. It had to be blocked off and the tunnel driven anew on a series of curves so as to cross under the buried valley higher up its course. The tunnellers also suffered another catastrophe when the air blast from an avalanche swept away the works canteen and its occupants.

The next generation of great Alpine tunnels was for highways, not for railways, but a deep level St. Gotthard railway tunnel 49 km long has been the subject of studies.

1.5.3 Rock tunnelling development

The development of rock tunnelling has been largely dependent on three things: rock drilling machines, drill bits, and explosives. Gunpowder gave way to the much more powerful nitroglycerine, quickly followed by dynamite, introduced by Nobel in 1867, and by gelignite, which are much safer to store and handle and more controllable in use. There have, of course, been improvements and refinements, but no change of scale or new principle.

For rock drills compressed air became the accepted motive power, although hydraulic power was preferred for a time in Europe and is again coming into favour. Much ingenuity went into the design of compressors, from the falling water devices of the Frejus tunnel to steam driven reciprocating engines and modern reciprocating or rotary machines driven by electricity or diesel power. The great problem with drills themselves lies in their self-destructive character-istics; they hammer themselves to pieces. The wear and tear on the points was first met by making them as detachable bits of the toughest possible steel, but then in turn the shanks had to be improved to endure the increased fatigue stresses, while the whole mechanism, subjected to hammer blows and vibrations, and to dust, grit and water, had to be kept within strict limits of weight so that it might be handled by men for horizontal and overhead drilling. The Alpine tunnels and, perhaps most of all, the Hoosac tunnel were the cradle of these developments, taking advantage as time went on of every improvement in steel technology. One of the great advances, as late as the 1950's, was the development of the tungsten carbide bit. It was in Sweden, where the abundant rock is mostly ancient and very hard, that ways and means of incorporating this material in long-lasting bits were found and brought into practical use.

1.6 NATIONAL SYSTEMS

During the 19th century various systems of tunnelling, principally for canals and railways, were given national labels from the countries in which they were developed. Every type of ground and tunnel section has its own problems so that each system was modified to suit the conditions and to overcome defects that appeared. Much more space would be required to describe each system and its development fully, but the details are hardly relevant now, when timber is so largely replaced by steel and concrete and when so many new techniques of excavation and ground control are available. In any case, there was always modification to adapt any system to the ground and the circumstances of the particular tunnel. The principles, however, remain of interest and are relevant when considering methods of construction. Apart from the structural adequacy of any system, old or new, its economy of materials can be vital, as can speed of construction which may depend on clear access to the working areas. Additional headings were frequently incorporated in order to assist transport of materials and so open out additional working points.

The English system comprised a top (crown bar) heading 3-6 m in length driven ahead of the main face. In this, two principal crown bars were set longitudinally, resting on the completed lining at the back and on props ahead. This heading was then enlarged laterally down to springing, the top being supported by additional crown bars ultimately propped from a substantial sill. The lower half of the tunnel was then excavated, the main sill being undercut progressively and propped down to the tunnel floor. This left a clear chamber within which a complete length of lining was built, roof timbers being removed progressively if possible but built in when necessary.

The advantage of this system is the clear building space, but it is dependent on the stand-up time and the ground loading being within the capacity of the crown bars.

The Austrian (cross bar) system was essentially based on a short top heading enlarged laterally to the full size of the arch, the roof being supported on timber segmental arch ribs at relatively short centres. The ribs usually had to be provided with radial props from sills which had to be changed as excavation progressed.

After excavation down to springing level the lower half was excavated in much the same manner as in the English system.

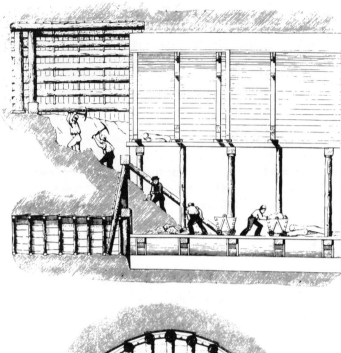

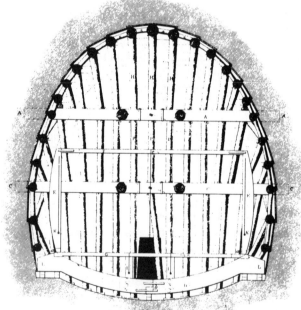

Fig. 1.5 – Two drawings reproduced from Simm's Practical Tunnelling (1896). The English System of Tunnelling, as used in the Bletchingley Tunnel (1840) in clay. (a) Longitudinal section showing top crown bar heading in advance of brickwork, and bottom heading. (b) Face timbering, ahead of brickwork.

The merit of the system lay in the ability to build the ribs at as close centres as necessary to resist high ground pressures, but successive repropping could result in relaxation of the ground causing increased loading. The lengths available for construction of the lining were liable to be rather short and obstructed by timber.

The Belgian (underpinning) system initially resembled the English system in the excavation of the arch section down to springing, but at that stage, before excavation of the lower half, the building of the arch was completed. The arch had then to be undercut and underpinned, which could be done in short lengths in small pits if necessary.

The principal advantage lay in the early completion of the roof structure, provided that the underpinning operations did not result in undue relaxation of the arch and consequent heavy loading.

The German (centre core) system was also claimed as a French system, having been used about 1803 in the Tronquoy canal tunnel. In this system the bases of the tunnel walls were first built in separate small bottom headings, followed by a succession of upper headings until the crown was reached and the arch completed.

The core of ground was left in as a 'dumpling' until completion of the lining and gave support to vertical and radial props. The advantages of working in small headings in bad ground are apparent, but could be nullified by squeezing and distortion of the core and also by difficulties of securing sound workmanship in the building of the lining in small units in confined spaces.

The Italian (invert arch) system was developed about 1870 for the very difficult Cristina railway tunnel through the Appenines. Very severe clay pressures were encountered, crushing timbering and masonry. In the system finally successful the invert was first built in solid masonry from a bottom heading, so as to provide a secure base for props and struts. This masonry was extended laterally and upwards in small units, including a thick temporary masonry arch over the working heading, so that the crown excavation could finally be timbered and the arch lining built with the temporary arch as centering.

The American system was not a standard national pattern in the same sense, but there was a common pattern resembling the Austrian system. A top heading was driven from which excavation was enlarged laterally to accommodate a polygonal timber arch rib down to springing level. Support at springing might then be by vertical side posts.

Alternatively, 'wall plate' headings might be driven first, the legs and cap of the arch rib being built up from the longitudinal sill comprising the wall plate. Having secured the top, excavation and timbering progressed downwards for the 'length' under construction.

It is clear that every one of these systems had its merits and disadvantages and the safe use of each depended on familiarity with the system in all its

details and with the ground being tunnelled. Adaptation and modification in
any particular tunnel was necessarily continuous.

1.7 SHIELDS AND COMPRESSED AIR

1.7.1 Tower subway

In the field of subaqueous tunnelling 1869 was an important year because it
marked the successful construction of the Tower subway in London using a shield
and cast iron lining. The tunnel was used for a cable-hauled car and then for
pedestrians until 1894 and now carries water mains. The scheme was Barlow's,
but his pupil, Greathead, became responsible for it and in particular the design
and development of the shield, which is the ancestor of almost all subsequent
shields. The subway was 402 m long lined with cast iron segments within a
2.18 m diameter circular excavation. The tunnel was driven through London
Clay 19 m below high water, with 7 m cover below the river bed.

The shield comprised a cylinder formed of 13 mm thick wrought iron skin
plates 1.45 m long, stiffened with cast iron rings and having a stiffening
diaphragm incorporating a rectangular doorway, which could be closed off
by dropping boards across it. Behind the diaphragm were six screw jacks,
thrusting the shield forward from the completed cast iron lining, which was
erected ring by ring within the tail of the shield. This permanent lining comprised three segments of a circle plus a short key segment, all flanged and
bolted together. Because of the thickness of the shield's tail skin and working
clearances the cast iron lining did not entirely fill the excavated void, and the
injection of cement grout was adopted to minimise ground movement, but a
hand syringe was not very effective. Progress of nearly 3 m a day demonstrated
the efficiency of the system, albeit in good ground. The importance of this
small tunnelling operation lies in its pioneering and developing and proving in
practice of so many devices essential to shield tunnelling in soft ground, namely:
rigid and simple shield, protective diaphragm, tail skin protecting building of
lining, cast iron lining providing, in combination with the principle of grouting,
immediate ground support.

In 1940 the tunnel was damaged by an adjacent bomb crater in the foreshore
near the low tide line. A length of about 50 m was repaired by enlarging to 3 m
diameter with cast iron rings using tunnelling methods. It is of interest that the
effect of the forces was to fracture the cast iron rings and crush the tunnel, at
one point to a diameter of about 1.3 m, but when exposed in the re-excavation
the clay outside had flowed plastically to the new diameter, and appeared
unchanged except for a skin of about 50–75 mm.

Barlow in 1864 had patented most of these ideas, but Greathead receives
the credit for putting them into practical shape. Working possibly from Barlow's
1864 patent, Beach in New York built a shield for a pneumatic subway under
Broadway, brick lined 2.4 m diameter. The body of his shield was of timber with

iron cutting edge and tail, and he used hydraulic rams. His tunnel was successfully driven through sandy soil in 1869-70, and a shield of his design was again
used for a 2.4 m sewer in Cincinnati in 1871-2.

Although the Mersey and Severn tunnels were major subaqueous railway
tunnels in rock, the techniques were not fundamentally different from the other
railway and canal tunnels. Water, of course, was an even more dangerous enemy
there than on land because any breach to the river opened up an unlimited
source of supply, but the distinctive problems of soft ground subaqueous
tunnelling, exemplified in Brunel's Thames tunnel, were not faced again on that
scale until the attempt to tunnel under the Hudson River between Jersey City
and New York started in 1879.

1.7.2 Hudson River Tunnel

New York had from an early day railway connections from the north leading
eventually to the terminus at Grand Central Station but no direct links from the
west and south where the Hudson river was a formidable barrier dependent on
ferry transport for the crossing until 1908. That was the date of completion of
the Hudson River Tunnel for which a preliminary shaft was sunk in 1874. At the
chosen site the tunnel is almost entirely in silt but the use of compressed air[†]
appeared to offer a means of excluding water and holding the ground, initially
for an iron plate lining, followed by a brick lining. Work started in earnest in
1879. After installation of an air lock and breaking out from the base of the
shaft it was thought that 'the great problem that the silt would hold the air and
the air would hold the silt was practically solved'. Unfortunately, the balance
was too unstable and either drying out of the silt or intrusion of water caused
falls of ground. In 1880 a serious accident, in which 20 lives were lost, occurred
when trying to form the junction at the shaft. The tunnel was inundated, but
was recovered and work proceeded until 1882, when funds ran out and the
tunnel was sealed off. This was the first large scale use of compressed air[†] for
tunnelling, though a small tunnel in dock works in Antwerp had been driven
under compressed air a few months earlier. The use of compressed air for shaft
or caisson sinking for bridge piers was well known, but no earlier use in tunnels
is recorded. A patent for working in compressed air had been taken out in 1830
by Lord Cochrane. It included shaft sinking and also tunnelling with the use of
an air lock for entry. Brunel's Thames tunnel would have benefited from
employment of compressed air; it is said that the idea was brought to his
notice in 1828 by a Dr. Colladon. It may be worth noting here that there is

[†] Footnote:
Previous references to compressed air have been to the use of high pressure air (at pressures
of about 7 atmospheres) as the driving power for machines such as rock drills. The current
reference is to the compression of the whole atmosphere within the tunnel in which the
miners work and breathe at a pressure of the order of one or two atmospheres, calculated
to balance in some degree the water pressure acting at the face of the tunnel. The sense in
which the term is used is usually clear from the context.

Fig. 1.6 – Hudson River Tunnel. Excavation in silt in compressed air, with use of Greathead shield and cast iron lining (1890).

an inherent instability in this use of compressed air to exclude free water at the vertical face of a tunnel because the water pressure is so much greater at the bottom of the face than at the top while the air pressure is the same all over, and so must either be inadequate at the bottom or excessive at the top.

The combination of shield and compressed air together with cast iron lining was first proved on the City and South London Railway tunnelling as described later. With advice from Baker and Greathead the techniques were adopted successfully in the Hudson tunnel when work was resumed there in 1889, under a contract with Pearsons. The silt was so soft in places as to be extruded into the tunnel through apertures in the shield when this was jacked forward. The tunnel was not, however, completed under this contract, which was suspended for lack of funds in 1891; another contract was let in 1902 and tunnelling by the same method was completed in 1905. The length driven by shield was 1070 m and the external diameter of the cast iron lining 5.9 m.

An important contribution to compressed air working was the introduction at the Hudson tunnel in 1889 by Moir, Pearson's agent, of the 'medical lock' for treatment of caisson disease, whereby complete relief was given in ordinary cases, and fatalities were reduced from the appalling figure of 25% of the men employed in a year to two deaths in 15 months out of 120 men.

1.7.3 London tube lines

The construction of the City and South London Railway 1886–90 (now part of the Northern Line in the London underground system) provided the first large-scale use of the Greathead shield system, and also the first use of shield, compressed air and segmental cast-iron lining in combination. This was also virtually the first electric railway. The tunnel was driven as twin cast-iron lined tubes, starting on the north bank of the Thames near London Bridge and crossing under the river and running south for 5.07 km to Stockwell. The first third of the tunnel was only 3.100 m in diameter and the remainder only 3.200 m. Most of the drive was in London Clay but water-bearing gravel was encountered for a length of 180 m near Stockwell. It was for this work that compressed air was introduced. The unsatisfactory grouting technique of the Tower Subway was replaced by Greathead's device of the grouting pan, using high pressure compressed air to inject the mixture through holes provided in the cast-iron segments.

The original Metropolitan and District lines had been constructed by cut and cover, but disturbances to the surface and to property were unacceptable. The success of this scheme therefore pointed the way first of all to Glasgow to build its 6½ mile loop subway (1897), passing under the river Clyde in difficult conditions, and then to the expansion of London's underground system. The same tunnelling principles were followed in construction of the Bank—Waterloo railway (1898) where clay-pocketing was introduced by Dalrymple Hay; the Central London railway (1900); the Bakerloo line (1906); the Piccadilly line (1906); and the modern Victoria line (1968) and Fleet line (1979). All the lines have been extended, partly in tunnel but also, in the outer suburbs, by running on surface lines.

A notable development of the original City and South London railway was its enlargement to standard 3.56 m diameter and lengthening of stations in the early 1920's, some of the work being carried out with trains running through annular tunnelling shields, and some in compressed air. The Eastern Extension of the Central line (1935–39) was marked by some very difficult compressed air working in bad ground and the use of chemical ground treatment, and also by the introduction of pre-cast concrete segments for the tunnel lining where the ground was good enough and cast-iron was not deemed essential. The construction of the Victoria line introduced digger shields, and flexible joined segments. The projected route of the Fleet line ran through difficult water-bearing gravels in the south-east and, in anticipation, trial tunnelling to develop the 'Bentonite shield' was carried out successfully. Another aspect of such a railway system is the very complex tunnelling for interchange stations, such as

Euston, where the main line terminus at the surface is served by stations on six deep tube tracks and the two shallower tracks of the Inner Circle. These, with connecting passages and escalator tunnels on a slope of 30°, make a very intricate three-dimensional pattern.

1.7.4 General adoption

Following the success of the City and South London railway the combination of shield and compressed air was adopted before the end of the century for a number of tunnels. In America—apart from the second instalment of the Hudson river tunnel—the earliest and most notable was the 6.4 m diameter cast-iron lined Sarnia tunnel for the Canadian Grand Trunk Railway, passing from Ontario to Michigan under the St. Clair river, and completed in 1890. Air pressures ranged from 0.7 to 1.9 bar* and the shield was provided with an erector arm to handle the C.I. segments. In 1892-94 a gas main tunnel under the East river, New York, was started in good rock but ran into trouble with bands of decomposing felspar which washed out when acted on by water. A shield, compressed air up to 3.6 bar, and a cast-iron segmental lining were necessary to complete the trouble-some sections. The use of timber for initial lining of some other small pipe tunnels is of interest.

In Great Britain, apart from tube railways and the Blackwall tunnel, described more fully below, this period saw the Vyrnwy aqueduct under the Mersey rescued by use of a shield and compressed air, while in Scotland three 5.2 m diameter tunnels 210 m long were driven under the river Clyde for the Glasgow Harbour authority in 1890-93, providing an early example of a sub-aqueous highway tunnel, although it may be noted that access to the tunnels for vehicles and pedestrians was by lift only. Edinburgh also in 1893-4 con-structed twin 5.3 m highway tunnels in compressed air under the Mound, compressed air being used to give support rather than to expel water.

In France the method was used at the end of the century for a number of sewer tunnels of diameters of 2 m to 3 m under the rivers Seine and Oise in the vicinity of Paris.

In Germany a 4 m diameter tramway tunnel 373 m long was driven under the river Spree in 1896-99.

In Australia, the City of Melbourne built some 11 km of tunnelled sewers with diameters ranging from 1.5 m to 3.5 m; seven lengths totalling 1620 m were constructed in compressed air, and cast iron lining and concrete was used for six of these lengths and concrete blocks for one. For the free air tunnels, cast-iron, concrete, bluestone, and even timber segments were used.

1.7.5 Blackwall Tunnel

The Blackwall Tunnel (1892-97) under the river Thames may perhaps be considered as the achievement of Brunel's vision of a highway under the

---

* 1 bar in the metric (SI) system is $10^5 N/m^2$ and equals 14.50 psi, nearly 1 atmosphere.

river, built by a public authority and free for public use. It was in many ways a bold pioneering work. The tunnel was deliberately located at a level where cover at the deepest part of the river was no more than 1.6 m of gravel. Reliance was placed on the combination of shield and compressed air, which at the date of the decision had not been proved elsewhere, and on the protection of a clay blanket dumped in the river bed. In fixing the level the limiting depth was decided as 24 m below high water, to limit maximum air pressure to 35 lbs/in^2. Near the critical section the tunnel was twice inundated to a depth of 2½ m, fortunately without casualties.

The advances since Brunel's day included the rigid structural steel circular Greathead shield with stiffening girders and two safety diaphragms, cast-iron segmental lining bolted together within the tail of the shield and pressure grouted, and the use of compressed air to keep the water under control. Other features were the use of hydraulic power for the main rams, which were 28 in number, subsequently increased to 34, capable of a total forward thrust of 5000 tonnes, and the provision of a segment erector arm working in the tail of the shield to handle the heavy cast-iron segments.

Two shafts were sunk on each side of the river and shield tunnelling started from No. 4 on the south bank. The shield, weighing 220 T, was assembled in a shallow pit near the shaft and then floated along a channel to the shaft and lowered into place by pumping out the water with which the system had been filled. From shaft No. 4 the shield was driven through shaft No. 3, then under the river to No. 2 and on to No. 1. At each end a length of tunnel was built as cut-and-cover and beyond that a ramp in open cut up to surface level.

The ground comprised river gravels overlying London Clay on both banks, with the variable Woolwich and Reading beds below the clay. Under the river the clay thinned out altogether so that the tunnellers had a face of gravel entirely open to the river, except for the protection afforded by depositing a 3 m thick 'clay blanket' over the worst section. The shield face when necessary was kept closed up by a system of horizontal steel planks held by jacking screws, much as in Brunel's shield, and released one by one as each move forward was made. For the most critical part only a small 'window' in each plank was opened. In good ground, where sand and shale underlay the clay, progress up to 4 m in 24 hours was made, but in mid-river no more than 1½ m in a week was possible. Other points of interest in this tunnel were the use of electric lighting in the tunnel, the provision of hydraulic power by pipe line from surface pumps, the repair of damage to the cutting edge of the shield in the invert caused by striking rock in the early stages of the drive. Very great precautions were taken in subjecting men to the compressed air working and in the event no lives were lost while only three cases of permanent illness were recorded.

The internal diameter of the tunnel was only 7.5 m allowing a 4.9 m roadway with restricted headroom. The alignment was straight between shafts but with sharp bends at the shafts. This was acceptable in the days of horse-drawn dock traffic, but became intolerable for modern vehicles. A new tunnel was built adjacent in 1960-68 in which again shield, compressed air and cast-iron lining were used, but with the additional device of extensive ground treatment by injection of complex grouts from top and bottom pilot tunnels, to make the ground coherent and watertight. After completion of this new tunnel some improvements in the old tunnel were made, in particular to improve clearances at the bends and each of the pair of tunnels now carries one-way traffic only.

Other highway tunnels under the tidal Thames, also shield driven in com-pressed air, are at Rotherhithe (1904-08), very close to Brunel's tunnel, and at Dartford, 22 km down river from Blackwall tunnel, where a pilot tunnel was driven before 1939 but work on the main tunnel was not resumed until 1956, the tunnel being opened in 1963. The design of shield closely resembled that for Blackwall, including segment erectors, and hydraulic pipe lines, but the bore under the river was mostly in chalk and the more difficult strata were near the river banks where the top of the face was in gravel on one side and in soft silty clay on the other. Duplication of this tunnel was completed in 1980.

1.8 20TH CENTURY TECHNIQUES

By the beginning of the 20th century the basic techniques for bored tunnels had been devised and proved the hard way, so that most ground could be tunnelled if the promoters were prepared to pay the price. The new century therefore saw a steady expansion of tunnelling throughout the world to serve many and varied purposes. A system of tunnelling widely adopted in recent years has been the submerged tube for river crossings where the tunnel is prefabricated in long lengths in a dry dock, floated out into the river and sunk into a pre-dredged trench where the lengths are connected up. Much work by this system has been done in Holland, and also in the U.S.A. Excavating machines working within a tunnel have been developed and have been combined with shields in very powerful tunnelling machines. Ground treatment by injection of a wide range of chemical grouts has proved a valuable technique in difficult ground, both for reducing its permeability to influx of water and improving its cohesive strength. Freezing whether by brine circulation or by use of liquid nitrogen can also provide temporary cohesion and impermeability. In rock, preservation of the integrity of a rock mass by rock bolting is a method of growing importance. Sprayed concrete linings immediately after exposure, can prevent progressive loosening of the rock.

For small tunnels and large pipes, pipe jacking has become a useful method. It may be considered as shield tunnelling in which the tunnel lining itself con-stitutes the shield. All of these techniques are further described in later chapters.

1.8.1 Railways

Tunnels for main line railway systems have continued to be built throughout the world, with many notable achievements on the Alpine scale. New Zealand built the Otisa tunnel (1923), 9 km long through crumbling shale, and the Rimutaka tunnel (1955) of similar length, and others. Italy's Bologna–Florence Diretissima (1934) included thirty tunnels, of which the Great Appenine tunnel, 18½ km long through soft clay and running sand with methane gas, was the most formidable. In the U.S.A. and Canada old summit tunnels have been and are being replaced by longer tunnels at a lower level and with easier gradients and curves to handle heavy goods traffic more efficiently. Japan has engaged in major railway development in recent years to improve communications in their mountainous country, and has built many notable tunnels, both for the general railway system and for the new high speed lines.

The Channel tunnel project, and the Seikan tunnel, are described in Chapter 10.

1.8.2 Metro systems

Most cities having a population of the order of a million or more, and some smaller, are finding the problems of surface transport so difficult that they are using the third dimension, depth, to tunnel underground for railway construction. The various names—Underground, Metro, Subway, U-bahn, Rapid Transit—can perhaps best be generalised under the term Metro, whether this be thought of as deriving from Paris or from London's first system, the Metropolitan Railway.

The varieties of system are many but almost all have in common tunnelling for at least some sections of their city routes. Some were planned as self-contained lines usually radial but sometimes as a loop like the Glasgow Subway. Others develop from city tramway or street car routes, which are run below the surface to clear the streets of congestion. Others again arise from the extension of main line or suburban railways into the heart of a city or from interconnection of existing termini.

Insofar as generalisation is possible the independent lines tend to be deep level bored tunnels, while the extensions and tramways tend to be shallow, constructed largely by cut-and-cover methods.

Before the end of the 19th century, in addition to London, lines were constructed in Glasgow (1896), Budapest (1896), Boston (1897) and Vienna (1898). The Mersey Railway into Liverpool (1886), now extended into a city loop, might also be put in this category. After London, the next major system was the Paris Metro, whose first line was opened in 1900, followed by Berlin in 1902. New York had then an elevated railway but also went underground progressively from 1904, with Jersey City following in 1908 and also Philadelphia.

New York's problems of crossing the Hudson river, and more so the East river, were solved for main line and metro railways by driving numerous tunnels. Six railway tunnels in all were built under the Hudson river in the years 1902-08; eight were built under the East river from 1903-09 and eight more from 1914-20. All are single track tunnels lined with cast-iron 4.6 to 5.0 m diameter, shield driven in compressed air through varying strata of silt, sand and rock.

Additional tunnels were driven from time to time and more recently a tunnel to carry four tracks under the East river has been constructed, the river section being a submerged tube approximately 12 m x 11 m in section with rail tracks at two levels, but connecting into bored tunnels.

The first quarter of the 20th century saw underground city lines opened in Hamburg (1912), Buenos Aires (1913), and Madrid (1919). In 1935 the first section of the Moscow Metro was opened, since when it has been steadily expanding. It has been followed in the U.S.S.R. by Leningrad, Kiev, Tbilisi and Baku.

Major world wide expansion began about 1950 and in the following twenty years eighteen cities began operating new systems, large or small, as well as many additions and extensions to existing systems, and planning and construction in progress on many others.

Toronto Subway (1954) was the first in Canada, followed by Montreal Metro (1965). In Japan, Tokyo opened its first line in 1927, then Osaka (1933), Nagoya (1957), and Kobe (1968). In the U.S.A. the earlier Metros in Boston, New York and New Jersey, Philadelphia and Chicago (1943) grew out of overhead railways, but the new Bay Area Rapid Transit (BART), opened in stages from 1972, is a landmark of careful planning for a very high standard of comfort and speed in an attempt to attract traffic away from the private car. Its 10 km underwater tunnel across the bay was constructed in prefabricated lengths sunk into a dredged trench by submerged tube methods. A noteworthy feature is the design of tunnel end joints to meet the contingency of earthquake movements.

Rotterdam's line across the river Maas (1968) was also built as a prefabricated submerged tube in concrete, and the method was even adopted there for the city streets in which canals were first dug so that the units might be floated and sunk.

Almost every method of tunnelling has been used in these Metros: cut-and-cover, shield tunnelling with or without compressed air, digger shields, rock tunnelling with explosives or machines, and as described, submerged tubes. They vary in size of tunnel from the Glasgow Subway which in cross-section is a circle of 3.35 m internal diameter, up to a circle of 8.70 m diameter for the Paris express line, while the rectangular section adopted for cut-and-cover construction is usually for double track with a span of about 7½ m. The largest span is 34 m for the Brussels main line link. Depth below surface may exceptionally be as much as 60 m.

Although a city may initially build a shallow subsurface line, later lines are forced deeper at crossings and cut-and-cover methods have to be supplemented by deep tunnelling techniques in increasing degree. Access to deep stations by escalators or lifts provides a new range of tunnelling problems.

Melbourne is currently completing city loops with main line capacity linking up the various suburban lines and providing through running.

So many new Metros are now planned and under construction that further enumeration or description is impracticable.

1.8.3 Highway tunnels

Tunnelling for highways did not become a common practice until much later than for railways. Because of gradient and curve limitations railways needed tunnels early and often, but much steeper gradients and very sharp bends were at that time acceptable on highways when they did not carry heavy long-distance traffic and were not the subject of large capital investment. Short road tunnels through rocky spurs and ridges are numerous in mountain areas and on coastal roads, but the longer highway tunnels are now either subaqueous or carry the modern highway with its increasingly heavy vehicles and loads through ridges and mountains for exactly the same reasons as formerly applied principally to railways—gradients, curves and large capital investment. There is also now a third situation demanding highway tunnels, namely, city congestion, eased by underpasses short or long.

The Thames tunnel (1843) was, as described, the frustrated forerunner of highway tunnels and although hill tunnels were built in the 19th century it is significant that the major early road tunnels were subaqueous tunnels in port and dock areas. Blackwall (1897; 1361 m) fulfilled Brunel's dream and was followed by its near neighbour Rotherhithe (1908; 1482 m), both shield driven in compressed air and lined with cast-iron rings. In Hamburg a tunnel under the river Elbe (449 m) was opened in 1911, and in Pittsburg the Liberty tunnel (1800 m) in 1924, but the first of the modern generation for motor vehicles was really the Holland tunnel (2600 m) in New York, opened in 1927 to provide the first road access other than by ferry, to the city from the west.

The Holland tunnel was planned and designed for modern motor traffic which is characterised by emission of poisonous carbon monoxide. The problem of ventilation became for the first time an issue of vital importance and was very fully studied and so successfully provided for that the system has worked satisfactorily without major change for nearly fifty years. The tunnel, under the Hudson river, was shield driven in compressed air and lined with cast-iron (8.33 m int. dia.) through the same ground that had proved so difficult in the 19th century. Six hooded shields each 9.19 m diameter were employed to drive the twin tubes: the tunnel face had to be kept close timbered, and in some sections clay pocketing round the hood was found necessary. Over some lengths the shield face, which was divided into 19 compartments, was kept closed except for small areas in the bottom and the silt was extruded through these slots into the invert and thence removed. For a short section on the New York side rock in the invert had first to be excavated in a pilot heading and replaced by a concrete cradle.

The success of this tunnel led to the construction of the Lincoln tunnel, also under the Hudson river between New Jersey and Manhattan Island. Three two-lane tunnels of lengths 2280, 2510 and 2260 m were built, also shield driven with cast-iron lining, and were opened in 1937, 1945 and 1957. Under the East river the Queen's Midtown tunnel was opened in 1940.

The Mersey Queensway tunnel, opened in 1934, was another major highway tunnel. It was driven essentially by rock tunnelling methods—drilling and blasting—under the river Mersey to connect Liverpool with Birkenhead. It was lined with cast-iron under the river, with an internal diameter of no less than 13.4 m in order to provide for four lanes of traffic between its main entrances in the city centres. The lane width is only 2.7 m. Two two-lane branch tunnels were driven direct to the dock areas, but because of the problems of crossing traffic they are not now much used. The main tunnel is 3237 m long and the branches 504 m and 478 m. Ventilation was a major problem, more costly than originally foreseen, but satisfactorily solved. A second tunnel, Mersey Kingsway (2487 m) opened in 1971 and duplicated in 1973, was built about a mile downstream, through the same Triassic sandstone, by use of a full face excavating machine, again with a circular segmental lining but of concrete faced with steel. In this case a pair of two-lane tunnels 9.67 m diameter each providing two 3.7 m lanes was preferred to the single large diameter tunnel. The Dartford tunnel (1963; 1429 m) and second Blackwall tunnel (1968); 1174 m) have already been mentioned. Similar subaqueous tunnels, driven in compressed air and cast-iron lined were completed under the Clyde (1963; 762 m) and under the Tyne (1967; 1684 m).

A new pattern in highway tunnel construction was set in Oakland, California by the Posey tunnel (1081 m) opened in 1928, which was probably the first highway tunnel constructed by the submerged unit method, although a railway had already in 1910 been carried under the Detroit river by similar means. Circular steel shells in 62 m lengths were encased in concrete and lowered into a dredged trench in the bed of the river, then joined up to form the tunnel, the trench being backfilled over the tunnel. This tunnel was duplicated in 1962 by the Webster Street tunnel.

The submerged tunnel has perhaps now become the commonest method for subaqueous tunnels in the U.S.A., some of the longer examples being: Detroit—Windsor (1930; 1191 m), Virginia—Elizabeth river (1952; 1020 m, 1962; 1280 m), Baltimore (1957; 2331 m), Virginia, Hampton Roads (1957; 2280 m), Chesapeake Bay (1963; 1749 m and 1661 m), together with many others under 1 km.

In Europe, Holland has been the leader in this method, but with substantial differences in construction technique, using precast concrete units of rectangular

Fig. 1.7(a) – First Mersey highway tunnel. Mersey Queensway Tunnel (1930) in sandstone. Excavation and erection of 13.4 m dia. cast iron lining for upper half, using pilot heading.

Fig. 1.7(b) — First Mersey highway tunnel. Mersey Queensway Tunnel (1930) in sandstone. Completion of excavation of lower half, with cast iron lining underpinning upper half.

section for such tunnels as: Rotterdam, Maas (1942; 1075 m), Amsterdam, Ij (1967; 1037 m), Amsterdam, Coen (1967; 587 m). In Belgium also the method was used for the J. F. Kennedy tunnel (1968; 690 m), and France, Sweden and Denmark have completed similar tunnels in recent years.

Japan has built a number of long highway tunnels, mostly by rock tunnelling methods, such as the Kanmon tunnel (1958; 3461 m) connecting the islands of Honshu and Kyushu, and the twin Teenosan tunnels (1963; 1390 m and 1453 m) for the Nagoya–Kobe expressway. Under construction is the Enasan tunnel (8450 m) on the Tokyo–Nagoya highway which was briefly second only to the Mont Blanc tunnel in length. Submerged tube methods have also been used in Japan but principally for short Metro system tunnels.

The Alpine railway tunnels have been succeeded by a generation of highway tunnels of which Mont Blanc (1965; 12650 m), Grand St. Bernard (1964; 5800 m), San Bernadino (1967; 6596 m) and St. Gotthard (1980; 16320 m) are the longest. The same problems of water, cold or hot, and swelling rock producing extremely heavy pressures, and rock bursts, as well as avalanches, have had to be faced. Although so much more is known and equipment and tools are so much improved, the difficulties remain formidable.

1.8.4 Water

Water tunnels may be looked at broadly in two major divisions, namely: aqueducts and hydro-electric schemes. A third, of lesser magnitude, is for cooling water systems in thermal power stations.

Aqueducts follow the ancient tradition of the Persians, Greeks, Romans, and others in carrying water supplies for long distances from mountain areas not only to cities but also for irrigation.

The Great Lakes in America were the scene of some early subaqueous tunnelling. Chicago drove a brick lined 1.5 m x 1.5 m tunnel 3221 m long out under Lake Michigan in 1867 to ensure ample clean water, and has gone on extending the system ever since. Cleveland in a similar enterprise under Lake Erie in 1874 had much difficulty with methane gas, but also has added to its tunnels subsequently. In southern California a number of cities have combined to draw water from the Colorado river in 370 km of aqueduct of which 148 km is in bored tunnel and 88 km in cut-and-cover. The work was started in 1932, and includes 29 tunnels of 4.9 m diameter, the longest being the East Coachello (29 km) and the San Jacinto (21 km) at depths up to 200 m. The New York City–Delaware water tunnel of 4 m diameter is said to be the world's longest at 137 km.

London's Metropolitan Water Board in 1955–60 drove a 2 m tunnel 30 km long to transfer water from west to east into the system of reservoirs based on the river Lea. The long lengths carefully sited as far as possible in the London Clay stratum stimulated development of soft ground tunnelling machines together with expanded concrete linings which are assembled without bolting

immediately behind the digger shield and wedged out so as to fit tight against
the machined surface of the clay without the usual need for grouting. The
success of this first tunnel was followed by further similar tunnelling in
London and elsewhere and the adoption of the idea of the expanded lining
also for Metro construction in the Victoria line.

In South Africa the Orange River Project for diversion of water from the
Orange river into the basin of the Fish river for irrigation and also for supply
to Port Elizabeth, has as its key link one of the world's very long tunnels, the
Orange–Fish tunnel, 82.4 km of 5.34 m finished diameter concrete lined tunnel,
driven through rock by drilling and blasting, working from seven shafts up to
278 m deep.

Hydro-electric power schemes are typically in mountain areas and depend
on storage of water at high level and utilisation of its energy of descent to
turbines situated as far as possible below storage level. Tunnels are normally
required to feed the turbines and frequently also for the discharge, but also
through the mountains to supplement the supply available in one valley with
that from an adjacent collecting area. With improvement of rock tunnelling
techniques it has also become advantageous in some schemes to site the turbines
deep in the heart of the rock in caverns excavated for that purpose. The
advantages lie in the shortness of the pressure tunnels leading to the station,
and also in protection of the generating stations.

An early example of tunnelling for water power was at Niagara in 1890,
where water was drawn off above the falls and returned to the river lower
down after utilisation of its energy. Further power and control schemes have
followed to make use of as much of Niagara's water as possible without too
serious interference with the spectacular flow over the falls.

Sweden built a small underground power station in 1910 at Mockfjord, and
followed with the first such major station in 1910-14 at Porjus, within the
Arctic Circle. This has a 530 m supply tunnel feeding five shafts 50 m deep
and a 1152 m tailrace. The machinery chamber is 12 m x 20 m x 90 m long
at a depth of 51 m. Power was required for a railway serving iron ore mines,
and underground construction was adopted partly to ensure freedom from
freezing up in winter. The construction techniques have been continuously
improved, sizes increased and costs reduced, so that the Stornorrfors station
opened in 1958 has a generator chamber 18.5 m x 29 m x 124 m and a tailrace
16 m x 26 m in section and 4000 m long. The power generated is 375 MW.
More than half of Sweden's power is now produced in such stations. Similar
underground stations have been constructed in most countries with suitable
topography.

Apart from complete underground stations, there has been much tunnelling
done to feed turbines above ground and to link up sources of supply as well as
for pumped storage schemes. Scotland has many miles of such tunnels. Australia's
Snowy Mountains scheme has required extensive tunnelling. Generation com-

bined with river control and irrigation is typified on the Indus river by the Mangla Dam, where five 11 m tunnels each 500 m long were driven by means of a Robbins Mole, the same machine being subsequently adapted to drive the twin tubes of the Mersey Kingsway tunnel. The hazards still to be encountered are exemplified by the collapse of ground into the tunnels at the Tarbela Dam, also on the Indus river.

In hydro-electric water tunnels there is an important distinction between those in which water is contained at high pressure and those in which it flows as in a covered channel. In high pressure tunnels the rock is most unlikely to be sufficiently watertight and the relations between stresses in the tunnel lining and in the surrounding rock are of vital importance if cracking and leakage are to be avoided. The science of rock mechanics has been developed in recent years to deal with this problem among others.

1.8.5 Sewers

The growth of cities, often astride rivers, makes sewerage an ever-increasing problem, if the discharge is to be collected and disposed of efficiently. The volume to be handled is similar to the volume of water supplied, and there are special problems of additional surface water flows in rainstorms. The critical requirement of small but steady gradients leaves little choice as to pipe depths so that tunnelling soon becomes necessary, even for pipes, and much more so for the larger trunk sewers. The largest sewers do not often exceed a few metres in diameter but they have to be driven in conditions that are often very difficult, because the level can rarely be determined to suit easily tunnelled strata and the sewer must be driven typically through very variable alluvial deposits and even through made ground, in the vicinity of building foundations and other sub-surface structures peculiar to cities.

London was the first great city to provide comprehensive sewerage. Before 1817 contamination of drains was a penal offence but in 1847 it first became compulsory to drain houses into sewers, which had previously provided only for surface water drainage. Eight independent bodies were superseded by a series of Metropolitan Commissions of Sewers and eventually in 1856 by the Metropolitan Board of Works. Abolition of cesspools was followed by shocking pollution of the river Thames from the direct discharge into the tidal river. Bazalgette, as Engineer to the new Board, planned and executed a major scheme of some 70 miles of interception sewers up to almost 3 m diameter, discharging into the river 12 miles downriver. Numerous tunnels were necessary under streets, rivers, canals, railways, and house property. While many were through clay, others were through water-bearing sand and gravel and through 'quicksands'. Bazalgette developed a very satisfactory method of ground water lowering by sinking pumping wells to 2 m below excavation level, providing a shingle filter at the bottom and laying earthenware drain pipes below the invert of the proposed sewer. The whole scheme was substantially completed by 1865.

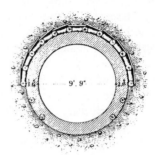

LOOKING WEST.   LOOKING EAST.
TRANSVERSE SECTIONS.

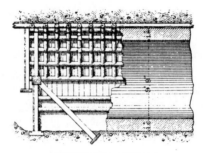

LONGITUDINAL SECTION.
MIDDLE LEVEL SEWER. TUNNEL UNDER NEW INN YARD.

SECTION OF SEWER IN TUNNEL   SECTION OF SEWER IN TUNNEL
NEAR THE UPPER MALL, HAMMERSMITH.   UNDER QUEEN STREET, HAMMERSMITH.

Fig. 1.8 – Sections of sewers, illustrating Bazalgette's paper of 1865 to the Institution of Civil Engineers.

No doubt the varied tunnelling in progress at this time stimulated thought and experiment, and contributed to Greathead's development of the shield for the Tower Subway in 1869.

Bazalgette's great plan for London was substantially enlarged in the years 1898-1912 when a further 75 km of main sewers were built, about 57 km being tunnelled. Cast-iron linings were used for some 25 km, about half with the aid of a shield and compressed air.

The brickwork in these sewers was built to very high standards of workmanship, and generally they still continue in use.

Shields and compressed air were widely used before the end of the century for sewer tunnelling in such diverse cities as Cincinnati, Melbourne and Paris.

In many cities now the greater demands of growing population and industry, and higher standards for rivers makes continuous improvement necessary, including large tunnelled intercepting sewers to eliminate direct discharge into rivers or sea. Extensions of existing outfalls into the sea to much deeper levels further offshore are being demanded. A notable example is that of Los Angeles, where a 4 m tube has been extended 8 km into the Pacific to a depth of 60 m of water; this was laid by submerged tube methods—perhaps more akin to pipe laying than to tunnelling—in exposed oceanic conditions to this great depth. Sydney, Australia, now proposes sea outfalls 4 km long.

Another city with special problems is Mexico City, built on deep lacustrine deposits which continue to subside steadily under the weight of the city's buildings through the years, so that a surrounding canal which used to drain the city is now left high above it.

1.8.6 Other tunnels

Tunnels to carry cables or pipes are numerous and important but have not usually been of large dimensions or otherwise remarkable in construction. The cable tunnel under the river Severn has already been mentioned. A similar cable tunnel was driven through chalk under the river Thames near Tilbury. The London Post Office tube railway runs for some 11 km between Paddington and Liverpool Street and carries mails in automatic trains without drivers. It was tunnelled over the years 1914-17 but not equipped and commissioned until 1924-27.

Tunnels for storage of oil and other materials have been constructed widely, as well as tunnels for shelter and defence purposes, as for example in Gibraltar where provision was made for all requirements for a garrison to remain underground for a long period. Another aspect of underground construction is for car parking in cities, but not necessarily by tunnelling techniques.

Many new methods of excavation have been proposed including rock fusion and hydraulic jetting, but none has yet been sufficiently developed to supersede some form of digging tool for soft ground, and drilling and blasting or mechanical excavations for hard rock—merely developments of the primitive antler pick and fire setting.

1.9 FUTURE PROGRESS

Perhaps the most fitting conclusion for this chapter is to record an international beginning and continuing developments. An O.E.C.D. Advisory Conference was held in Washington in 1970 and attended by representatives of nineteen countries. The main aims of the conference were:

(1) to assess the most important strengths and weaknesses of present-day tunnelling technology;
(2) to identify the principal needs for improvement; and
(3) to recommend government policies—including policies for research, development and demonstration—designed to stimulate rapid progress in tunnelling technology.

According to a survey some 13000 km of tunnels were constructed in the decade 1960-69, and twice as much was expected in the succeeding decade. This excludes mining tunnels.

The conference agreed on five recommendations. They are too lengthy to be quoted in full but their subjects may be indicated as follows:

(1) That each country should designate a national agency for coordination and stimulation of improvement.
(2) That in every urban area a single agency should maintain records and a master plan.
(3) That in evaluation account be taken of indirect as well as direct costs and benefits.
(4) That each country should promote application of technical advances in tunnelling.
(5) That working ties be established between national agencies as well as through an international commission.

Since that conference, the professional aspects of tunnelling have progressed steadily. The International Tunnelling Association was formed in 1974 and meets annually, principally these days to review the progress of its various working parties each covering some specialised aspect. Its twenty six member nations include almost all the major countries to whom tunnels are important.

Tunnels have been the subject of an increased amount of research at universities and laboratories (such as the Transport and Road Research Laboratory in Britain), and there are now regular conferences on tunnelling in many countries and a vastly increased exchange of information internationally.

All this activity has helped to bring the potential value of tunnels to the attention of politicians and planners, and although many projects have been delayed recently by the widespread recession, it seems certain that tunnels will play an increasing role in the future.

BIBLIOGRAPHY

A short bibliography appears at the end of each Chapter. A comprehensive bibliography will be included in the second volume.

There are a few books which specifically deal with the history of tunnelling, and much additional historical material is to be found in descriptions of methods and projects, in biographies and incidentally in recorded discussions at meetings of the Institution of Civil Engineers and elsewhere.

The appended list first gives some early classic books and papers *in order of date of publication* followed by books primarily historic in their content. It is far from exhaustive, and reference should be made to other chapters, although some titles may be repeated.

Simms, F. W., *Practical Tunnelling*, Crosby Lockwood, 1844 (revised and enlarged 1859, 1877, 1896).

Bazalgette, J. W., 'On the main drainage of London, and the interception of the sewage from the River Thames', *Min. Proc. Instn. Civ. Engs.* 1865, **24**.

Brunel, I., *The Life of Isambard Kingdom Brunel, Civil Engineer*, Longmans, 1870.

Drinker, H. S., *Tunneling, explosive compounds and rock drills*, J. Wiley, 1878.

Gripper, C. F., *Railway tunnelling in heavy ground*, Spon, 1879.

Baker, B, 'The Metropolitan and Metropolitan District Railways,' *Min. Proc. Instn. Civil Engineers*, 1885, **81**.

Wolfe Barry, J., 'The City lines and extensions (Inner Circle Completion) of the Metropolitan and District Railways , *ibid*, 1885, **81**.

Burr, S. D. V., *Tunneling under the Hudson River*, J. Wiley, 1885 (reprinted A. A. Mathews, Arcadia, 1968).

Fox, F., 'The Mersey Railway', *Min. Proc. Instn. Civ. Engs.* 1886, **86**.

Walker, T. A., *The Severn Tunnel*, Bentley, 1888 (reprinted Kingsmead, 1969).

Greathead, J. H., 'The City and South London Railway; with some remarks upon subaqueous tunnelling by shield and compressed air', *Min. Proc. Instn. Civ. Engs.* 1895, **123**.

Leitch, W. O., 'Iron Tunnels', *ibid*, 1896, **125**.

Hay, D. and Fitzmaurice, M., 'The Blackwall Tunnel', *ibid*, 1897, **130**.

Dalrymple-Hay, H. H., 'The Waterloo and City Railway', *ibid*, 1899, **139**.

Halcrow, W. T., 'A Century of Tunnelling', *Proc. Instn. Mech. Engrs.*, 1941, **146**.

Rolt, L. T. C., *Isambard Kingdom Brunel*, Longmans, 1957.

Lampe, D., *The Tunnel; the story of the world's first tunnel under a navigable river, dug beneath the Thames, 1824–42*, Harrap, 1963.

Sandstrom, G. E., *The History of Tunnelling*, Barrie & Rockliff, 1963.

Coleman, T., *The Railway Navvies*, Hutchinson, 1965.

Clements, P., *Marc Isambard Brunel*, Longmans, 1970.

Beaver, P., *A History of Tunnels*, P. Davies, 1972.

2

Functions and Requirements

In any systematic consideration of tunnels and the appropriate methods of construction, the function of the finished tunnel is of fundamental importance. The purposes of tunnels—and consequently their size, shape and lining—are diverse. In planning and construction important factors to be examined in relation to function include: situation, ground, dimensions and geometry, structural form, construction method and permanent equipment. The object of this chapter is to review the range of uses and the interactions between function and these other factors. Particular functions, structures and methods are dealt with in more detail in later chapters.

Costs are not discussed in any precise terms. Too much space and time would be needed to abstract comparable figures and to present them in any useful form, even apart from making proper allowances for inflation and other changing conditions. The resources demanded by practicable alternatives may be the most significant measure. Another aspect is cost/benefit analysis which takes account of indirect social and environmental costs as fairly as possible.

2.1 FACTORS RELATED TO FUNCTION

The factors referred to above may here be explained a little more fully in general terms. They are mutually interdependent and are not separate aspects for decision.

1. 'Situation' for a tunnel may be through a mountain or hill, or subaqueous, or urban.
2. 'Ground' may be anything from soft silt to hard uniform rock covering a very wide range of behaviour in excavation; water may play an important part. Any choice of ground implies changes in geometry, structural form and construction method.
3. 'Dimensions and geometry' are those of the finished tunnel: width, height and length, together with levels and gradients and curves. Specified limits may be very narrow or offer a wide range of possibilities.

4. 'Structural form' may be circle, horseshoe, rectangle or other shape incorporating cast-iron, concrete, brickwork, sprayed concrete, etc., to carry the
loads imposed. The nature of the ground and method of construction
influence strongly the structural form.

5. 'Construction methods' range from boring by drilling and blasting, or by
tunnelling machine, or with or without a shield, to cut-and-cover in various
sequences, and submerged prefabricated tunnels. The choice of method is
limited by the ground conditions, but also by available resources in the
widest sense.

6. 'Equipment' of the completed tunnel includes such features as roadway or
rail track, lighting, ventilation, decorative and functional finishes, control
systems. The special needs of each category of tunnel will be further referred
to.

All of these things should be taken fully into account in the planning and design
of the project. It is usually most unsatisfactory and inefficient to make substantial additions or alterations at a later stage, except where proper provision
has been made in the original planning.

2.2 PRINCIPAL FUNCTIONS

The principal functions for which tunnels, other than mining tunnels and
military sappers' tunnels, are built include:

A. Transportation
   1. People and goods: pedestrian and cycle subways
                               railways and metros
                               highways
   2. Water: canals
                               city supplies
                               irrigation
                               hydroelectric power
                               cooling water
   3. Sewers:
   4. Cables and piped services:

B. Storage and Plant
   1. Car parks
   2. Cavern storage of oil
   3. Underground power stations
   4. Military stocks
   5. Disposal of radioactive waste

C. Protection of People
   1. Shelters
   2. Control posts

2.3 SITUATION

The reason for tunnelling for transportation is to pass underneath obstacles, which may be hill or mountain ridges, rivers or seas, city streets and buildings or other structures.

2.3.1 Mountain Range

If the obstacle is a mountain range passage through it by tunnel can effect a great saving in time and energy and, indeed, may make practicable a crossing which would otherwise demand gradients and curves quite unacceptable for the purpose. The progression from canals, which must be level except for steps at locks, through railways, where gradients greater than about 1 or 2% are unsatisfactory, to highways with acceptable gradients of 3 or 4% marks also the historic sequence of tunnel development.

 If the attempt is made to plan the layout of a surface route up a valley having a col at the head to be crossed, progressive difficulty is to be expected as the col is approached and the valley becomes narrower and steeper. The ruling gradient of railway or highway can only be worked to by attempting to climb as quickly as permissible from the starting point, utilising the sides of the valley and cutting steadily upwards across the contour lines. With increasing steepness and reducing width for deviations the col may be unattainable, and a summit tunnel becomes inevitable. Such a procedure offers the minimum length of tunnel, but there is usually the alternative of driving a longer tunnel at a lower level with shorter or easier gradients and easier curves, effecting operational savings in distance, climb, fuel consumption and time, but at greater capital cost. This is the typical problem that becomes extreme in the Alpine type of tunnel, whether for rail or road. The long costly tunnel justifies the capital investment if sufficient traffic can be attracted.

2.3.2 Subaqueous

Examples of passage under waterways have been described in their historical context. The choice of a tunnel rather than a bridge for the crossing of a river or estuary depends on the factors peculiar to each situation. Where numerous traffic lanes are wanted and where foundation conditions make possible moderate spans, the bridge may well be the cheaper alternative but the cost of very long bridge spans increases disproportionately, and if foundation conditions are unfavourable and if shipping requires long spans and high clearances, the tunnel becomes the better choice. However aesthetically exciting great bridges may be in their main spans, long approaches at high level through a city are as a rule far from pleasing and can form a serious obstruction to traffic circulation and land use at ground level.

 Another advantage of tunnelling may arise from construction in stages. An ultimate requirement for a six-lane river crossing as traffic develops over a period of years can be met by a series of two-lane tunnels as needed, whereas virtually the whole capital cost of a six-lane bridge would be incurred in the initial construction and it would remain under-employed for a long period. The successive construction of two-lane tunnels in this pattern of development is illustrated by the Lincoln tunnels in New York, opened in 1937, 1945 and 1957, and in England by the Mersey Kingsway tunnels opened in 1971 and 1974 and the Dartford tunnels opened in 1963 and 1980.

In the case of surface railways the subaqueous tunnel is handicapped by the need to descend far below ground level and rise to the surface again while providing a gradient much flatter than is acceptable for road transport. This does not apply in the same degree to metro systems which generally remain well below ground level.

2.3.3 Urban
Tunnelling under city streets has now become a common activity for nearly all the types of transportation listed except canals, but long urban tunnels are principally for metros, water supply, and sewers. Much shorter tunnels are required for highway underpasses and pedestrian subways, most usually constructed in cut-and-cover. Longer highway tunnels are sometimes suggested but problems of access and ventilation add greatly to the difficulty and cost, against which preservation of surface land and gains in environmental amenity may prove a quite inadequate offset.

2.4 PEDESTRIAN AND CYCLE SUBWAYS
2.4.1 Pedestrian subways
Pedestrian subways are in many ways the least demanding of tunnels—perhaps they are also the most primitive—because the pedestrian is able to descend and ascend steps and quite steep gradients, and to turn corners sharply. The absolute limitations on tunnelling are therefore few, but most modern pedestrian subways are intended to offer an attractive alternative to the use of the surface, as in crossing a street, and therefore most go far beyond minimum standards. The old gloomy passage, brick-lined, damp and poorly lit is very different from the modern subway of the city centre—spacious and bright, lined with decorative tiling and having easy approach ramps.

The shallow subway will probably be constructed in cut-and-cover, but for connecting passages in metro stations at deeper level, bored tunnelling will be necessary. Minimum space requirements are: headroom of about 2.3 m, width for passing of at least 2 m, and preferably more, and moderate gradients which should be less than 10%. Where steps are acceptable the rise can be as steep as 1 in 2, but the total rise of each flight should be no more than about 3 m.

Drainage, adequate for the worst rainstorm, must be provided, utilising storage and pumping if necessary. Emergencies such as tidal flooding and bursting of water mains must be examined at the design stage and provided for, at least to the extent necessary to prevent major catastrophes.

Lighting should be of the highest standard practicable and of robust construction, vandal-proof if possible in exposed situations.

The usefulness of a subway can be greatly enhanced by good decorative finishes which attract users. Ceramic tiles or terrazzo provide such a finish: vitreous mosaic tiling is perhaps even better and less easily damaged, but there are many other suitable finishes depending on situation and usage.

It is usually important also that a subway should be as shallow as possible so as not to discourage the user by long descents and ascents. This implies minimum roof construction depth and may make it difficult to incorporate ceiling lighting.

2.4.2 Cycle subways

There is in some highway systems a need to provide separate accommodation for cyclists. Their use of the main carriageways may be dangerous and obstructive. A subway similar to that for pedestrians may be provided at street crossings, but with gradients not exceeding about 1 in 10 and, of course, without steps.

A special requirement appears where a subaqueous tunnel is built to replace a ferry in an industrial area where cycle transport is important. For the Tyne crossing a separate cycle tunnel (and also a pedestrian tunnel) served by an escalator was built (see Fig. 2.1). In the Clyde tunnel a cycle track and pedestrian path were incorporated in the invert of the main tunnel beneath the road deck.

2.5 RAILWAYS

Tunnels for railways are discussed at greater length in later chapters and therefore the references here are only intended to relate their special features to those of other tunnels. The typical situations for main line railways are mountain ranges, hills and subaqueous crossings. Every kind of ground is liable to be encountered. In mountain ranges, complex patterns of folding and faulting present various strata dipping at any angle and including belts of shattered rock and squeezing rock. Water is usually encountered, sometimes at high pressure and temperature. In undulating country, the conditions are likely to be less severe, but clays may involve particular difficulties.

For subaqueous crossings, tunnels have been cut through anything from the near liquid silts of the Hudson river to the volcanic and other beds of the Seikan tunnel, and water is always a hazard.

The typical railway tunnel is about 5 m wide x 7 m high for a single-track tunnel and about 8.5 m x 7 m for twin tracks, the choice depending on volume of traffic, and also on problems of rock support in a wide tunnel. What governs the longitudinal profile of all railway tunnels is an acceptable gradient. Less than 1% is preferred but steeper gradients may have to be adopted in many

Fig. 2.1 — Pedestrian and Cycle Tunnels under river Tyne.

circumstances. The ability to restart a stopped train on a rising gradient is an operational necessity. The ultimate controlling factors are loco power and rail adhesion. The other principal geometrical factor is curvature, which is governed by much the same rules as on the open line in relation to speed.

The commonest structural form for railway tunnels is probably the horseshoe, the ground being protected and supported by a lining wherever there is any looseness or uncertainty about the exposed rock. In the past brickwork and masonry from local sources were often used. In modern tunnels sprayed concrete, steel arch ribs and *in situ* concrete are most usual in sound rock. Where the tunnel is through clay slow plastic movement is to be feared and the bottom must be protected with an invert arch or at least a strut across the base of the side walls. A complete circular form with segmental concrete or even cast iron lining has been constructed in some cases.

Construction methods are not peculiar to railway work except where rail rather than road access and transport are adopted.

Equipment comprising track, signalling and other features are dealt with in Volume 2.

2.6 METRO SYSTEMS

As with main line railway tunnels the requirements for metros are dealt with in later chapters in more detail, but are outlined here. They differ significantly from main line railways in many respects. The tunnel, the rolling stock and all the equipment are, or should be, designed as an integrated system if it is reasonably self-contained. Sometimes it is necessary to accommodate main line or suburban rolling stock, but this is unlikely to lead to overall economy unless the metro line is essentially a subsurface section of a primary surface railway.

Metro tunnels are intrinsically urban, but will frequently include subaqueous sections, because few major cities are without rivers to cross, and many are sea ports. Hill tunnelling on a minor scale is also encountered, but not mountain tunnelling in its full sense. In general, metro tunnelling is as shallow as practicable because of the importance of easy and rapid access to and from the surface.

Many major cities are situated on rivers and built on alluvial ground, with the consequence that if their metro tunnels are immediately sub-surface they must be through soft, and usually water-bearing ground. In many other cities, however, rock is present at quite shallow depth or outcropping at the surface in hilly areas. Typically, metro tunnels present a wide range of soils and usually considerable variability along any line.

Gradients may be steeper than with main line tunnels, because the system does not have to accept heavy goods trains but can be equipped with relatively light coaches with multiple motor drives. In contrast to some main line tunnels, watertight linings are usually considered essential and rails are therefore dry enough to give good adhesion. Gradients of 3.5% are acceptable, and, indeed, were unavoidable in some cities such as, for example, Toronto where the whole land slopes up at about that rate from the shores of Lake Ontario. In Montreal, steeper ground required gradients up to 6.3%, and pneumatic-tyred drive was adopted in order to improve adhesion, and hence acceleration, as well as for smooth riding.

There is sometimes merit in a deliberate switchback profile, whereby trains climb up to stations, the gradient providing assistance in braking, and reabsorbing kinetic energy, while a corresponding descent aids acceleration out of stations. An additional advantage may lie in having the stations less deep than would otherwise be the case, but, conversely, greater depth of excavation in cut-and-cover between stations might be impracticable.

In dealing with shape, size and structure there are substantial differences according to whether construction is by bored tunnel or cut-and-cover. The choice of method is a complex matter, but cut-and-cover is likely to be preferred where it is possible to follow a shallow subsurface route without unacceptable disruption of streets and services, while deeper tunnelling is progressively more necessary in heavily congested city areas.

In cut-and-cover twin tracks are usually accommodated in a rectangular reinforced concrete box with a central wall or line of columns. Dimensions and clearances can follow normal railway principles adapted to the rolling stock provided, and any abnormal loads which may be specified.

In bored tunnels a circular tube with cast-iron or concrete lining is almost invariable with the diameter designed to be a minimum, because cost increases disproportionately as excavated area increases. Accuracy of alignment is then more vital than for any other tunnel, because clearances between rolling stock and structure are so small. For high speed operating, modern track is laid with precision, embodying transition curves and superelevation to which the tunnel lining must conform. Inevitable errors of shape and position may necessitate rebuilding of lining which is a troublesome and time-consuming operation, and sometimes hazardous. Within limits, redesign of the curves and realignment of the track is usually possible while maintaining basic standards.

Even in sound rock some lining is desirable to protect passenger trains against even trivial falls of rock which could be disproportionately troublesome.

In deep systems station tunnels are much larger than running tunnels; they may be bored, or may be built in deep pits from the surface. High standards of watertightness with aesthetically acceptable linings, finishings and lighting are called for. These requirements, together with those for track, signalling, fire precautions, passenger amenities generally, and ventilation and movement of air are discussed in greater detail in volume 2.

2.7 HIGHWAYS

Highway tunnels may be in any situation where tunnelling is possible.

For long tunnels with heavy traffic the proper furnishing and equipment become quite elaborate and are dealt with in more detail in Volume 2. Here the broad differences from other tunnels are outlined.

In comparison with main line railways a very important difference is the permissible gradient, which may be at least three times as steep. This is particularly relevant to subaqueous road tunnels where a descent of the order of 30 m is necessary in order to pass under a navigable waterway. A gradient of 3½% to 4½% is normal, and in special conditions, such as the Clyde tunnel, short approach ramps on a restricted site may justify as steep a gradient as 6½%. It may be noted that a 30 m descent at 3% requires a length of 1000 m, much of it in tunnel, whereas a 6% gradient halves this length.

In summit tunnels steep gradients do not usually present a problem as the climbing is done before the tunnel is entered and its profile is likely to be nearly level with sufficient slope only to ensure drainage.

Although steep gradients are negotiable by road vehicles there are three factors that make them progressively more undesirable. On a long ascent of 1 in 30 heavy vehicles fully loaded can usually maintain a moderate road speed, but if the climb is steeper many will have to change down to low gear and will slow down all traffic to perhaps 15 kph or less, thereby reducing the capacity of the tunnel. In climbing steep gradients the output of noxious fumes—CO from petrol engines and smoke from diesels—increases disproportionately and makes greater demands on ventilation. A third objection to a steep gradient is the danger from vehicles running down out of control.

There are, of course, mountain tunnels having an overall one-way gradient through spurs or ridges. This gradient must be governed by the ruling gradient of the road system as a whole, but with special consideration of the three factors described above.

Horizontal curves may be much sharper than for railways if necessary although both for construction and for use the driving of a tunnel on a sharp curve should preferably be avoided. A radius of 400 m is not difficult for construction or traffic, and even sharper curves are practicable. At the north end of the Tyne tunnel there is a semi-circle having a radius of 128 m, built in tunnel to allow the roadway to emerge in a level area and provide access to a road junction close to the river bank.

Vertical curves at change of gradient are subject to much the same considerations as on the open road, but with the additional factor, not generally of major importance, that in a dip the sight line is restricted by the tunnel ceiling. A radius of 1000 m gives a reasonable road profile, especially as very high speeds need not be usually allowed for.

Dimensions of highway tunnels have increased with the steady development of road vehicles. It has been usual to provide at least two traffic lanes rather than single lane one-way tunnels in which it would be very difficult to ensure access to accidents. Road widths for two lanes have grown from 4.9 m in the early Blackwall tunnel (1897) up to 7.3 m in many modern tunnels, and occasionally 7.5 m. Preferred headroom in British tunnels is currently 5.4 m but in Europe 4.5 m is widely accepted: sometimes, however, greater height is provided in port areas.

In all tunnelling, increase in width imposes increase of cost not only in direct proportion but additionally by the structural consequences of increased roof span. In circular tunnels the vertical diameter is similarly increased and the excavated area then increases as the square of the diameter. A further increase may be necessary in the strength of the lining and therefore in its thickness. For subaqueous tunnels whose level is determined by minimum cover under a channel or rock surface, extra height imposes a lower road level and in turn longer approach ramps. Constructional problems of increased size are discussed in a later chapter. Economy of dimensions is obviously most important, and any substantial increase can be very costly.

It is these factors that lead to the construction of two-lane units and discourage the provision of wider carriageways, which are sometimes suggested as advantageous in preventing complete stoppage when a single vehicle breaks down.

The Mersey Queensway tunnel (1934) is exceptional in having a four-lane carriageway in a single circular bore, although the road width is only 11.0 m. The tunnel was driven through rock in free air and the main midriver section is a 13.4 m diameter circle, cast-iron lined. There was much unoccupied space beneath the roadway, thought suitable for carrying a tramway but not so employed, and now used for ventilation and for cables and pipes.

Submerged unit tunnels of rectangular section are much less sensitive to increases of width; wider lanes and as many as are justified by traffic needs can be accommodated in a single structure. For this form of tunnel comparison with a multi-lane bridge, referred to above, is much more direct.

Highway traffic cannot be constrained to run on any precise track like rail traffic, and therefore it is essential to allow adequate tolerances in deciding on the dimensions of the tunnel. Construction must follow as precisely as possible the designed line and dimensions. As in the case of metro tunnels, but with rather more latitude, it is likely to be necessary to prepare a three-dimensional 'wriggle diagram' to fit the required road geometry into the tunnel space.

Ground encountered and methods of construction are so varied and cover such a range that no aspects peculiar to highways invite comment. Shield drives, drill and blast, TBM's, cut-and-cover, and submerged units all have their applications, and even the small tunnel methods, including timbered headings and pipe jacking may serve ancillary purposes.

Lighting and ventilation can both have important influence on construction. They are more fully discussed in Volume 2. Artificial lighting of a very high standard is essential in all but the shortest tunnels. The human eye adapts quickly, but not instantaneously to changes in luminosity and, particularly in driving from bright sunlight into a tunnel, the provision of graduated diminution of light is most valuable. Such devices as sun visors outside the portals and much extra lighting within the portal area are used. At night the lighting within the tunnel is likely to be as good as or better than that outside; the transition boost lighting is then switched off and perhaps the tunnel lighting is also reduced.

Ventilation is a large specialised subject in itself and can have an important influence on the construction of the tunnel. Working shafts can be planned for incorporation as permanent air shafts, and the air ducts and their connections into the tunnel space may provide complex problems of design, excavation and construction. The provision of power supplies and emergency arrangements for lighting and ventilation is again something to be planned from the beginning.

Drainage has two aspects: first, the drainage of ground water entering the tunnel through the lining and second, surface water entering at the portals, carried in on vehicles, perhaps as snow, and flooding from burst water pipes or from the use of fire hoses. The leakage of ground water is minimised by water-proofing techniques during construction and is not likely to be a major operating problem in a well-built tunnel even if water is deliberately drawn off from the lining in order to prevent pressure building up. Ground water in very small volume can however be a serious decorative problem, as major seepages quickly contribute to staining of any finishes and assist in the build-up of sooty deposits which may be corrosive. Seepage water will frequently carry lime or other salts in solution and deposit them where it emerges.

In summit tunnels and those on a steady gradient all water can be drained to the portals by gravity, but in a subaqueous tunnel or a city underpass all water drains to the lowest point where a sump and pumps must be provided of capacity adequate for all probable emergencies.

Other features special to highway tunnels are traffic control systems and fire precautions, and provision for breakdowns and accidents. All these systems have to be devised to operate in conjunction with a random sample of the public, many unfamiliar with the particular tunnel. One important feature should be an effective means of quickly stopping traffic from entering the tunnel if an incident gives rise to obstruction of the tunnel or any other danger.

Some highway tunnels permit the passage of pedestrians and cyclists. Such provision reduces the traffic capacity and adds disproportionately to the cost, unless separate space can economically be provided. Because overtaking in tunnels is not normally safe, cyclists will slow down the whole flow of traffic unless segregated. Also, cyclists and pedestrians will require a higher standard of dilution of carbon monoxide because they are exposed for a longer time and while taking exercise. If the obligation to allow pedestrians and cyclists the use of a tunnel is unavoidable, it may be met by provision of a separate tunnel, as described earlier.

2.8 WATER CONVEYANCE

Tunnels to convey water, or sewage, have various features in common. The principal characteristics required are smoothness, and watertightness, but the need for these differs in degree. There are important differences in tunnels required merely to allow water to flow through them at low pressure, often without the bore being full—free discharge tunnels—and those in which the water is under high pressure, possibly very high pressure, as in the supply to turbines or in a town supply aqueduct passing under a valley.

The importance of smooth lining depends on the velocity of the water and on the length of the tunnel. Smoothness is relatively unimportant for a canal where movement of water is minimal, but can be most valuable in maximising the flow through an aqueduct or in minimising loss of head in power development.

The requirement for watertightness is also dependent in part on pressure, internal or external. High pressure tunnels must be extremely well sealed against water losses which could quickly result in serious erosion. In sewers, also, water losses can cause dangerous contamination, and even very small leaks may be enlarged by chemical action. Drinking water supplies must be secured against contamination by inward leakage when running at low pressure. Canals are perhaps the least demanding in this respect, and indeed may benefit from inflow of water, but must be well sealed against outward leakage.

Another general requirement for water tunnels is a means of access for inspection, maintenance and repair. Any system of penstocks or dams must be planned with this in mind.

2.8.1 Canals

The absolute requirements of a canal tunnel are: a level tunnel, retention of water and space for passage of barges. These relate particularly to transport canals. In canals feeding hydro-electric schemes minimum loss of head may be the overriding consideration. The level requirement is, of course, fundamental, from which it follows that canal tunnels are through ridges only and cannot as such dip down under rivers. Sections of an irrigation or supply canal can, of course, be connected by inverted siphon pipes or tunnels under obstacles.

Retention of water can be very important, as canal tunnels are most common on a summit level, where adequate water supply is most difficult, but essential to the operation of locks on both sides of the summit. If water can be not merely conserved but collected within the tunnel it is an added advantage. Lining of the canal invert with clay puddle was a usual practice together with the use of timber boarding. Other linings such as brickwork may be required.

Historically, space for passage ranges from 2.2 m x 3.6 m for the British 'narrow boat' in the Harecastle tunnel up to 32 m x 15 m in the Rove tunnel. The Harecastle tunnel was one way only at a time and without a towpath, the boats being 'legged' through by the crew. The use of engines and of tugs in tunnels gave rise to ventilation problems which in some cases have been solved by use of an electrically operated tug.

2.8.2 City supplies

The supply of pure water by aqueducts to cities is an ancient need, often demanding tunnelling. The problems of collection and storage in mountain areas are discussed later; they are much the same whether the water is for town supplies, irrigation or hydroelectric power. The aqueducts from dam site to city may be pipes on or above the surface or in trench, but tunnelling becomes necessary where ridges have to be crossed, or economically advantageous, as in London's supply, where other obstructions are numerous and a convenient route is available at depth in the clay. For these tunnels generally the water is not at very high pressure and they may even flow only part full. The principal requirements are: an overall downward hydraulic gradient accordant with the required volume and velocity of the water, a smooth unobstructed bore, and a watertight lining.

Manning's formula, $v = k\ R^{2/3}S^{1/2}$ connects velocity of water, roughness of tunnel (k), hydraulic mean depth (R), and hydraulic gradient (S). k is a roughness factor ranging from 100 for a large tunnel with exceptionally smooth bore down to the very low value of 25 for an unlined rock tunnel. For a concrete lined tunnel an average value is about 80. From such figures as these the value of smooth lining can be assessed for particular conditions.

Although small losses of water by leakage from a short aqueduct may in themselves be unimportant unless the leaks are enlarged by erosion, the cumulative loss from a long aqueduct becomes excessive and therefore a high standard is essential. Contamination by inward leakage is less likely, except perhaps if the supply fails or the pipe is emptied, but must be guarded against.

Tunnel sizes are determined to carry the necessary volume, using the available gradient, and linings are specified to perform three principal functions: first, any required support of the excavated ground; second, provision of the appropriate smooth bore; third, watertightness in both directions. As there is a minimum practical diameter of about 2 m for tunnels other than the shortest headings, tunnel size will sometimes be more than is otherwise necessary. Control by penstocks, and facilities for inspection and maintenance will be necessary, and surge shafts may be provided. Rates of flow in city water supplies are likely to be much more uniform than in hydroelectric tunnels, or in irrigation schemes.

2.8.3 Irrigation

Tunnels may also be required at most stages of irrigation projects: for collection of water, bypass of dams, transfer of water, and distribution. The tunnel requirements and problems are very much the same as for city supplies. There are schemes combining the two, such as the very large Orange—Fish river scheme in South Africa. Combined irrigation and hydroelectric power schemes are also numerous.

2.8.4 Hydroelectric power

As described in Chapter 1, many modern hydroelectric generating stations are sited underground in mountainous areas, and the practice is growing of incorporating pumped storage systems in their design. The tunnelling becomes quite complex.

In terms of tunnel requirements there are, in addition to the access and cable tunnels, at least three separate functional tunnel types. These are:

a. Free discharge.
b. High pressure water tunnels ('penstocks') feeding into turbines.
c. Machine halls and transformer halls, excavated as caverns out of solid rock.

2.8.4.1 Free discharge tunnels

For collection of water from adjacent, or even remote, valleys, tunnels through mountain ridges may be required. Their function is simply to carry the available water as directly as possible to the main reservoir. The considerations as to size, gradient and lining are very much the same as for water supply; minor leakages are not likely to be important in themselves and smoothness of bore will only matter to the extent that it may make possible a smaller tunnel.

From reservoir to pressure shaft a tunnel will be continuously full, but at relatively low pressure. Minimum acceptable loss of head determines the appropriate diameter and smoothness, while a gentle gradient to permit the tunnel to be emptied for inspection and maintenance is usual. The hydrodynamic consequences of surges back from the pressure shaft must be studied in each particular system to ensure that no damage results and that no air is entrained.

Tail race discharge tunnels must be adequate to carry the maximum turbine discharge without any obstructive back pressure. As the turbines will be sited at a low level to utilise maximum head of water the gradient for the tail race will be as flat as possible. Therefore adequate area and smooth bore are likely to be important. There will also be a need to ensure against scour and erosion of the lining under any conditions of discharge. In some instances these discharge tunnels are designed to operate under pressure and require the provision of surge shafts or air shafts.

2.8.4.2 High pressure tunnels

The turbo generators being sited at low level as described above must be fed with high pressure water by the most direct line possible, minimising loss of head by friction and at bends and changes of section. A very steeply inclined or vertical shaft is usual. Hydrostatic pressures at turbine level are very high and additionally there are shock waves and surge pressures arising from the shutting or opening of turbine penstocks to vary output in accordance with demand. These pressures are kept within limits by the use of surge shafts or chambers. The hydrodynamic system comprising tunnels, shafts, pipes and turbines has to be designed as a whole to handle the very high energy of the moving mass of water. In the earlier stations it was usual for steel pressure pipes to run at the surface down the mountain side into the station, but pressure tunnels and steel-lined shafts now often take the place of the exposed pipes. In underground power stations this is necessarily the case as illustrated in the simplified section (Fig. 2.2).

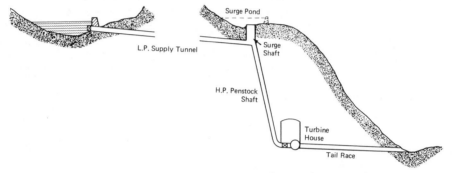

Fig. 2.2 – Diagram of hydraulic tunnels in underground power station.

The peculiar requirements of these pressure tunnels are therefore: a steep gradient requiring shaft sinking techniques rather than tunnelling and a lining capable of resisting high pressures and remaining watertight.

At great depths in rock it may be necessary to consider the natural undisturbed rock as being stressed hydrostatically under its own weight. After relaxation of this stress by virtue of the excavation the load may slowly build up again so that high stresses are ultimately imposed on the tunnel structure. To meet this condition the tunnel structure can be designed to comprise not only the lining but also such of the surrounding rock as can be integrated with it by sound construction methods.

The lining is likely to be a composite structure of concrete casing with a welded steel inner lining. The steel must not only be adequate in tension for the internal water pressure but must also be secured against the contingency of buckling when the tunnel is empty and external water and rock pressures develop. Against internal pressure substantial support to the steel plate is given by the concrete lining and also by the surrounding rock, but against external pressure the steel must be adequately anchored into the concrete.

High pressure grouting behind the concrete lining can be of great value, and indeed can be used to effect precompression of the concrete lining, which helps in avoiding tension from the subsequent high internal pressures. It was in the study of these varying stress conditions that much of the science of Rock Mechanics has been developed.

2.8.4.3 Machinery halls

Very large caverns are required for generating stations installed underground. Turbo-generators, transformers, switchgear and penstock controls must all be accommodated; and access for operation, maintenance and renewal will be needed, and cable runs and ventilation will also require tunnels or shafts.

The main chambers are usually much too large for full face tunnelling as a single operation. The chamber may have vertical walls and an arched roof with a span of 15 to 30 m. Sometimes the whole chamber is of horseshoe section. The typical procedure in its simplest form is for headings to be excavated along the springings of the arch followed by concreting of the skewback for the arch and then excavation for and construction of the arch, under the protection of which the bulk excavation can follow. The thickness of lining obviously depends on the quality of the rock, but unless the rock generally is reasonably sound it is unlikely that this type of station will be built. Much more complex sequences of construction may be necessary, depending on rock types and structures, and on the interaction of the various parts of the project (see Figs. 2.3(a) & 2.3(b)).

2.8.5 Dam bypass tunnels

In building a dam the problem of controlling the flow of water across the line of the dam, both during construction and in subsequent use, is frequently solved by tunnelling through solid ground at one side of the dam site. If this is through sound rock, lined as necessary, the river can be diverted from its normal channel while the dam foundations are laid in relatively dry conditions. If tunnels are of sufficient size to take the river in full flood work can proceed throughout the year without interruption. There is also the further advantage of allowing the dam to be built as a continuous structure without temporary apertures which have to be made good subsequently.

Whether or not diversion tunnels are used for construction, tunnels for draw off may be required. Water may be required from the same reservoir both for irrigation and for power generation, and there may also be a need for release of flood water. Separate tunnels in parallel can serve all these purposes. Except for power generation extreme smoothness is unlikely to be necessary but very high velocities and turbulence may be expected in dealing with floods, so that the tunnel must be properly lined unless the rock is absolutely sound.

The magnitude of such tunnels may be illustrated by those at the Mangla Dam on the River Indus where five tunnels of about 11 m diameter and each 500 m long were driven with a Robbins full face 'Mole'—later re-used for the Mersey Kingsway tunnel. The dangers of these great flows of water are apparent from the experience at the Tarbela Dam, also on the River Indus, where four diversion/draw off tunnels were used. When filling the reservoir in 1974 an enormous cavity developed over one of the concrete lined tunnels and some

Fig. 2.3(a) − Cruachan Pumped Storage − Machinery Hall: during excavation (Edmund Nuttall Limited).

Fig. 2.3(b) – Cruachan Pumped Storage – Machinery Hall: during installation of machinery (Edmund Nuttall Limited).

60 m of tunnel was washed away and a million cubic metres of ground, with loss of at least a year's use of the works.

2.8.6 Cooling water tunnels

Thermal and nuclear generating stations also require considerable supplies of water for efficient operation of the condensers, and tunnels are frequently necessary for the cooling water system. The usual hydraulic ideals of low velocity, large smooth bore, and absence of abrupt bends or changes of section apply to these tunnels so that pumping costs may be kept to the economic minimum.

The tunnels have to be driven in very varied and sometimes extremely difficult conditions where power stations are sited close to rivers and estuaries and varied alluvial deposits are encountered. Intakes and outfalls may have to be established in deep water, below the lowest tide level, involving difficult junctions between tunnel and shaft. Compressed air working is frequently necessary.

An unusual requirement for additional water at the oil fired Bankside power station in Central London, just across the river from St. Paul's Cathedral, was for gas washing to clean the sulphur oxides from the exhaust gas before discharging it to the atmosphere. Acid resistant lining in the discharge tunnel was necessary. As the river flow reverses with the tide, separation of the intake and outfall had to be effected by siting them on opposite sides of the river to avoid recirculation of warm water. The outfall tunnel was driven right across under the river bed into a shaft sunk from bed level. Another instance where difficult compressed air tunnelling was necessary through gravel and sand was for the nuclear generating station built on the Dungeness shingle promontory in Kent, where an old ship's timbers were encountered in the tunnel excavation. Submerged units sunk in the sea bed have been utilised at Kilroot in Co. Antrim.

2.9 SEWERS

All of the water that is supplied to a city has to be discharged again to a river system, and, because sewers start as pipes a little below ground level, the available head for discharge is normally very limited. In any case, there must be a continuous falling gradient along each sewer, no steeper than is adequate to carry the flow. Tunnelling becomes necessary when pipe depths become too great for trench excavation or when disturbance of the surface cannot be tolerated. Another tunnelling requirement arises when old sewer outfalls direct into a river or the sea are no longer permitted and new main collecting sewers must be built to carry the flows to treatment plants. Outfalls discharging limited quantities of untreated sewage into the sea are still considered satisfactory but must be carried out well beyond the tide line and may have to be tunnelled.

In comparing the mileage of tunnelling in Great Britain for various uses, other than in mine development, much the greatest is for sewers, and even although the tunnel diameter is not large, averaging perhaps about 3 m, the total excavated volume still exceeds that for any other purpose.

The primary needs for a sewer tunnel are precise gradient, smooth bore, watertightness and resistance to corrosion and erosion.

The flow in a sewer will vary greatly from dry weather flow to storm flow and the gradient must be such that adequate velocity is maintained at all times to carry solids and to prevent sand and grit from settling out. The capacity must be such as to carry the maximum storm flow. In order to maintain velocity when flow is minimal a large bore tunnelled sewer may be designed with a small half round channel in the invert, or as an egg-shaped section. Ventilation to avoid accumulation of noxious gases must always be provided.

The importance of watertightness is obvious. Brickwork of very high standard was widely used in the past; concrete is now commoner. If cast-iron is used for the structural lining it is likely to have an inner lining of brick or concrete. For the invert, blue engineering bricks provide a hard smooth surface resistant to corrosion. Very corrosive effluents from factories have sometimes to be accepted, or may be discharged accidentally. Scouring by sand and grit can also cause serious erosion unless a hard invert is provided. In hot climates, particularly where scarcity of water results in sluggish flow of concentrated sewage, linings above water level may be severely attacked by bacterial and acid action.

The smallest practicable size for driving a tunnel is about 0.7 m wide x 1.2 m high, excavated as a rectangular timbered heading, within which a pipe can be laid up to about 0.5 m diameter. It will be appreciated that a man can only work with difficulty in such restricted space and that so small a tunnel can hardly be continued for any great length. A system of tunnelling with a shield of 1 m diameter followed by lining with concrete rings built of three circular segments has been introduced.

In urban conditions there is often very little choice of route for a sewer and practically no choice of gradient; it must therefore be driven through whatever it meets, and the strata immediately beneath a city are likely to be very variable. Pipe jacking and tunnel jacking are of growing importance for sewer construction. The technique is more fully described in Chapter 4. Limitations on length are not serious if access manhole shafts can be utilised as thrust pits. Control of gradients may be found difficult.

The difficulties of bad ground increase disproportionately in large tunnels so that the relatively small size of sewer tunnels in some degree counterbalances the ground difficulties. The size also restricts the use of mechanised equipment, but tunnelling machines can be employed for larger trunk sewers where the diameter exceeds 3 m.

Sea outfalls can with advantage be tunnelled to beyond the low water mark, where pipe lines whether on the surface or in trench, would be vulnerable to storm damage and subject to the very corrosive conditions of intertide exposure.

An interesting development is the Chicago scheme to use deep level tunnels of large size to store temporarily storm water flows from the shallow combined sewerage system, so that pollution of Lake Michigan by uncontrolled and untreated overflow is avoided. A pumped storage scheme for generation of electricity is combined with the scheme.

For sewer tunnels additional requirements are the provision of means of access for inspection, cleaning and maintenance.

2.10 SERVICE TUNNELS

Increasing use is being made of tunnels to carry cables and piped services either under rivers or in cities. Where electricity cables carry much power they necessarily produce heat which must be dispersed. In some instances air cooling may be adequate but cooling by circulating water may be necessary. The Severn cable tunnel, 3600 m long, had to provide for heat removal amounting to 5000 kW by means of water circulated in pipes carrying the cables which are at 400 kV. Heating effects from trunk mains carried through highway tunnels may require special provisions.

Consideration has been given to the operation of cables at temperatures close to the absolute zero ($-373°C$) to take advantage of superconductivity, which eliminates all electrical resistance and the consequent heat losses. Such cables requiring very special arrangements for refrigeration and a very high standard of heat insulation would almost inevitably have to be carried in tunnels.

Telephone networks also make use of tunnels on a substantial scale in cities, allowing access for laying and inspection and room for expansion, and providing protection from the hazards of ducts laid in the ground.

Gas pipes are easily accommodated in tunnels specially provided for the individual service. Precautions are necessary against leakage and to monitor any escapes which might result in the build-up of a toxic or explosive atmospheric mixture. Proposals have been made for tunnels to be used for combined high pressure and low temperature storage and supply. A single kilometre of 3 m tunnel could provide a large storage capacity and reduce greatly the need for surface storage and also for big mains to handle peak flows.

It may be asked why so few examples exist in cities of tunnels designed to carry in a single subway the multiplicity of services required which are instead buried separately in trenches under the highways. The answer lies partly in the *ad hoc* manner in which the towns and cities—and the services themselves—have developed, partly in the numerous companies and authorities involved and partly in quite genuine difficulties of mutual occupation and safety.

Fig. 2.4 – Water mains in service tunnel under Manchester Ship ➤ Canal (Liverpool Corporation).

Among the special problems of mutual interference of services are: flooding from leaking or burst water mains, risks of explosion from leaking gas, induced electric currents interfering with telephone circuits or causing electrolytic corrosion, heat effects from electric cables carrying heavy currents. All those problems, as well as details of points of entry of each service to the tunnel and arrangements for repair and maintenance, need careful study and planning, not only for a common services tunnel but similarly if any such services are to be run through a highway tunnel. In a long highway tunnel the explosion risks from a very high pressure gas main might be quite unacceptable.

Nevertheless, there must be great potential savings to the community in this area. The cost of a sewer tunnel of minimum economic diameter is, in advantageous circumstances, no greater than the basic cost of digging a trench and providing and installing a 0.5 m diameter piped sewer. That comparison is valid without making any allowance for the disruption caused to surface traffic by the roadworks involved, and emphasises yet another important reason why service tunnels are so rare. The undertakings which dig up our highways to install and maintain services do not have to pay for the disruption they cause (indeed would be exceeding their terms of reference to do so), and the resulting distortion of the overall economics of the operation militates strongly against the construction of tunnels.

2.11 STORAGE AND OTHER TUNNELS

2.11.1 Storage
Storage underground is an ancient practice. Its most extensive modern use is probably for oil in bulk, having advantages of security against damage and fire, and causing minimal visual intrusion in areas where landscape is considered important. In suitable strata unlined cavern storage is possible at depth, oil drawn off being replaced temporarily by water to maintain a pressure balance until the oil supply is replenished. Tunnelled storage has also been used extensively to provide protection for explosives and other defence supplies and is a possible method for disposal of radioactive waste.

Underground car parks might be considered either as storage or as a facet of transportation. They are almost always constructed in cities, usually as basements in buildings, or under park areas.

2.11.2 Protection
Provision of a protected environment has been an important preoccupation of governments, particularly as a defence against nuclear weapons. Tunnelled shelters and control centres have obvious merits, particularly if massive rock is accessible. The special problems are perhaps less those of tunnelling than of structural resistance to explosives, and preservation of life and activity for a long period in a sealed environment.

2.11.3 Military
For the sake of completeness the sappers' art should be included. It has an ancient history in the undermining and breaching of fortifications, castles and city walls. Whether or not espionage tunnels fall into this category is a debatable question. The actual tunnelling methods are substantially those of driving of headings, with necessary timbering. Extensive tunnelling operations largely in chalk took place in France in World War I. More recently military tunnelling activity has been reported from Korea.

2.11.4 Mining
Apart from actual mining operations, many access tunnels and shafts are required in opening up coal and ore mines. The methods and machinery developed are very relevant to tunnelling for other purposes.

BIBLIOGRAPHY
The bibliography appended lists important books of general application to tunnel construction. A comprehensive bibliography will be included in Volume 2.

Virtually the whole range of tunnelling might be seen as covered by this chapter, but because highway, metro and railway tunnels are treated in more detail in separate chapters in Volume 2 the relevant brief bibliographies appear there. Tunnels conveying water and sewage are not further described as such in the book and some relevant publications on these subjects are therefore listed below.

General Tunnelling
Copperthwaite, W. C., *Tunnel shields and the use of compressed air in subaqueous works*, Constable, 1906.
Hewett, B. H. M. and Johannesson, S., *Shield and compressed air tunneling*, McGraw-Hill, 1922.
Richardson, H. W. and Mayo, R. S., *Practical tunnel driving*, McGraw-Hill, 1941 (Revised edn., R. S. Mayo, 1975).
Hammond, R., *Tunnel Engineering*, Heywood, 1959.
Pequignot, C. A. (ed.), *Tunnels and Tunnelling*, Hutchinson, 1963.
Szechy, K., *The art of tunnelling*, 2nd English edn., Akademiai Kiado, 1973.
Muir Wood, A. M., 'Tunnelling', chp. 30 *in* L. S. Blake (ed.), *Civil Engineer's Reference Book*, 3rd edn., Newnes-Butterworth, 1975.
Golder Associates and James F. MacLaren Ltd., *Tunnelling Technology*, Ontario Ministry of Transport and Communications, 1976.

Water, Sewage etc.
Humphreys, G. W., 'The main drainage system of London', *Min. Proc. Instn. Civ. Engrs.*, 1917, **204**.

Watson, D. M., 'West Middlesex main drainage, *J. Instn. Civ. Engrs.*, 1937, **5** (Apr.).

Scott, P. A., 'A 75 inch-diameter water main in tunnel: a new method of tunnelling in London clay', *Proc. Instn. Civ. Engrs.*, 1952, **1** (May).

Fulton, A. A., 'Civil engineering aspects of hydro-electric development in Scotland', *ibid*, 1952, **1** (July).

Tattersall F. and others, 'Investigations into the design of pressure tunnels in London Clay', *ibid*, 1955, **4** (July).

Jaeger, C., 'Present trends in the design of pressure tunnels and shafts for underground hydro-electric power stations', *ibid*, 1955, **4** (July).

Cuthbert, E. W. and Wood F, 'The Thames to Lee tunnel water main,' *ibid*, 1962, **21** (Feb). *See also* discussion 1962, **23** (Dec.).

Guthrie Brown, J., *'Hydro-electric engineering practice'*, **1**, *Civil Engineering*, Blackie, 1964.

Young, W. and Falkiner, R. H., 'Some design and construction features of the Cruachan pumped storage project', *Proc. Instn. Civ. Engrs.*, 1966, **35** (Nov.). *See also* discussion, 1967, **37** (Aug.).

Haswell, C. K., 'Thames Cable Tunnel', *ibid*, 1969, **44** (Dec.). *See also* discussion. 1970, **47** (Oct.).

Various authors, 'The Chicago Sewer System (Tunnel and Reservoir Plan – TARP)', *Proceedings Rapid Excavation and Tunnelling Conferences*:

1st, Chicago, 1972, Session 3, Chapters 57-61.

2nd, San Francisco, 1974, Session 4, Chapter 18.

3rd, Las Vegas, 1976, Session 11, Chapter 44.

4th, Atlanta, 1979, Session 19, Chapters 93-96.

Household, H., *The Thames and Severn Canal*, David & Charles, 1969.

Haswell, C. K., 'Tunnel under the Severn and Wye estuaries', *Proc. Instn. Civ. Engrs.*, 1973, **54** (Aug.). *See also* discussion, 1974, **56** (Aug.).

Crockett, A. S. and Dugdale, J., 'Development of Edinburgh's sewage disposal scheme', *ibid*, 1976, **60** (Feb.). *See also* discussion, 1976, **60** (Nov.).

Lander, J. H. and others, 'Foyers pumped storage project: planning and design'.

Land, D. D. and Hitchings, D. C., 'ditto: construction', *ibid*, 1978, **64** (Feb.). *See also* discussion, 1978, **64** (Nov.).

Hadfield, C., *British Canals*, 6th edn., David & Charles, 1979.

Muir Wood, A. M. and others, 'Dams and their tunnels', *Int. Wat. Pwr. Dam Constr.*, 1980, **32** (Feb., Mar., Apr. and May).

3

Investigations

3.1 PLANNING

Before a tunnel can be planned in outline and designed in detail much information on the physical aspects of the project must be sought in addition to, and having a direct bearing on, economic studies. The need for detailed and extensive investigation is probably greater than for most other types of construction. Tunnelling is necessarily costly, but it is false economy to save on the information required to make the best choice of line, level and methods.

This chapter deals with the physical aspects which must be investigated before and in the course of tunnelling. There are also the problems of economic utilisation, including traffic surveys and forecasts for transport tunnels, and general cost/benefit studies taking account of environmental aspects and, particularly in urban conditions, problems of disruption during construction.

The topography of the area concerned must be studied to the fullest practicable extent, together with the history of any relevant ground disturbance, as must its geology and geotechnology. Of course, the extent and scope of the investigation will be dependent on the size of the project and on existing knowledge and experience of the characteristics of the ground from previous excavations and works. However good the past records, each new project will benefit from additional borings and other site exploration.

Investigations for a tunnel should be a continuing activity throughout its planning, design and construction. As each item of information is utilised new and more detailed problems appear and further investigations become necessary.

The general planning of possible routes and levels based on the broad topography is followed by more detailed examination of possible alternatives to the point where the most favourable alignment apparent can be selected. Even at quite a late stage a substantial change of level or line may be found advantageous, where more competent rock may be found, or ground more suited to particular equipment. In any case further and fuller information on the ground structure through which the tunnel is to be driven will be a continuing requirement, and it is likely that there will be a need for probing ahead through the tunnel face where there are any doubts about variations in the ground.

3.2 TOPOGRAPHY

The first approach is the study of existing maps to the largest available scale, including contours or other information on levels. A site inspection will be advisable at an early stage and as often as possible thereafter in order to appreciate the significance of the features mapped and the general characteristics of the area. From the first tentative tunnel routes drawn on the map the extent of more detailed topographic survey required becomes apparent. Figure 3.1 shows a contoured topographic survey, used to enable the best route for a tunnelled railway to be selected from several possibilities.

Chapter 9 describes surveys more fully. They will usually be tied in to the national grid or other reference system and will comprise a triangulated network or a closed traverse establishing a coordinate system for the tunnel, together with infilling of details as the layout of the project is determined. Accurate levelling related to national bench marks and establishing additional reference bench marks for site control is a part of the basic survey. The choice of permanent reference points in positions which will remain undisturbed through the construction is fundamental.

The requirements will vary considerably according to the purpose of the tunnel as described in the previous chapter, and the character of the terrain.

The work may be in open country, mountainous or alluvial, or in a city centre with large and important buildings, a suburban area or an industrial area. The survey may be required to include accurate location of existing tunnels whether to avoid interference or to join up. Metro station work is particularly demanding in this respect, while in sewer work levels are of the utmost significance.

Aerial photographic survey can be most valuable both in speed and in accuracy of recording detail. It is well known that in the countryside it may sometimes reveal the unexpected presence of ancient workings.

The framework of the survey should be used as a basis of a full and accurate record of the construction including more particularly such ultimately concealed parts of the structures as temporary shafts and adits, or any areas of extensive overbreak in tunnel, or temporary excavations refilled.

3.3 SITE HISTORY

It is often important, particularly in mining and industrial areas, that the history of the site should be known. Mine workings have often been abandoned without particulars being incorporated in maps, but sometimes records exist in various

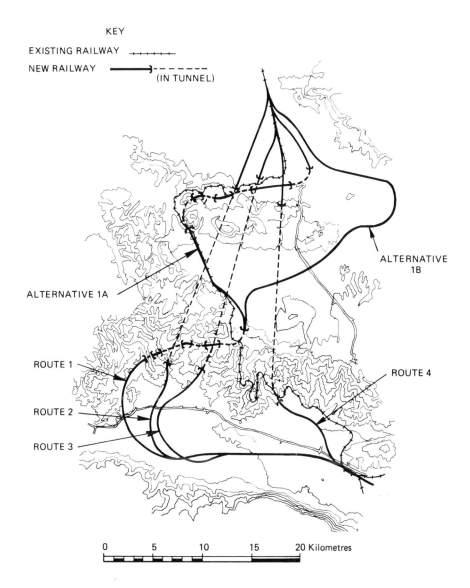

Fig. 3.1 — Contoured topograhic survey.

archives, or in deeds relating to the purchase of land from which the presence
of abandoned shafts and adits can be ascertained or at least suspected. Quarries
also have often been refilled after being worked out and at such a site a tunnel
supposedly in rock might emerge unexpectedly into soft filling. Wells, likewise,
are a hazard, particularly in some urban areas underlain by reliable aquifers.
Even an old borehole may be troublesome if not properly sealed, in that it may
provide a passage for water, or for the escape of compressed air.

Another unusual danger in shallow tunnelling is the pollution of the ground
by industrial wastes, where contaminants have seeped down into the underlying
strata over a long period. In the Blackwall tunnel the ground beneath the site
of an old gasworks was heavily contaminated with tarry residues. In another
case of a cable tunnel through chalk at a depth of about 20 m, hydrogen sulphide
dissolved in the ground water was encountered. Under a steelworks site spent
sulphuric acid discarded into soakaways in the past made necessary the use of
special acid-resisting linings. Under old colliery waste tips excess of carbon
dioxide and deficiency in oxygen has been encountered. This hazard of
deoxygenated air can occur also in natural ground in which air rather than
water occupies the pores of a soil or stratum with a content of organic silt
or pyrites or other readily oxidisable substance. The deoxygenated air may be
drawn into the tunnel by a fall in atmospheric pressure or may be forced into
the tunnel by use of compressed air in adjacent workings.

3.4 GEOLOGY

Geological survey and geotechnical studies of surrounding ground are fundamental
to planning, design and construction. Stratigraphy, petrology and tectonics are
all relevant but much finer detail of structures and variations is necessary for
tunnelling than for broader geological purposes. Soil mechanics and rock
mechanics studies follow the basic geology to assist in predicting the mechanical
behaviour of the ground during excavation and its interaction with supports,
temporary and permanent.

Initially, geological information is available from published maps and
memoirs which are often supported in greater detail by unpublished records
accessible to those interested. The alluvial deposits, drift and types of rock
occurring in the area and their interrelationship will be shown on maps but
precise interface positions and changes in texture and strength are likely to be
of great significance in tunnelling and must then be the subject of fuller
exploration.

Any records of previous borings may be of great value. Inspection of
exposures in quarries, pits, shafts and mines is almost always worthwhile and
also in cliffs and stream beds and any excavations. Records of earlier tunnels
should be sought and also of wells and deep foundations.

The major items of geological and geotechnical information required include:

1. Geological description with details of lithology and variability.
2. Location and orientation of discontinuities and planes of weakness relative to tunnel excavation—bedding planes, joints, faults, shear zones.
3. In situ stresses.
4. Geomechanical properties.
5. Ground water.

These are discussed in more detail in Volume 2.

3.5 SITE INVESTIGATION

The principal means employed to obtain additional knowledge of the tunnel are borings, trial pit shafts and exploratory headings. The objective is to identify and locate precisely each stratum relevant to the proposed tunnelling and to assess its characteristics and variations, and its behaviour during excavation.

The strata are identified and their characteristics ascertained from samples taken and from inspection and tests both in situ and in a laboratory. The whole programme needs to be very carefully planned so that the right questions are asked and the necessary answers obtained as economically as possible and without overloading a particular project with a mass of superfluous or irrelevant tests and studies. This again emphasises the advantages of a progressive investigation programme in which the areas of uncertainty are narrowed down.

As an example, a roadway may be required to form the descent from the surface through an open cut approach into a tunnel which passes under an obstacle. If the tunnel section can be sited so as to be wholly or mainly within a thick stratum of uniform character then borings for that section need be only sufficient to check that uniformity and to ascertain the relevant mechanical properties and behaviour, always subject to the proviso that thicknesses may be less than expected and characteristics may vary locally. Any place where an anomaly, such as a buried channel or a fault is suspected will require much more detailed study.

The approach ramps which may be through much more variable strata including soft water-bearing ground will also call for a detailed study with careful consideration of the methods of construction. These might include open cut construction supported on piles followed by cut-and-cover tunnelling involving the use of ground water lowering techniques and ground treatment by injection grouting.

Variations from typical characteristics may occur locally due to weathering, particularly in the vicinity of a fault or fissure, or an ancient land surface. As an example, the London Clay of Eocene age has a thickness of up to 100 m or so, but its surface has been eroded in the past and is cut into by old channels or swallow holes, so that any tunnel driven near its upper surface may encounter such an anomaly unexpectedly.

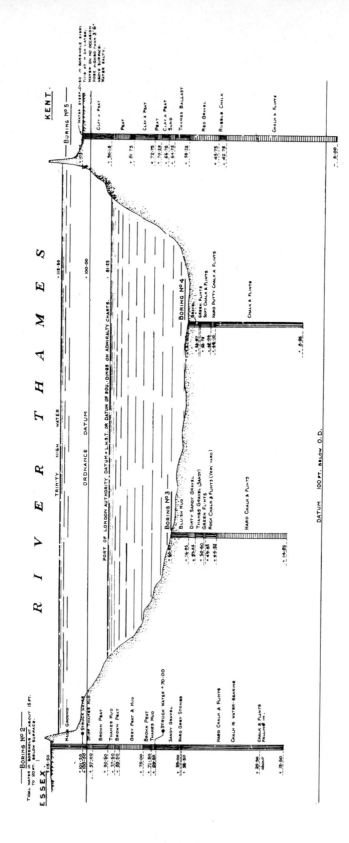

Fig. 3.2 – Section showing preliminary boreholes for Dartford Tunnel. Note that vertical scale is 10 times horizontal scale.

No pattern of borings can be sufficiently closely spaced to identify all such anomalies but the number of borings will in general be influenced by the variability expected or found.

In the first stage of site investigation by borings there should at least be sufficient to check the presence and levels of the expected strata and their principal characteristics. Some of these boreholes should be taken well below the intended invert of the tunnel to ascertain what lies below and to provide information on which a judgement can be formed as to the best level for the tunnel. Such deep borings may also identify the presence of aquifers under pressure (artesian water) or other significant features.

Following this first stage, tentative decisions on the tunnel route and suitable methods of construction are possible, and a second series of borings will furnish reasonably complete sections along and across the tunnel, but always in the knowledge that conditions between boreholes cannot be interpolated with absolute confidence. The closer and the more numerous the boreholes the more reliable is the cross section if similar strata are encountered consistently. Particularly in alluvial ground changes may be very rapid; in built-up areas and areas worked for minerals former excavations may have disturbed the uniformity of pattern; in rock unexpected faults, fissures and zones of weathering may occur.

The third stage of site investigation is to check at critical points, as design and geometry of the tunnel are finalised, to fill in gaps of information to resolve uncertainties. A pilot tunnel or exploratory heading may assist in these functions. Even after all these investigations excavation in any tunnel is exploratory and in many cases probing ahead should be adopted as a standard procedure.

The sinking of boreholes is by far the most widely applicable method of investigation for reasons of flexibility, speed and economy. They may range from hand augering to depths of a few metres in holes of about 40 mm diameter up to 1 m diameter pits, but for most tunnel purposes boreholes will be in the range of 100 mm to 400 mm diameter with depths normally less than 100 m, but much more where necessary.

3.6 METHODS OF BORING

The various methods of boring may be listed as:

1. Hand auger boring, for shallow holes in soils.
2. Light cable percussion boring adaptable for almost all ground other than deep holes in hard rock.
3. Mechanical augering, for cohesive soils.
4. Rotary open hole or core drilling, for rock.
5. Wash boring, for sands, silts or clays where sampling is unimportant.

Hand auger boring is very limited in its application to tunnelling. Depth cannot exceed about 5 m and the hole is uncased.

Light cable percussion boring is the most adaptable system for general use. The equipment comprises tripod, winch, light cable, drill rods, excavating tools and sampling tools. Relatively light and simple equipment can produce most of the essential information and samples. In its most portable form, the equipment can be dismantled into small units and transported to and set up on any part of

Fig. 3.3(a) — Drilling rig and tools — Mobile drilling rig, with percussion and auger capability (Engineering Laboratory Equipment Ltd.) . . . .

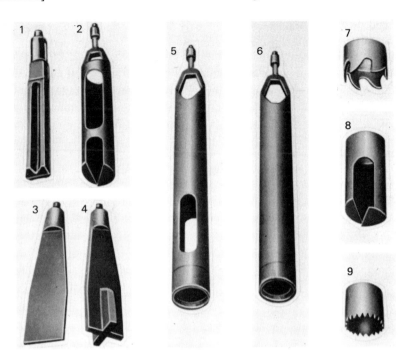

Fig. 3.3(b) — Tools for use with drilling rig. 1 Drilling bit for rock: 2 Auger bit for soft ground: 3 & 4 Chisels for breaking out rock: 5 Clay corer: 6 Shell for cleaning out hole after drilling: 7, 8 & 9 Gravelling, auger and serrated shoes for use with shell (Engineering Laboratory Equipment Ltd.).

any site, without requiring the construction of special access roads or elaborate levelling of a working site. it can be set up and operated in a limited space with a minimum of preparation and disturbance. To ensure the best use of resources, and reliable information with properly taken and prepared samples for tests, highly expert supervision is essential, but relatively unskilled labour can be used for much of the site work.

A hole is made by percussion methods, lifting and dropping a shell bit at the bottom of the hole for granular strata, or turning by means of rods an auger bit or clay cutter for cohesive soils, or lifting and dropping a chisel bit for rock or boulders. As the hole is sunk it is normally lined with steel tubes driven down. Unless water is present in the ground, a piped supply is needed for use of the shell in granular material to assist in collecting and drawing up the material.

In all these methods the excavated debris is extracted and examined at the surface, samples being preserved as appropriate. The samples are inevitably much disturbed and unless taken very frequently will be mixed by the process of drilling but they allow the soil at each level to be identified and classified broadly.

To obtain samples for more precise identification and for testing, boring must be interrupted while a suitable sampling tool is mounted and used in the undisturbed ground at the bottom of the hole. Granular soils cannot be sampled without disturbance, particularly where particle size is large in relation to borehole diameter. Degree of compaction is inevitably disturbed, fines are lost and moisture content is changed by the operation; sampling is better in very large diameter holes. In situ cone penetration tests can be used to provide information on behaviour of the ground.

Relatively undisturbed samples of clays—and marginally silts—can usually be obtained by means of suitable sampling tubes skilfully used. Grain structure, moisture content and strength properties from tests on the samples can be correlated with expected behaviour of the ground.

Rock will be fragmented by the chisel but can usually be identified. Undisturbed samples require the use of an annular bit, producing a core.

Mechanical augers are continuous flight augers usually with a hollow stem and having an outside diameter of 150-250 mm and a stem of half that diameter. They are normally vehicle mounted and therefore require adequate road access and a firm and level working area. They are used in cohesive soils, and have a hollow stem, which is plugged in general use, but can be used for sampling or for core drilling into rock below the soil. Larger augers drilling out a one metre diameter inspection shaft can be very useful in suitable conditions.

Rotary drilling is used mainly in rock but also in hard cohesive soils and the bit may either cut out all the material leaving an open hole or be of annular form preserving a relatively undisturbed core. Cores are usually 70 mm diameter but may be only 55 mm, or may be larger.

Diamond bits are usual and hollow rods to carry down fluid to lubricate and flush the operation.

3.7 SAMPLING

If open hole drilling is employed any required samples have to be taken separately, interrupting progress for the purpose. In any strata affecting tunnel construction, a continuous core is very desirable to help in determining the presence of discontinuities and the degree of fragmentation of the rock. Horizontal bedding and other joints will be reasonably well shown in a vertical bore but vertical and steeply inclined joints are unlikely to be adequately represented. Inclined boreholes designed to cut across such joints can, in special circumstances, provide very valuable additional information.

Wash boring is a relatively cheap, quick and easy way of probing through sands, silts or clays but information of the character of the soil at any level is minimal. It can provide a useful check on rock level where cover is shallow and variable.

Sampling may be adaptable to many purposes but not all may be relevant to a particular project. In granular soils particle size and grading, density, moisture content, and permeability are the principal items on which information is sought. Particle size and grading in particular will govern the behaviour of the soil in tunnelling and the passage through it of water and other fluids such as grouts or compressed air (Fig. 3.4).

In cohesive soils the same items are repeated with the addition of strength characteristics, namely: shear strength and compressive strength and also Atterberg limits which provide a guide to changes in plasticity with varying water content.

To allow most of these to be determined in a laboratory it is vital that the samples should be as nearly undisturbed as possible and that they should be carefully sealed off against change of moisture content immediately after securing the samples.

In rock the samples are used to determine corresponding characteristics; more particularly: density, permeability, crushing strength, mineral composition, and sometimes elastic moduli. Natural water content may be significant in some rocks and under some conditions. Of major importance is the structure of jointing and fragmentation in the rock and any changes caused by deep weathering. These properties are not readily mapped from test samples and may have to be explored by site tests and geophysical methods.

In all sampling the determination of the properties of the soil or rock sample specimens is subordinate to assessment of properties in the mass as actually encountered *in situ* when tunnelling. The hardest rock if sufficiently fragmented by faulting and crushing may behave in the mass like a granular soil. Under high pressures and stresses and in the presence of water shaly rock may resemble clay in plasticity, flow and swelling. Weathering from a surface exposed in the past or from a fault may disintegrate an otherwise sound rock at depth. These features may not be disclosed by borings and samples and may only appear during construction, but some indications can be obtained from site testing or geophysical exploration, or from exploratory shafts or headings.

3.8 IN SITU TESTS

As part of a scheme of exploratory borings *in situ* tests of ground behaviour can be valuable. The Standard Penetration Test measures the local resistance to the driving of a cone or sampler at the bottom of a borehole by use of a falling weight. In cohesive soils the Vane Test for resistance to rotation of a vane evaluates local shear resistance. Permeability may be assessed in a borehole, or an isolated length of a borehole by measuring acceptance of water under constant head or under falling head, or outflow of water. In a trial pit or shaft

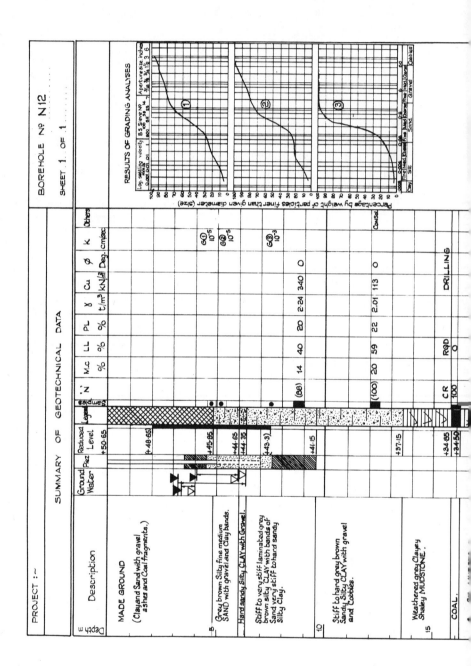

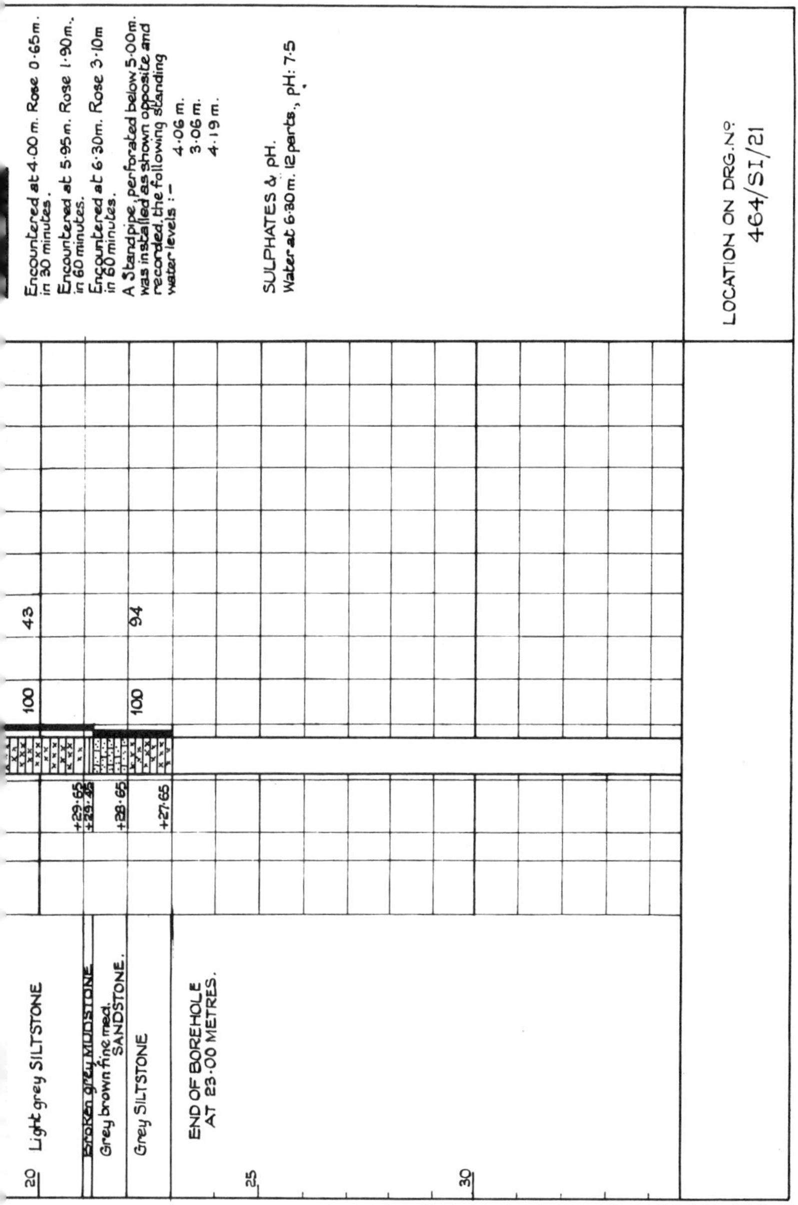

Encountered at 4.00 m. Rose 0.65 m. in 30 minutes.

Encountered at 5.95 m. Rose 1.90 m. in 60 minutes.

Encountered at 6.30 m. Rose 3.10 m. in 60 minutes.

A standpipe, perforated below 5.00 m. was installed as shown opposite and recorded, the following standing water-levels :–
4.06 m.
3.06 m.
4.19 m.

SULPHATES & pH.
Water at 6.30 m. 12 parts, pH: 7.5

LOCATION ON DRG. Nº 464/SI/21

20 Light grey SILTSTONE

Broken grey MUDSTONE
Grey brown fine med. SANDSTONE.

Grey SILTSTONE

END OF BOREHOLE AT 23.00 METRES.

100   43
100   94
+29.55
+28.25
+28.65
+27.65

25

30

Fig. 3.4 – Typical borehole log, with grading curves.

of sufficient size plate loading tests may be made to determine the bearing strength of the ground at that level.

Geophysical methods include seismic refraction and electrical resistivity on land surfaces and seismic profiling and echo sounding for underwater exploration. For large scale geological phenomena magnetic and gravimetric surveys may provide information. All these methods in application to tunnelling need to be based on and carefully referenced to a sufficient number of fully sampled boreholes.

3.9 TRIAL EXCAVATIONS

Within their limitations of availability and cost, trial excavations in pits, shafts or headings will provide more useful and detailed information than any other method.

In pits, excavated under expert supervision from the surface and lined, the nature and succession of strata can be observed exactly, numerous samples of any size can be obtained with minimal disturbance of the samples, and any appropriate *in situ* tests can be made. Such a pit can remain accessible for inspection and further tests at any stage of the project. The limitations on this are: first, site availability; second, time and cost of construction; third, the presence of water may necessitate pumping with consequent disturbance; fourth, depth may be restricted.

Lined shafts have most of the same merits and may be carried to greater depths. They may also comprise part of the tunnelling scheme, either for temporary access or with a permanent function, but this will limit the choice of site and may restrict scope for tests and samples.

For tunnel construction a heading is probably the most informative exploratory system. It may be driven into the hillside as an adit, or may be driven from a shaft. It may constitute a pilot tunnel driven on the line of the main tunnel and subsequently enlarged, or it may be driven to serve ultimately as a drainage or ventilation tunnel, or to carry services such as cables or pipes. Even although a pilot tunnel explores the actual ground through which the main tunnel is to be driven, there may still be surprises in store in effecting its enlargement. The disproportionate importance of size in tunnel excavation is discussed in Chapter 4. A fault, of trivial significance in a small tunnel, driven and supported quickly, may give serious difficulty when the unsupported span of ground is greater and it remains open for longer and when the driving of the pilot may itself have initiated some disturbance.

This was exemplified in the Mersey Kingsway tunnel (1971) where a fault required only some extra timbering and propping in the pilot tunnel, but made necessary multi-heading construction in that area during enlargement. In the Eisenhower Memorial tunnel, also mentioned in Chapter 4, a pilot tunnel was driven to study the ground thoroughly, but over a lengthy section enlargement proved unexpectedly difficult because of squeezing rock.

Ground exploration is, of course, only one function of a pilot tunnel: others are access for ground treatment, reduced face loads and extra support in main tunnel, improved access, ventilation and drainage.

3.10 HYDROLOGY

The importance of water to tunnelling can hardly be over-estimated and information on its various manifestations is essential. It appears at the surface as springs, streams, rivers, lakes, estuaries and the sea. Below ground it is present as pore water almost everywhere below the water table, but is usually present also above the water table where held by capillary action or by adsorption; it may be static or may flow through permeable ground or fissures, or as underground streams, particularly in limestones. Its relevance to tunnelling is fourfold:

1. It may flood a tunnel, breaking in at an exposed face, or as surface water entering from a shaft or adit.
2. The presence of water in the ground adds hydraulic pressure to the loading on a watertight lining.
3. Pore water modifies significantly the plastic properties and strength of soils and water in fissures may reduce the strength of rock by lubricating joints.
4. Water intruding into beds of anhydrite or other minerals may act chemically on them causing swelling and disruption.

These aspects are further discussed in Volume 2.

3.10.1 Surface Water

Records of river levels and flows and lake levels are frequently available and are particularly useful if correlated with rainfall. In the absence of records systematic observations may be advisable.

Where tunnelling is in the vicinity of tidal water, tide tables recording as fully as possible times and heights of tides are indispensable together with any available information on tidal surges which may be superimposed on normal tides and, in estuarine conditions, any records of river floods.

In addition to surface flooding problems, changes in these surface levels will as a rule eventually affect water table levels in the ground and therefore pressures and rates of inflow in tunnelling. If compressed air is being used adjustment of working pressure will be required. The surface openings of all shafts or adits, particularly if sloping downwards, should of course be sited above maximum flood levels or be provided with appropriate protective walls or bunds or with flood gates. In urban work, the possibility of surcharges in adjacent sewers should not be overlooked and also possible backflow of water along pipes which have been intercepted but not adequately sealed off.

Another aspect of water standing in lakes or marshes or in peat is that methane gas may be generated where vegetation has decayed in the sediments; its explosive characteristics call for special precautions.

3.10.2 Ground Water

The water table is the significant level of ground water. In any stratum it is the level at which water will stand in an open hole connecting only to that stratum. It must be appreciated that the water tables in successive strata in a borehole may differ. For example, the water table in the shallower soils overlying an impermeable clay may be a little below ground surface, but penetration of a permeable stratum below the clay may tap artesian water having a level of water table above ground surface.

In variable ground with lenses of granular soils alternating with silts and clays there may be 'perched water tables' over limited areas.

The determination of water table levels is an important function of site investigation by borings and requires careful observation of water levels and flows in boreholes. As the operation of boring may involve the addition and extraction of water, natural undisturbed levels can usually only be observed during interruptions of boring long enough for equilibrium to be established. Every opportunity to make such records should be utilised. To ascertain longer term variations in water level, standpipes or piezometers carefully set into boreholes to respond to a single stratum may be established and observed over any suitable period.

Permeability of water-bearing strata is an important factor in determining the inflow of water to be expected and its influence on ground behaviour. It is also fundamental to any injection grouting processes which may be contemplated (Volume 2).

3.11 GASES

Gases in tunnelling are significant because of explosive or toxic properties. The most common as a tunnelling hazard is probably methane (Chapter 4) which may originate in strata having an organic content and may emerge in adjoining areas. It is particularly common in the vicinity of coal seams but also arises from decaying vegetation in lake beds or from peaty deposits and sometimes from rubbish tips. It is considerably lighter than air (rel. density 0.56) and is easily ignited in mixture with air at concentrations of 5% or more with a resulting explosion. If strata of this nature are present tests for methane should be made in any investigation.

Hydrogen sulphide (H_2S) may also appear as a product of organic decay and can be highly toxic. It may be present in existing or abandoned sewers.

Carbon monoxide (CO) is most familiar as a constituent of petrol engine exhaust gas but may be generated in smouldering coal seams or any fires where combustion is incomplete. It is highly toxic and is very slightly lighter than air (rel. density 0.97).

Carbon dioxide (CO_2) results from complete combustion in coal or other fires or where acid acts on limestone. It is not itself toxic, but can be dangerous by displacing air or reducing the proportion of oxygen present in the atmosphere. It is denser than air (rel. density 1.53) and therefore tends to accumulate in pits and sumps.

Sulphur dioxide (SO_2) is toxic. It results from combustion of sulphur and its compounds and may appear naturally in volcanic areas.

3.12 STRUCTURES

Investigations into existing structures below ground should be comprehensive, not merely to ensure clearances, but also to allow the risk of settlement to be minimised.

Most existing tunnels are recorded but may need to be surveyed precisely and in detail unless very adequate clearances from the projected tunnel and its zone of disturbance are assured. Deep foundations and piles are not always as well documented as is necessary and may have to be the subject of special surveys, trial pits, or borings.

Early mines, whether for coal or other minerals, are rarely recorded in detail and may be altogether forgotten. In any such areas the preliminary investigations need to be extensive and the methods of working adopted should take into account the contingency.

BIBLIOGRAPHY

The requirements outlined in this chapter are described in considerable detail in a series of publications of the TRRL and reference should also be made to British Standards and Codes of Practice, and other publications listed below.

Glossop, R. and Skempton, A. W., 'Particle-size in silts and sands', *J. Instn. Civ. Engrs.*, 1945, **25** (Dec.).

Harding, H. J. B., 'Site investigations, including boring and other methods of subsurface exploration', *ibid*, 1949, **32** (Apr.).

In situ investigations in soils and rocks, British Geotechnical Society, London, 1969.

Safety in wells and boreholes, Institution of Civil Engineers, London, 1972.

Subsurface exploration for underground and heavy construction, American Society of Civil Engineers, New York, 1974.

B.S. 5573, Code of Practice for safety precautions in the construction of large diameter boreholes for piling and other purposes (revision of CP 2011), British Standards Insitution, London, 1978.

B.S. 5930, Code of practice for Site Investigations (revision of CP 2001), British Standards Institution, London, 1981.

Laboratory and Supplementary Reports, Transport and Road Research Laboratory, Crowthorne. There are also special site investigation studies, listed in the main bibliography (Volume 2):—

Dumbleton, M. J. and West, G., *Preliminary sources of information for site investigations in Britain, LR 403,* revised edn., 1976.

Dumbleton, M. J. and West, G., *Guidance on planning, directing and reporting site investigations, LR 625,* 1974.

Dumbleton, M. J. and West G., *A guide to site investigation procedures for tunnels, LR 740,* 1976.

BRE/TRRL Working Party, *Probing ahead for tunnels: a review of present methods and recommendations for research, SR 171,* 1975.

4

Tunnelling in Soft Ground

4.1 SCOPE

Tunnel construction is a complex operation and is only efficient to the extent that the various elements are satisfactorily integrated in the construction process. What is under discussion here, and in Chapter 6, is work at the face in bored tunnelling, the essence of which is excavation from inside and underneath. Three items from the list of fundamentals in Chapter 1, namely: excavation, immediate support, and management of water, interact so closely in soft ground that they cannot be isolated. Permanent support is more fully considered in Chapter 8, dealing with lining of tunnels. Survey also receives separate treatment, although it is vital at every stage of excavation in giving accurate guidance, for which purpose it is essential that clear sight lines must be available, unobstructed by plant and equipment or any other obstacle.

All recent development has been towards integration of design and construction as a unified industrial process, labelled 'systems engineering'. Many of the problems are logistical, concerned with the best methods of removing the excavated spoil and bringing in materials for lining, and the provision of essential services—light and power, pumping and water supply, ventilation, etc.— and the continual extension forwards of those services as the tunnel advances. Spoil handling is of particular importance to the economics of rapid tunnel excavation and the choices are briefly outlined below. It remains of the utmost importance that any system adopted is sufficiently flexible to cope with the unforeseen hazards almost inevitably encountered in course of excavation.

In these chapters the aim is to concentrate on the basic work at the tunnel face, that is to say the excavation and support of the ground and related management of ground water. Although soft ground and rock tunnelling differ obviously in their practices, they also have much in common, and the same principles, and many similar techniques, are applicable, more especially in difficult ground in which there is a need for continuous and detailed support of exposed ground. Much of what is said here is therefore relevant to the chapter on tunnelling in rock.

Fig. 4.1 – Spoil disposal by skips on rail track.

The fundamental difference lies in the elastic properties and strength of intact rock which are not greatly modified by the presence of water, and which allow a cavity to remain self-supporting, in contrast to the lower strength of soft ground and the dependence of its properties on the presence and movement of pore water and its pressure pattern.

The geologist uses the term 'rock' comprehensively for all deposits with which he is concerned, but his 'unconsolidated sediments' correspond to the tunneller's soft ground, typically such deposits as clays, silts, sands, gravels. These are characteristic of valleys and plains, which are the usual sites of cities, and therefore much urban tunnelling, which is generally shallow, is in soft ground. Mountain tunnels, in contrast, are cut through ridges, which have resisted erosion by reason of the presence of hard rock. Subaqueous tunnels may be of either type according to whether the river crossed is currently running in and eroding a rocky bed, or has, above rock level, sedimentary deposits of adequate substance and thickness for the tunnelling process adopted.

The association of soft ground tunnelling with urban needs is reflected in metro construction, sewers, water supply and other services. In some cities rock is encountered widely at shallow depths and most tunnelling must be in rock. In metro construction there is often a choice between cut-and-cover and bored tunnelling, discussed in Volume 2. Sewer tunnels, of small to medium size, probably involve a greater mileage of tunnelling than all other uses added together. They are likely to be shallow tunnels driven through very varied strata, often in built-over areas. Water supply tunnels are less characteristically urban where they transport remote supplies citywards, but they are also driven within metropolitan boundaries for trunk mains in preference to pipes laid in trench.

4.1.1 Spoil Handling

The economic importance of efficient spoil handling and disposal is particularly relevant in a long tunnel, whether in soft ground or rock. The problems are logistical rather than structural. For every tunnel the choice of appropriate methods must be made in the light of the expected volume, the rate of output fixed by the excavation cycle, the working space underground and at the surface, the machinery and equipment available and the ultimate disposal facilities or requirements.

So many different types of handling equipment, frequently designed for use in mines, are available, and such varied combinations are possible, that detailed consideration in the present context is not practicable.

In general, where work proceeds from a shaft, there are four phases to consider, namely: loading at the face, transport to the shaft, hoisting and ultimate disposal. At all stages the nature of the material, its bulking, fragmentation and particle size, and water content affect significantly the choice of plant and necessary capacity. The choice of transport method, broadly rail skip, conveyor, road vehicle or slurry pumping, is the key to all the other phases. The commonest method is probably by rail skip hauled by battery locos or, in large well ventilated tunnels, by diesel locos. In small tunnels man haulage may be appropriate. This system involves track laying and maintenance, with frequent extension as the face advances and provision of passing facilities to allow empty skips to be brought up as the loaded skips are moved back. Loading at the face presents problems of access to the skips, depending on their capacity in relation to volume of output.

Material from tunnelling machines is likely to be passed back by conveyors to a loading point. In small hand excavated tunnels direct shovelling into skips may be necessary, or there may be room for a mechanical shovel, or a loading conveyor.

At the shaft a hoist may be installed with a cage into which skips may be run to be lifted to the surface, or a crane may be used. Discharge can be either direct into a road vehicle, or to a spoil heap or a storage hopper, providing a reservoir to smooth out operations. Other shaft hoisting operations are, of course, possible such as a bucket elevator, or a conveyor in an inclined shaft.

For the main transport from face to shaft, or to portal, or for part of the way a conveyor may be preferred to rail skips, but, of course, other transport is necessary to carry lining materials to the face. Conveyor systems may require transfer points which can cause difficulty if there is excessive spillage.

In some tunnels, where there is direct road access through the portal, road vehicles are used for the whole operation, with mechanical loading at the face.

Another system is conveyance by slurry pumping. This is an integral feature of the Bentonite Shield method. It has also been used in other tunnels such as the first Dartford Tunnel, driven in compressed air through chalk. The spoil was crushed and mixed to a slurry with water, flints being either screened out if large, or crushed. The slurry was pumped out through a 150 mm pipe to settling lagoons. One great advantage was that no 'locking out' operation was necessary.

Ultimate disposal may be by tipping to waste locally, or for reclamation of old quarry sites, or for building road or other embankments.

4.2 PATTERN OF GROUND STRESS

In undisturbed ground, whether rock or soft, there exists a state of stress increasing with depth. The largest component is normally vertical compression proportional to the weight of overburden, usually accompanied by horizontal compression. The magnitude of the horizontal stress is commonly about a quarter of that of the vertical stress, although conditions may be very different where geological forces, recent or ancient, have operated, and where rock structure is not uniform.

The presence of a cavity within the ground mass inevitably changes the pattern of stress. The simplest illustration of the nature and order of magnitude of the stress changes is, perhaps, the two-dimensional case of a circular hole

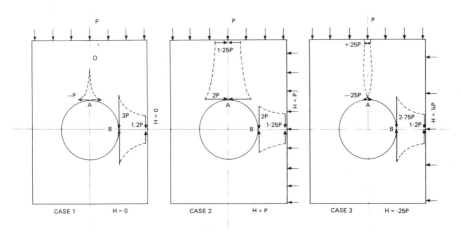

Fig. 4.2 – Patterns of ground stress.

representing a tunnel cut out of a uniform elastic solid in which there is a vertical stress, P, and a horizontal stress H (Fig. 4.2).

Three cases are considered:

$$H = O, \quad H = P, \quad H = \tfrac{1}{4}P$$

The second case represents a hydraulic pressure pattern, and the third case is more typical of natural conditions.

The stresses of particular interest are the circumferential stresses at the crown of the tunnel (A) and at the axis level (B). In the first case, with vertical loading only, tensile stress of P develops at A and compressive stress of 3P at B, but if followed outwards for a distance of one radius along the vertical and horizontal radii respectively both revert nearly to the general stresses which are respectively zero and P.

In the second case, compressive stress of 2P occurs at both A and B, again diminishing outwards to the general stress P at a distance of one radius.

In the third case, a small tensile stress is experienced at A, and a compressive stress of about 2.7P at B.

In all cases, radial stresses are necessarily zero at the cut surface. They increase outwards to their general values. Rock bolting may be used to increase them.

The implicit arching action is apparent, with the need for horizontal thrust or tensile strength at the crown, and the increased loading at springing. What is also of importance is the rapid diminution outwards of stress changes, showing such a tunnel to be very localised in its effects.

The assumptions of uniformity and elastic behaviour are rarely borne out in practice, but the indication of ground stresses in the range −P to +3P is helpful, when correlated with the compressive strength of the ground, as a guide to the need for structural support. Local containment of the exposed surfaces against ravelling, weathering, or swelling is a separate requirement.

In mountains, where much folding and faulting has occurred ground stresses may be high and irregular. Residual geological forces can be enormous and when they act on rock having some plasticity, very high squeeze pressures may make soft ground excavation methods necessary.

The indication of possible tension shows a need for support in soft ground, which has little or no tensile strength. The magnitude and timing of the support comprises much of the art of soft ground tunnelling. If the ground is allowed to loosen much heavier loads are to be expected and progressive deterioration. Stand-up time is a useful concept, as being the time for which a length of tunnel excavation can be left unsupported without detriment to the integrity of the remaining ground and without loss of strength. It may range from less than five minutes in very soft clay, silty sand below the water table or gravel, up to 24 hours or more for dense sand or gravel with a binder, or stiff continuous clay.

4.3 EXCAVATION IN SOFT GROUND

In the tunnelling sense soft ground broadly comprises gravels, sands, silts, clays and alluvial deposits generally. From the aspect of behaviour Terzaghi has classified such ground into the categories: Firm, Ravelling, Running, Flowing, Squeezing, and Swelling. To a very great extent properties and behaviour will depend on water content and movement of water, the management of which is a vital aspect of safe and efficient working.

In soft ground, of any category other than firm, some form of immediate support is always necessary, by timbering, shield, permanent lining or a combination of these. Water management may employ variously: pumping, ground water lowering, freezing, grouting, and compressed air.

4.3.1 Granular soils

Gravel or sand, unless cemented naturally or by grouting, will tend to slip at any exposed face until its angle of repose is attained; any inflow of water is liable to wash out the fine sand. This sort of movement is quite unacceptable on any but the smallest scale and timbering at the face becomes necessary to prevent its initiation. The crown of the tunnel is, of course, particularly vulnerable to gravel flow, and timber poling is necessary to hold the top except where a hooded shield is effective or suitable ground treatment. Support at the face in compact gravel or sand is rather to prevent initiation of movement than to carry any great thrust, because in compact granular material, in the absence of disturbance, arching action will develop quickly ahead of the face. There is, however, little or no cohesion and no tensile strength in such ground and any small cavity developing must be quickly secured to prevent loosening of a large volume. Close boarding of a face, using narrow horizontal timbers advanced one at a time from the top downwards, keeps to a minimum the exposed ground and the risk of a slip.

Water flowing in at the face may wash out the fines and loosen the ground. This emphasises the importance of really close-fitting timbers, but also of lowering by underdrainage the water level at the face as close to invert as practicable.

To effect this a filter well in the invert, or sunk from the surface outside the tunnel may be used, or relief drainage in the lined section of the tunnel where the ground is already secured. In special cases compressed air working or grout injection may be employed. If water-bearing gravel or sand is likely to be encountered for a long distance the Bentonite Shield may be the best solution.

4.3.2 Silt

Silt is much finer grained and calls for even more care, particularly in the presence of water. Its cohesive properties are very sensitive to water content. It is characteristic of silts that there is a very small moisture range between the plastic limit and the liquid limit. If allowed to dry out silts become brittle and crumble away readily; if wet they quickly become fluid. Their permeability is lower than that of sands, but high enough for water to be absorbed or discharged quite readily. Compressed air is a most valuable aid in tunnelling silt. Close timbering is essential unless the conditions are particularly favourable —a high clay content in the silt, no excess water, rapid progress of excavation. Grouting is usually unsatisfactory in silt because of failure to permeate the fine pore structure unless very expensive chemical grouts of low viscosity can be used. The presence of thin layers of silt interleaved with sand and gravel can inhibit effective grouting. Freezing has proved satisfactory in such conditions.

4.3.2.1 Organic soils

Mention should also be made of organic silts and clays, in which decaying vegetable matter is a typical constituent. Their physical properties may differ appreciably from inorganic soils, their permeability being low and their compressibility high. The organic content frequently gives rise to discharge of noxious gases, typically: carbon dioxide, sulphuretted hydrogen, or methane. If encountered in tunnelling very adequate ventilation becomes necessary and monitoring of incidence. The explosion hazard from methane gas is more fully described in Chapter 6.

4.3.3 Clay

Clay has very valuable cohesive and plastic properties which can provide excellent tunnelling ground except where too soft or badly fissured.

Its permeability is low and except to the extent of fissuring provides a seal against entry of water. It may, however, swell slowly when exposed in an excavation and exert increasing active pressure on any support or lining. This may make the time occupied in a cycle of operations critical.

The plasticity of clay allows it to deform under change of loading and to creep in at the face, slowly in stiff clay but more rapidly in soft clay; the deformation must be restrained within small limits if disturbance of the ground and its stress structure is to be limited. Heavy timbering becomes necessary for a big face but not necessarily close boarding.

Water entering along fissures may wash out material and enlarge the water passage; it may also soften the clay. All wet spots in a clay face must therefore be regarded with suspicion. This is particularly so where the tunnel is near the upper surface of the clay stratum and is overlain by water-bearing sand or gravel, as is often the case in London.

The swelling of clays is usually attributable to pore water moving into the space where previously existing stress has been relaxed by the excavation. The pore water moves slowly inwards from the surrounding ground, not outwards, as sometimes supposed, from the exposed surface. The phenomenon is particularly significant in overconsolidated clays, which previously have over a long period been subjected to heavy loadings squeezing out much of the pore water.

In the extreme case, clay or silt may be so soft and plastic that a shield can be advanced with a closed face, or with small shuttered openings through which as much ground as necessary is extruded into the tunnel. At the other extreme, clay may be so stiff and sound that, in a small tunnel, no immediate support is required.

4.3.4 Tools
The basic tools of excavation where explosives are not used are the pick and shovel, but with mechanical aids and elaborations. In clay tunnelling the pneu-matically-powered clay spade and pick are the most used digging tools, to break out and trim the face. Where size of tunnel and other conditions permit, the operation may be more fully mechanised by use of the roadheader type of machine which excavates by rotation of a multi-pick head on a hydraulically operated arm. Continuous excavation may be by a drum digger or similar full face rotating machine, or by oscillating cutting heads. Tunnelling machines are more fully dealt with in Chapter 7. The Greathead shield also may function as an excavating, or more precisely, trimming tool.

4.4 TIMBERED HEADINGS

The fundamentals of soft ground excavation are best dealt with by describing examples: first, a timbered heading in sound clay, followed by the more elaborate procedures necessary in a piled heading in running ground.

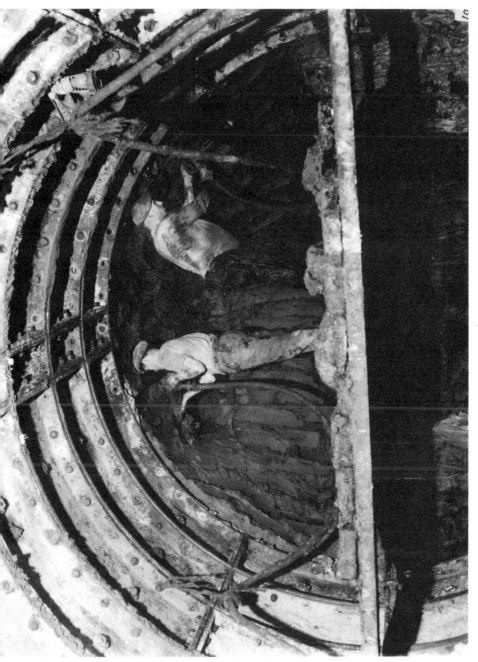

Fig. 4.3 – Excavation in stiff clay, without timbering, for C.I. tunnel lining.

4.4.1 Headings in clay

Headings like this may be used for such purposes as access to form a break-up for a larger tunnel, or for laying a sewer or other pipe, or for construction of walls preliminary to excavation and roofing of a passage or chamber. They may also function as pilots ahead of a large tunnel for advancing and supporting the crown, or for construction of arch skewbacks or wall footings or for ground treatment by grout injection.

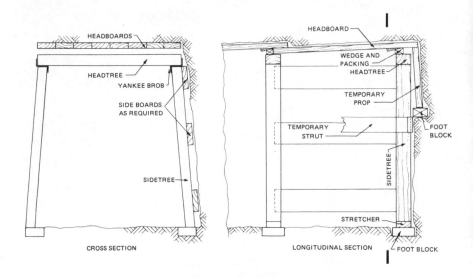

Fig. 4.4 – Timbered heading in clay.

Figures 4.4(a) and (b) show a heading about 1.5 m x 2 m in section being advanced in 1.2 m settings in sound clay. To advance the heading by one frame:

1. The top is excavated for a length over the width of two or more boards.
2. The headboards are tucked back over the previous headtree and propped temporarily at or near the face. These props must be secured at the toe, resting on footblocks with the clay face below strutted against shear failure.
3. The whole width of the top is excavated progressively, and the remainder of the excavation is completed.
4. A headtree is fixed in place to take the load from the headboards.
5. Sidetrees, wedged up to the end of the headtree, are caught at the top by 'yankee brobs' of bent steel plate and rest at the base on footblocks. They are set with 'sprag' of 1 in 12, or more, so that any lateral loading from the ground tightens them.
6. Side boards may, or may not, be required.
7. The temporary props at the face are removed, everything is wedged up tight, and all is ready for another setting.

4.4.2 Forepoling

In running ground, such as water-bearing sand or silt, or in fragmented or squeezing rock, wherever it is dangerous to expose even small areas for a short time—where, in fact, the stand-up time is so brief that support must be fixed in advance of excavation—forepoling may be found necessary. This is the use of poling boards or steel spiles as horizontal piles driven ahead of the tunnel face before it is opened up. The hooded shield embodies this principle, but in some conditions grout injection or freezing may offer alternatives.

A piled heading of similar dimensions to that already described exemplifies the principles, but details are likely to be much varied to suit the ground. Support of the face in such ground by close boarding adequately strutted at all stages is essential. Figure 4.5 illustrates the description.

The narrow head boards are cut to a chisel edge at the leading end and are driven into the ground ahead through the last completed setting. They have to be inclined upwards at about 1 in 6 so that they pass above the position of the next headtree with sufficient clearance for the next setting of boards to be driven under them and above the headtree. The upward slope may be greater than this clearance requires because it may be determined by the board having to be started with its tail beneath the previous headtree.

In the simplest case, the head boards, starting at the centre are first driven to their full length, and the side boards are similarly driven, inclining outwards. The top face board can now be removed, allowing the ground behind it to be scratched out to about half the length of the head boards. The top face board is advanced and refixed in this new position and is strutted back. The whole

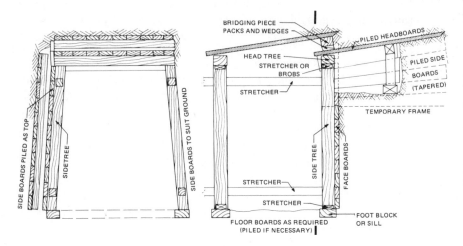

Fig. 4.5 – Piled heading.

face is advanced to the half length in this manner, one board at a time, working downwards until a headtree, sidetrees and a sill, constituting a midway frame can be completed to support the head, side and face boards. These are securely wedged at the frame, which is also strutted back to the frame behind. The excavation is again advanced one board at a time to the full length of the setting, where a permanent frame is similarly fixed but with bridging pieces and packings carrying the head and side boards which are packed out to allow for insertion of the next setting of boards.

The midway frame may be removed if the boards are sufficiently strong, or may be left in place if necessary.

As always in tunnelling, the exact procedure and details will be governed by the actual behaviour of the ground, the dimensions of the heading, the timber sizes being used and the skill and speed of the tunnellers. The necessary upward slope of the head boards and the outward inclination of the side boards leave the angle between top and sides exposed, unless tapering boards are used and very accurately driven. Any exposed area of ground must be spanned by short timbers, while small gaps may be stuffed with bags, straw, etc.

In some ground it may not be practicable to drive the piles their whole length at one time and it may be necessary to drive a little beyond half way, excavate, provide temporary support and wedge up and then redrive ready to excavate the second half.

The essence of the whole operation is carefully planned workmanship to ensure that no large area of ground is ever left unsupported, and that every piece of timber is accurately placed and tightly wedged at all times except when actually being moved.

4.5 CIRCULAR TUNNEL SEGMENTAL LINING

For a tunnel with segmental lining driven in soft ground without a shield, timbering of the top and face is likely to be required.

The structural strength and spacings of the timbers will be determined by the nature of the ground, the time during which the support is required, and the importance of safeguarding the overlying ground against any settlement. Figure 4.6 shows a typical case of a small tunnel of about 3.5 m diameter where close boarding is appropriate. In stiff clay such close timbering is unlikely to be necessary except during periods when work is interrupted, but the principles of supporting top and face should be followed at every ring by provision of the main structural elements of the support system.

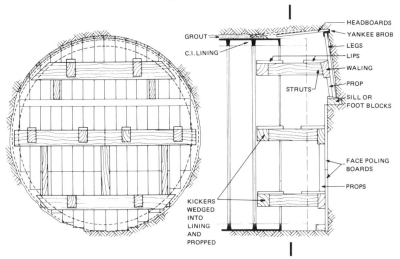

Fig. 4.6 – Close boarding in a small tunnel.

In the case illustrated the tunnel is advanced one ring at a time (exceptionally a two-ring step may be feasible). The cycle of operations, starting after erection and grouting of a ring is:

1. Excavate top and provide support by head boards which rest at the back on the completed ring and are supported by a front 'leg' set on a footblock on a bench in the clay face. The excavation proceeds from the centre working outwards to both sides until the top bench (about 1 m to 1½ m deep) has been advanced the distance of one ring.

2. Excavate a second bench. For this some head boards at the perimeter may or may not be required. Face boards and a waling are assumed necessary. The footblocks of the top legs must not be undercut and the face of the ground on which they rest must be kept strutted to secure it against shear failure.

3. Complete excavation to invert, shaping invert carefully so that segments can be set in place accurately.
4. Erect segments from invert upwards to key, checking accuracy of positioning of each segment. Unless the ground is unsafe, head boards can usually be recovered as segments are erected.
5. Pack at front of ring and grout up with cement grout.
6. The timbers are moved forward progressively into the next ring.

When the full face in a big tunnel has to be fully timbered, experience and craftsmanship of a high order are called for, Fig. 4.7 shows such a face.

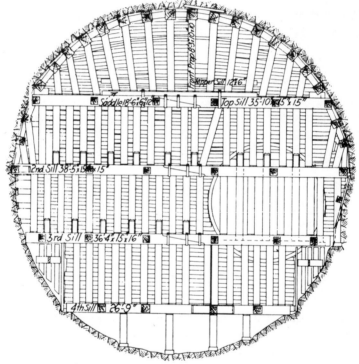

Fig. 4.7 – Timbering of 11 m face on the extension of the City and South London Railway.

4.6 GREATHEAD SHIELD

The Greathead shield, devised originally for tunnelling in clay under the River Thames, is primarily a device to provide continuous ground support. It can also in minor degree function as a cutting and trimming device. The shield comprises a cylindrical steel shell stiffened by ribs and diaphragms and provided with hydraulic jacks to propel it forwards. In addition to these basic elements many ancillary devices may be incorporated in or attached to a shield.

The fundamental operations in using such a shield are:

1. Excavate ahead, timbering face as necessary.
2. Shove shield forward one ring length by jacking from completed lining. The shield may be used to trim the excavation neatly provided excessive thrust is not required.
3. Withdraw shove rams and build segmental lining in clear space behind shield.
4. Grout up all voids between segments and ground.
   Repeat cycle of operations.

4.6.1 Ancillary equipment

Among the ancillary devices which may be used are:
  Face diaphragm
  Vertical and horizontal stiffening girders
  Hood
  Bead
  Tail
  Segment erectors

The face diaphragm helps to stiffen the shell but primarily enables the face to be shut off in the event of a run of ground. It must, of course, have apertures for access to the face so that men may get in and out to excavate and timber the face. In a small shield a sliding door, or grooves to take stop logs, may be suitable. Complete closure of the face may be considered unnecessary but a muck trap may be used. In this the diaphragm is in two parts, the front one covering the upper half of the face with a margin below axis, while the rear diaphragm covers the bottom half and a margin above axis. In a big shield (9 m diameter) such as that used at the first Dartford tunnel, there may be three such muck traps at different platform levels. A single trap of this kind can function as a water trap in emergency if the tunnel is being driven in compressed air.

In general, face timbering will be fixed in front of the diaphragm as excavation proceeds downwards from the top but some special devices have been used. In the Blackwall tunnel (1897) the shield was provided with two complete diaphragms equipped with air locks intended to make possible the use of higher air pressure ahead of the diaphragm than in the tunnel. It had also a system of steel shutters at the face, which replaced timbering, and could slide back into the shield under control of guide screws during a shove by the main rams. The use of differential air pressure was never in fact practicable.

The extreme in soft silt is tunnelling by displacement where the shield is shoved ahead without any opening or with a small opening only. In the river bed of the Hudson river this technique was employed in the original rail tunnel and also in the construction of the Holland and Lincoln road tunnels. In the latter, with apertures in the shield of only 0.5% of the face area, it was reckoned

Fig. 4.8 – Rear view of Greathead Shield in Dartford Tunnel, showing main rams, thrusting against completed C.I. lining, segment erector arm, muck shoots and skips for disposal.

that 30% only of the ground was excavated and 70% went in 'heave'. The soft silt was extruded through the shield in a plastic condition and sliced off. A similar technique was adopted in the Chicago Subway construction, described in detail by Terzaghi in which the aperture in a 7.6 m shield with 7 m cover was varied from 4% to 20% in an attempt to control the heave. In fact, the heave ahead of the shield ranged from 0.03 to 0.10 m and was followed by a subsidence of about 0.15 m.

Vertical and horizontal girders may be necessary to stiffen the shield and the diaphragm. They can also serve to provide working platforms at different levels and to divide the face into working compartments.

Such girders can carry a system of face jacks which support the face timbering and which can be designed to maintain pressure on the face during a shove and yet to allow the shield as a whole to move forward into the face without crushing the timber. Sometimes 'gun struts', where the inward movement is restrained by friction from screwed clamps, are preferred to the hydraulic complexity of jacks.

Hood: A hood is a forward extension of the cutting edge in the upper half of the shield which acts like the piles in forepoling and is kept buried in the ground ahead to secure the roof at all times. In gravel where the necessary force to drive in such a cutting edge is excessive and might cause dangerous disturbance, clay pocketing can be employed, but it will only be unwillingly resorted to. In this hand operation a handhole is formed in the ground ahead of the cutting edge and is refilled with puddled clay, and the operation is repeated all round the hood until there is a prepared clay part ring into which the shield can be shoved, the clay serving both to provide a water seal and to lubricate the passage of the shield.

Bead: The radius of the cutting edge is often enlarged to be a centimetre or two greater than that of the shield skin by attaching a bead. The objective is to reduce friction between the ground and the skin when the shield is being driven forward, and to reduce stresses in the shield (and in the ground) when minor directional changes are required. Beads do not always extend around the invert of the shield. Clearly beads can contribute to the settlement of ground and structures above a tunnel drive.

Tail: An extension of the shield skin forming the 'tail' is required unless the ground is so reliable that it will stand up unsupported during the erection and grouting of the lining. Normally the lining is erected within the protection of the tail which still overlaps it by a small amount after the shove. There is a tendency for grout deposits to build up on the tail skin, and it may sometimes be necessary to stop and break them off.

Segment Erectors: In any but the smallest tunnels, erection of precast segments makes necessary mechanical lifting equipment. The design and dimensioning of segments may be governed by the problems of handling and erection. A large shield will usually be equipped with one or two radial arms in the tail which can lift and place segments. The arm, operated hydraulically, is pivoted near the tunnel axis and is extensible, with a head devised to pick up the segments from the delivery point in the invert and lift and place them in position for bolting up.

4.6.2 Developments
The drum digger and other digger shields have been developed from the Greathead shield by devising rotating heads to cut into the face as the shield is advanced. This is only suitable for ground with adequate stand-up time to allow timbering to be dispensed with. The linings also have been developed as part of the same system, using wedging out of the lining directly against the excavated ground in place of bolting and grouting. These machines and methods are more fully described later.

The Bentonite shield may be the ultimate development of the closed shield for use in granular water-bearing soils. In it there is a complete closed diaphragm ahead of which any space is charged with Bentonite mud. There is a cutter head rotating full circle and the spoil, immersed in Bentonite mud, is passed back through a special device set in the diaphragm functioning as a valve. The whole face is thus pressurised and the excavation and disposal is fully mechanised. This machine also is more fully described in Chapter 7.

4.6.3 Steering and guidance
Control of a shield to keep it on line and level is not an easy problem. Precise survey and setting out are necessary and at the most frequent intervals practicable the shield's position must be accurately checked and recorded and also its attitude in terms of 'lead', 'look-up' or 'overhang' and 'roll'. Errors must be corrected as quickly as practicable, normally by selective and controlled use of the shove rams. The accuracy of the last completed ring must also be ensured. These problems are more fully discussed in Chapter 9.

In controlling a shield the ratio of length to diameter is of great importance. If the ratio is much more than about 1 : 1 it becomes difficult to correct errors of direction; the shield has cut for itself a passage through the ground which leaves little room for turning.

4.7 TUNNEL JACKING

4.7.1 Pipe jacking
In recent years pipe jacking methods have been developed and elaborated to tunnel jacking. No precise borderline is definable, but when a man can operate in the pipe, somewhere above 1 m diameter, it may be considered as a form of tunnel construction. Even at smaller diameters it may be a useful ancillary to tunnel construction as, for example, when pipes are jacked ahead at close centres to form a roof beneath which a tunnel can be mined, or to retain roof and sides

of a small passage. The technique is most suitable for relatively short straight lengths of small diameter in soft ground, but the limitations imposed by all these factors can be overcome.

Pipe thrusting, in which the ground is displaced and not excavated, is essentially a small bore pipe method. Horizontal auger boring is feasible for pipe lines up to approximately 1½ m diameter but for limited lengths. In pipe jacking, a line of pipes is jacked into the ground, being furnished with a cutting edge or shield at the leading end and with means for removing the displaced ground through the bore of the pipe. Diameters up to 3 m are not unusual and lengths of the order of 100 m, while longer drives are possible with intermediate jacking stations. Tunnel jacking may be the more appropriate term as the size increases and as rectangular or other special purpose structures rather than pipes are required. Pipe jacking is first outlined here.

Pipe jacking has been widely used as an alternative to open trench work, or lengths of timbered heading, where surface access is difficult and where settlement at the surface must be minimised. Sewers and culverts or other pipe crossings under a railway or road embankment, or under a canal or other obstacle can be so constructed, as can pedestrian subways at ground level through an embankment. The method also lends itself to sewer construction, where manhole shafts divide up the work into relatively short straight lengths and can be used as successive thrust pits. The technique has been adopted and adapted for more complex structures through embankments, further referred to later.

Its direct cost is usually greater than cut-and-cover, but surface disturbance and disruption are much less in congested areas, and working areas need not be so large.

The essential features of a pipe jacking installation are:

1. Thrust pit
2. Jacks and thrust ring
3. Pipes
4. Cutting shield

1. The thrust pit must be at tunnel depth and of sufficient length to accommodate the jacks, the thrust ring, and one length of pipe, with space for insertion and any jointing detail. The rear wall of the pit must be adequate to take the maximum thrust from the jacks and to spread that load into a sufficient area of ground. For large pipes and long drives the load is likely to be several hundred tons at its maximum as the drive nears completion. The whole success of the operation may depend on having ample jacking capacity and proper support for it. In a shallow pit or soft ground the back wall of the pit may not offer adequate support and it may be necessary to drive piles for the purpose, or install ties through the embankment or ground anchors.

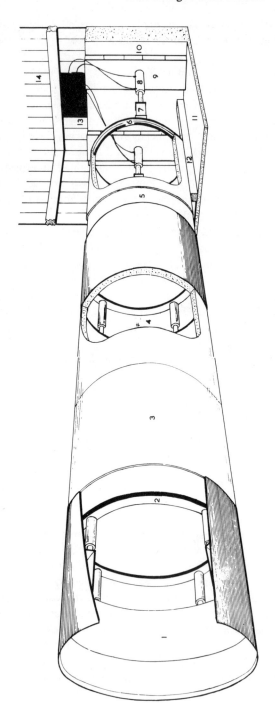

1   jacking shield
2   steel thrust ring
3   concrete lead pipe
4   interjack station
5   interjack pipe
6   steel thrust ring
7   spacer blocks

8   hydraulic jacks
9   steel pressure plate
10 concrete thrust wall
11 concrete floor
12 guide rails
13 power pack
14 thrust pit

Fig. 4.9 — General arrangement of pipe jacking equipment (Pipe Jacking Association).

2. Hydraulic jacks, operating at high pressures to achieve compactness, are installed on the floor of the pit. There may be one, two or more jacks, depending on the diameter of the pipe. They are symmetrically disposed and act on the rear of the pipe line through a thrust ring designed to bear safely and evenly on the pipe end. The stroke of the jacks is likely to be substantially less that the pipe lengths and a series of spacer blocks of increasing length will be necessary for successive insertion after each stroke until an advance of a full pipe length has been effected.

As the whole length of pipe is in contact with the ground the frictional resistance to advance increases progressively. It is possible to limit the resistance by installation of intermediate jacking rings whereby the leading end of the pipe only is first thrust forward and the rear part is then pushed up to it by use of the pit jacks. A further elaboration is to use a separate set of jacks to advance the shield only at the leading end and to follow up with intermediate jacks and pit jacks. In such cases it may be advantageous to be able to control the shield jacks individually so as to guide the shield and correct any misalignment.

3. Pipes. For many purposes reinforced spun concrete rings, rather thicker than ordinary sewer pipes are suitable, with joints substantially watertight but allowing some flexibility. Provision for grouting may be advisable not only to seal off any residual leakage and fill voids, but also to permit lubrication of the sliding surface during jacking, by Bentonite slurry or other suitable fluid.

Steel pipes of normal diameter may be employed in long lengths, but satisfactory external protection against corrosion is difficult to ensure because of scratching during thrusting. They may advantageously be used as sleeves through which a smaller service pipe is threaded. A pit long enough to enter each pipe length and to accommodate the jacks is, of course, necessary and there must be room for them to be threaded down any shaft and turned into position.

4. Cutting shield. The minimum necessary is the provision of a sharp but robust circular cutting edge secured to the leading pipe. For a steel pipe, no more than the pipe itself may be necessary. Beyond this, the shield may be elaborated up to the dimensions, strength and complexity of a soft ground tunnel shield, with hood, thrust jacks, face jacks, platforms and working compartments, stiffening rings and diaphragms, as pipe jacking develops to full scale tunnel jacking.

The essential difference from orthodox soft ground tunnelling then is that erection behind the face of segmental rings is dispensed with, the complete rings comprising the lining being built into the tunnel structure at the pit and thrust forward.

4.7.2 Tunnel jacking

As a tunnelling operation in its own right, jacking has been used for drives up to 4 m diameter and a record drive was completed in Chicago (1977) for a sewer with outside diameter 2.9 m for a length of 490 m.

A number of underbridges to carry roads through railway embankments have been constructed in the U.K. with the aid of jacking techniques, usually to construct the abutments and foundations in advance of the deck, which may be slid across subsequently in open cut. In most cases multiple prefabricated units have been jacked through in stages at one, two or three levels. In some cases half of the complete bridge up to 9 x 4 x 21 m has been built at each side and jacked forward in open cut, not really constituting a tunnel operation, except possibly for guide paths first built in timbered headings.

As compared with shield tunnelling, the limiting factors are:

    1. Thrust
    2. Size and weight of units
    3. Control of alignment

1.   The thrust necessary for large bores may be 1000–1500 tons. It can be minimised by ensuring a smooth outer surface without lipping at the joints and by lubrication with Bentonite slurry or otherwise at the sliding surfaces. The thrust can be further reduced by separating that for the shield or cutting edge from the friction on the lining. A separate set of shield jacks are provided for the shield and boring machine which may slide forward from within a protective 'can' as it advances, the 'can' being anchored in the ground to provide the thrust reaction. After advance of the shield the 'can' is in turn moved forward leaving a rear shield, or tail, into which the lining can then be shoved. If necessary additional intermediate jacking stations are possible. An adequately supported thrust block at the rear is, of course, essential.

    Another thrust problem, particularly with a rectangular section with shallow cover, is the drag exercised on the block of soil immediately above the structure. Patented devices, known as 'drag sheets', have been used where strong flexible sheets, of thin steel or fabric, are fed in and anchored back as the units are advanced in order to separate the force of the sliding friction from the ground above and reduce disturbance.

2.   Problems of transport and handling down the shaft will normally impose a weight limit for each unit, possibly up to 25 T.

3.   Alignment within 1% or so is very difficult to maintain in simple pipe jacking, even when the initial pipe is set most precisely. Jacking independently at the cutting head as referred to above can give control comparable to that of an orthodox TBM, and intermediate jacking with individually controlled jacks can help.

    Within the scope of these limitations, the method may be competitive, for sewer work in particular, with shield tunnelling in which a segmental lining has to be erected and grouted as part of the sequence of operations at the working face. The limitations on length are not serious in sewer work, where manholes at moderate intervals are normally required. Control of level is important.

The face support, and management of water present very much the same problems as in orthodox shield tunnelling with similar solutions, such as ground treatment and ground water lowering. The tunnel jacking method is one of growing importance but not for major tunnels. It may be noted that although most usually applicable to soft ground it is readily adaptable to soft rock, and hard rock can be dealt with if encountered.

4.8 SIZE OF TUNNEL

It will already be clear that the size of a tunnel may be fundamental in governing methods of excavation. In opening up a face, disturbance of the existing equilibrium of forces and stresses inevitably results in movement and in redistribution of forces. Among the difficulties which increase with size of face, mostly in disproportionate degree, are:

1. Volume of ground disturbed and extent of movement.
2. Access to all parts of face.
3. Strutting of exposed face.
4. Volume of excavation per ring and time of cycle of operations.
5. Water pressure differential between top and bottom of face.
6. Mixed face—more than one type of ground exposed.
7. Falling materials.

1. In a small face the volume of ground moving and relaxing will not be great and can often be tolerated or kept within acceptable limits by relatively simple timbering or other temporary support.

In a large face, the effects of relaxation of stress penetrate further ahead of the face and a larger volume of ground is involved over a longer period. Much stronger support becomes necessary to prevent weakening of the whole ground structure. Also, the risk of intersecting some fissure or other anomaly is much greater. The time factor is further disadvantageous in that there is a longer interval for trouble to develop between release of support of the ground ahead and its removal by excavation followed by new support. With increasing size full face excavation may cease to be practicable and the use of a pilot tunnel or a series of headings may be required. These limitations of size will apply much earlier in soft ground than in rock or in stiff clay.

In the Dartford tunnel (1963) one length of 9 m diameter tunnel through soft silty clay was driven in compressed air without a shield. A low level pilot of 3.5 m diameter with C.I. lining was first driven, followed by a pair of 3 m diameter similar top pilots. The full sized tunnel, also with C.I. segmental lining, was then excavated and built round this trefoil pattern of pilots. At no time was there a large area of face exposed and requiring support and at the same time the cycle of exposure and lining was greatly speeded up by the reduction in volume of clay to be removed per ring. There was also the advantage of anchoring back the face walings to the pilot tunnel iron which was bolted throughout.

This principle of using a sequence of small manageable headings to overcome conditions too difficult for full face working is repeatedly found to be the best expedient, even in rock. A small heading may be driven to get in the crown of a tunnel, or a pair of headings for the springing of an arched roof, or the whole of an arch may be built up progressively in this manner.

An outstanding example of this is the Eisenhower Memorial (originally Straight Creek) road tunnel through the Rockies in Colorado. Very severe rock pressures and movements made it necessary to build the main arch over a length of some 50 m by constructing a concrete arch in a sequence of thirteen headings, or drifts. Over adjacent lengths five or more headings were used to establish footings, springings, and crown.

2. The second aspect of size is that of ready access to all parts of the face, which is necessary for access and support. 'Man is the measure of all things', and accordingly, when a man's reach is exceeded stagings or other platforms must be provided, or with mechanised working gantry, jumbo shield or excavating machine. Brunel's shield was built up from 36 unit cells each about 2 m high x 1 m wide. Over a century later the Dartford tunnel shields were designed with 16 compartments separated by platforms and vertical diaphragms, the largest compartment being about 2½ m square.

3. The total thrust to be provided in strutting of the exposed face will increase with size not only in proportion to the increased area but also because of loss of arching action and the increased vertical depth on which pressure acts. Additionally, supporting walings and beams carry the loads across longer spans and must be proportionately stiffer.

The point may be illustrated simply by some rough approximations. Doubling the diameter of a circular tunnel quadruples the face area, the ground pressure may be supposed to be one and a half times as great, so that six times the load must be carried on beams twice as long, producing bending moments multiplied 12 times in a full length beam.

4. If the length of advance in each cycle of operation remains the same, the volume of material to be excavated and transported will increase in direct proportion to the area of face, or to the square on the diameter. The times for excavation and disposal and for the other elements in the total cycle tend to increase in larger tunnels. Therefore, the time interval between opening of the ground and provision of support will be substantially increased and heavier ground loadings are likely to develop.

5. In permeable saturated ground static water pressure at any level will be proportional to depth below the free surface. In fact, because of inflow, static pressure cannot develop unless the face is fully closed, but water problems will in any case increase disproportionately. Where compressed air is necessary the problems arising from difference of pressure between top and bottom of a big face can be formidable.

6. In a large tunnel the likelihood increases that the strata encountered will not be uniform but that different types of ground will be encountered at the top and bottom of the face.

Particular difficulties will be apparent if such strata as water-bearing gravel, sand or silt are met either at the top or at the bottom of a face, or if rock requiring the use of explosives occurs in a tunnel designed to be driven through soft ground. This was exemplified in both the Hudson river tunnel (1906) and the original Blackwall tunnel (1897). In the second Blackwall tunnel (1963), water at artesian pressure occurred in the invert so that the preparatory injection grouting scheme had to seal off both crown and invert.

7. The hazards from falling materials are obviously much greater in a large tunnel both because of the height of fall and the need for stagings, from which materials can be dropped.

It will be obvious that tunnels cannot just be scaled up, but that, even where a pilot tunnel has been successfully driven, the full scale enlargement presents further problems and difficulties.

There is also a minimum limit on dimensions as a man must have working room for himself, his tools and his timber within the tunnel, unless it is so short a heading that it can be constructed by reaching in from the ends. Apart from this, economic considerations of access and use of equipment may well make it cheaper to construct a 3 m tunnel than one of 2½ m diameter, but the actual limiting size will depend on the many construction factors of the particular project. Anything less than 2½ m is not likely to be economic for long tunnels. In the long London MWB water tunnel through the clay 2.54 m was adopted as a standard, and in the Scottish hydroelectric developments in tunnelling through hard rock the lowest cost per unit length was found to be for a tunnel of about the same diameter. For very long tunnels without intermediate working or ventilation shafts, the minimum economic size tends to increase with length, especially if the additional space has permanent value.

4.9 MANAGEMENT OF WATER

In most tunnels water is present in the ground to be excavated; a dry tunnel is unusual. Management of the water is a vital feature of excavation. It is probable that water more than any other factor has caused failures or unforeseen difficulties in tunnel construction. It is not only the spectacular troubles of inundation, as in the Thames tunnel, the Severn tunnel, the Lötschberg tunnel that emphasise the dangers from water and the importance of its management, but the multitude of small tunnels where costly delays have been caused by water, and subsidence and damage have resulted. The management of water is much more than a mere problem of oilskins and pumps.

Water, as a problem in tunnel construction, requires to be studied from three aspects:

1. Hydrology of the ground, both as existing before disturbance and as modified by the tunnel excavation and ancillary operations.
2. Soil mechanics, more particularly the changes in the properties and behaviour of the ground arising from changes in the pore water content and seepage pressures, and also any chemical reactions.
3. Logistics of provision and siting of pumps and pumping mains.

4.9.1 Hydrology

The inflow of water into the tunnel will be dependent on the water content and permeability of the various strata exposed and adjacent. The volume of water available to recharge the strata is important as is the rate of recharge.

In a subaqueous tunnel in which the source of the ground water is sea, river, or lake, the quantity is virtually unlimited. Much may depend on the existence or not of impervious strata protecting the tunnel excavation and on their thickness and characteristics. Although inundation from overhead is obviously the major hazard, artesian water in the invert may also be of importance.

The protection may be a bed of clay which virtually provides a water seal, but its continuity in adequate thickness above the tunnel must be constantly checked as the bed may thin out unexpectedly or its surface may be penetrated by a buried channel, or other hollow eroded in the past and refilled with alluvium. Such anomalies are not uncommon at the upper surface of the London clay which is usually overlain by water-bearing gravel.

Thin clay cover cannot be expected to provide much mechanical strength, therefore immediate support of the excavation followed as quickly as practicable by permanent lining and grouting becomes essential. In such ground any appearance of moisture at the face has to be regarded with extreme suspicion.

Such a protective stratum may be altogether absent as in the Blackwall tunnel (1897) where shield, compressed air, and an almost closed face supplemented by a clay blanket in the river bed were necessary and barely adequate. In the second Blackwall tunnel (1963) slightly more favourable ground was chosen, but with the added assistance of chemical injection grouting to reduce the permeability of the sand and gravel and to give it chemically some cohesive strength. Similar grouting treatment for a length of the invert also was necessary where artesian water was present.

A subaqueous tunnel may be in rock not completely impermeable but structurally adequate. Again there is a danger from buried channels and also fissures and faults.

Under the river Mersey such a buried channel of glacial origin eroded below the general bed level into the Triassic sandstone was encountered in the driving of the Mersey Railway tunnel (1886). There was generally at least 5 m of rock cover but locally the crown of the tunnel was in the clay and sand filling 1 m or so above the sandstone. The Mersey Queensway road tunnel (1934) encountered the same channel but the crown of the tunnel was kept low enough to provide a metre or so of rock cover, the pilot tunnel being lined locally with cast iron as a precaution. At the site of the Mersey Kingsway road tunnel (1971) this buried channel did not appear to be present, but a fault was encountered filled with soft material and communicating directly with the river. Protection of the critical length was provided by a reinforced concrete hood constructed in a series of small headings.

Where sources of water supply are not unlimited or where the recharging rate of the ground is limited by low permeability and adequate thickness, various methods of ground water lowering may be possible, as by well points, drainage tunnels, or well shafts with pumps. An invert heading kept in front of the face may be sufficient or pumping from a sump at the face.

Reduction of permeability by injection grouting to fill the pores can be used to check inflow, as can freezing. Compressed air also serves this purpose.

In mountain tunnels the water hazard is usually different. Fissures filled with water and recharged from the surface may be encountered, the water being at high pressure and possibly very hot. Such flows are likely to diminish with time both in volume and temperature but can be a very severe hazard. There is the added risk of such flows loosening and carrying into the tunnel large volumes of sand or other soft ground. A further hazard, particularly in limestone, is that of solution caverns filled with water and fed by underground rivers.

Examples of mountain tunnels in which water was a major problem include: the Lötschberg railway tunnel (1913), the Moffat railway tunnel (1928) through the Rockies in Colorado, the Tanna railway tunnel (1934) in Japan, the Tecolote water tunnel (1955) in California, the Litani water tunnel (1965) in Lebanon.

The level of the water table is not a simple concept in the context of tunnelling. In relatively shallow tunnels the strata are likely to be very variable with different permeabilities and rates of recharge. The significant questions are whether the ground is saturated and at what pressure, and what balance will be achieved between drainage into the tunnel, or ancillary drainage system, and recharge. This is a problem of dynamic rather than static equilibrium. Pressure gradients and seepage flows develop depending on permeability, source of water, and rate of pumping, and the excavation methods must take full account of this pattern.

4.9.2 Soil Mechanics
The interaction of water and solids in soils is a fundamental part of soil mechanics. The presence of water and its movement affects significantly the structural behaviour of soils exposed in tunnel excavation.

In the simplest case a damp sand will have some cohesive properties and will not run freely whereas the same sand either dry or saturated loses much of its cohesion and runs readily if unsupported. Water flowing through granular soil will tend to wash out the finer particles and will thus enlarge the passages, increase the flow and also cause settlement. A suitably graded gravel will, however, function as a filter retaining solids while allowing the water to pass.

Fine sands at the bottom of an excavation may boil up under the seepage pressure of rising water, creating an artificial quicksand, which can however be controlled by a proper gravel filter or by reducing the volume of seepage. The true quicksand results from a loose particle structure.

In silts water content is all important as described above. The original builders of the Hudson river tunnel in 1879 thought that regulation of compressed air pressure had provided the key to this problem, but found that stability could not be achieved.

In clays also water content and pore pressure control behaviour and properties, but changes are relatively slow so that time is usually available for the tunnelling cycle.

Following exposure by excavation there is a release of stress at the surface and increase of stress at depth as a consequence of which the clay acting as a sponge tends to draw in pore water from behind, which in many clays results in swelling. The time elapsing between excavation and final structural lining will govern the extent of this swelling and the resultant loading on the lining. In the case of a grouted precast lining some swelling usually occurs before grouting and some continues to develop and to impose a pressure on the completed lining.

4.9.3 Logistics
It should be clear that control of water before and as it enters the tunnel must be closely integrated with the method of excavation and support. The handling and disposal of the water is equally important.

In subaqueous tunnels it is usually necessary to drive much of the length on a falling gradient of about 3% to 5% for a highway tunnel. Water then inevitably runs forward and accumulates in the invert at the face where construction is in progress. All water must be pumped back along the tunnel and up to the surface where it can be discharged. Pumps at the face have to be moved continuously forward and therefore must be relatively light and mobile, transferring the water back to a fixed sump where a more permanent and mechanically efficient installation is possible. Clearly as much as possible of the water entering behind the face in the completed tunnel should be intercepted by a dam and sump before reaching the face.

If work is being carried forward beneath a river from a shaft it is likely that construction of a main sump and installation of permanent pumps there will be adopted. The pumping capacity must be adequate for all probable requirements with also ample standby capacity both against breakdown of plant and against unexpected influx of water.

In a long tunnel there are likely to be a series of pumps and sumps between working face and main sump at the shaft. Capacity of pumps and sumps, pipe sizes, and power supplies all need to be carefully planned to meet the maximum demand, bearing in mind that failure or inadequacy of the system may result in flooding of the tunnel and loss of the pumps.

4.10 ART OF TUNNELLING

In tunnelling the problems of excavation are more fully three dimensional than in other types of excavation. They are even four dimensional in the sense that time is a major factor because the stresses in ground that has been opened up are continuously changing and timing of support can become critical. The special characteristic of tunnelling is that ground is excavated from inside and from underneath. Therefore, it is, to a greater degree than in other excavation, exploration of the unknown. The weight of ground is always poised above, and its support at all stages must be ensured, as well as its protection from loosening by water.

The development of the various mechanised tunnelling systems should not lead to the conclusion that the tunnel miner's traditional skills in excavation, ground support and management of water are no longer required. Where ground conditions are suitable it is now possible to construct long lengths of tunnel with 'moles' or tunnel boring machines, erecting whatever permanent lining may be necessary in comparative comfort and safety. Even in ideal conditions it remains necessary to carry out much critical work by hand mining for such items as access headings, shield chambers, openings, junctions, and ventilation connections. The construction in tunnel of a station for an underground railway provides an example, where the station tunnel drive is not long enough to justify the installation of a fully mechanised system and where a whole network of tunnels has to be constructed at various levels, often beneath valuable surface property using great care and all the traditional skills.

In excavating tunnels in soft ground there is sometimes the likelihood and always the possibility that unexpected conditions, sometimes dangerous, will be disclosed as the face advances, however detailed and elaborate the preparatory investigations and studies.

Traditionally, skilled and dedicated tunnel miners with experienced supervisors lived with and cared for the working face, augering ahead to prove the ground, and placing support timbers where necessary. Work in difficult ground often proceeded for twenty-four hours a day for seven days a week, for reasons of safety as well as to increase progress, and it must be appreciated that continuous progress itself contributes to safety because of the limited 'stand-up' time of some ground.

With the mechanisation of tunnelling and the increased difficulty of arranging for work to be continuous over holidays, there is a danger that the traditional virtues may be lost. However modern the method, the need for caution remains and precautions such as regular inspection of the workings and the availability of emergency face supports and such items as standby pumps are as important as ever.

BIBLIOGRAPHY

The subject is dealt with extensively in the classic books, in particular those listed below, and incidentally in many papers and articles about particular projects which are included in the general bibliography in Volume 2.

Hewett, B. H. M. and Johannesson, S., *Shield and compressed air tunneling*, McGraw-Hill, 1922.

Richardson, H. W. and Mayo, R. S., *Practical Tunnel Driving*, McGraw-Hill, 1941 (revised edn., R. S. Mayo, 1975).

Terzaghi, K., 'Shield tunnels of the Chicago subway,' *J. Boston Soc. Civ. Engrs.*, 1942, **29** (July).

Terzaghi, K. 'Liner-plate tunnels on the Chicago subway', *Trans. Amer. Soc. Civ. Engrs.*, 1943, **108**.

Terzaghi, K. and Richart, F. E., 'Stresses in rock about cavities', *Geotechnique*, 1952, 3 (June).

Peck, R. B., 'Deep excavation and tunneling in soft ground', *Proc. 7th Int. Conf. Soil Mech. Fndtn. Engng.*, Mexico, 1969, State of the Art Volume.

Muir Wood, A. M., 'Soft ground tunnelling', *in The Technology and Potential of Tunnelling*, South African Tunnelling Conference, Johannesburg, 1970.

Peck, R. B. and others, 'State of the art of soft-ground tunneling', *1st North American Rapid Excavation and Tunneling Conference*, Chicago, 1972, **1**.

Szechy, K., *The Art of Tunnelling*, Akademiai Kiado, 2nd edn., 1973.

Bartlett, J. V. and King, J. R. J., 'Soft ground tunnelling', *Proc. Instn. Civ. Engrs.*, 1975, **58** (Nov.). *See also* discussion, 1976, **60** (Aug.).

Proctor, R. V. and White, T. L., *Earth tunneling with steel supports*, Commercial Shearing and Stamping Co., Ohio, 1977.

5

Compressed Air Working

5.1 USES AND LIMITATIONS

The use of compressed air in tunnel construction is to make practicable sub-aqueous tunnelling in conditions which would otherwise be unduly hazardous or impossible. It acts by providing a counterbalancing force against the inward pressure of water, reducing the inflow and supporting the ground. It is entirely practicable for men to work in compressed air, but there are physiological limitations and risks which make necessary strict observance of precautions, more particularly at higher pressures.

5.1.1 Decompression

The difficult physiological problems are those of decompression. During work under pressure air dissolves in the blood and is carried to the various tissues. The excess oxygen creates no serious problems except at very high pressures, nor does the nitrogen until pressure is reduced. Under reduction of pressure the nitrogen tends to form bubbles in the tissues and blood stream, and if these accumulate they may exert painful pressure on nerves and block the circulation with possible serious consequences. Decompression procedures therefore must be devised to minimise the risks. The principal means is controlled slow decompression providing enough time for harmless desaturation. The time necessary for decompression may be reduced by limiting the time of exposure to pressure to avoid saturation.

5.1.1.1 Diving

Diving has the same problem both in the ancient traditional diving to seek pearls or for salvage or other purposes and in helmet diving and modern scuba diving. Important differences from tunnel working are the individual self regulation of the diver and the higher peak pressures, the relatively short time of exposure to pressure, the problem of regulating decompression by slow ascent by stages, the temperature of the water and strong currents, and the extra difficulty of providing for any necessary recompression. The tendency has therefore been for diving saturation to be restricted by limiting the time spent at high pressure so that a quicker ascent is possible, whereas in tunnelling as long a shift as practicable is worked by a whole gang at moderate pressure, with the necessary sequel that decompression times, in somewhat more comfortable conditions, may be very lengthy. Techniques of saturation diving are being developed, and systems in which men remain under high pressure for days continuously. In very deep diving, gas mixtures such as oxygen and helium can be used to replace compressed air.

5.1.1.2 Flying
Decompression is also a problem of high flying in unpressurised aircraft. At about 5500 m atmospheric pressure is half that at sea level and at about 8500 m a third. Valuable research into the physiology of decompression in flying was therefore undertaken during and after World War II.

Airline services operate with pressurised aircraft. The pressure is not normally allowed to fall below that at 2500 m, namely 0.75 bar abs, but even so those who have been working in compressed air at 1 bar(g) or more are wiser not to travel by air for at least 24 hours after decompression.

5.1.2 Application
Its historical development as an aid to tunnelling towards the end of the 19th century is described in Chapter 1. Its earliest use was in dock work, but the main development was for river crossings by rail and road such as the Hudson river tunnel, the Blackwall tunnel and the Sarnia tunnel, and also for water and gas mains crossing under rivers and for metro tunnels and sewers at limited depths in water-bearing strata under cities.

These uses all continue to be important with the addition of structures associated with the development of electric power such as cooling water intakes and outfalls and cable tunnels for river crossings.

For major submarine tunnels such as the Channel tunnel and the Seikan tunnel the depths are too great for compressed air working. Their construction depends on finding rock strata competent, after suitable treatment and lining as necessary, to resist the stresses and water pressures.

5.1.2.1 Caissons
Historically use the of compressed air working for caisson sinking preceded that for tunnelling. It was a direct development from the diving bell and was first used in shaft sinking for mining operations by Triger in 1841 at Challonnes on the River Seine. Its earliest use for bridge foundations was for Rochester bridge

on the River Medway in 1851. In shaft sinking as a preliminary to tunnelling caissons are frequently used, and the method has also been employed for sinking prefabricated lengths of tunnel at relatively shallow depths where horizontal tunnelling was difficult.

In caisson work the water pressure is balanced at a single level, that of the cutting edge, and working pressure increases directly in proportion to depth. Problems of access differ considerably from those in tunnelling. Air locks are usually small, and decanting, referred to below, becomes the standard method of decompression for all but the lowest pressures.

5.1.2.2 Tunnelling

Compressed air tunnelling therefore is a valuable technique but calls for very careful planning and extensive provision of plant and equipment. Men must be trained in the proper use of air and must accept the disciplines of regulation and of medical supervision. In tunnelling about 3½ bar is the upper limit in standard rules. Higher pressures are practicable and are experienced in deep diving, but permissible exposure times at such pressures are so short and decompression times so long as to be uneconomic for tunnel work unless the circumstances are quite exceptional.

5.2 PHYSICAL ASPECTS

5.2.1 Units

In defining pressure a wide range of different units are employed. The most familiar is probably pounds (force) per square inch (lb/sq in) often written 'psi'. Other widely used units are kilograms (force) per square centimetre (kg/cm^2) or feet head of water or atmospheres. With the increasing use of the S.I. system, based on the metre, kilogram and second, it appears likely that for tunnelling the 'bar' will prove useful and convenient, as it is sufficiently close to 1 atmosphere to be interchangeable in ordinary use. The kilogram per square centimetre is also nearly the same and is sometimes described as a 'technical atmosphere'.

Air pressures are almost invariably stated as the excess over outside atmospheric pressure, sometimes written as 'pounds per square inch gauge' (psig). Absolute pressure is calculated by the addition of atmospheric pressure to the gauge pressure, and is significant mainly in the study of physiological effects. It is sometimes denoted by the symbol 'ATA' for atmospheres absolute. In what follows pressure will generally be stated in bars (gauge pressure), except where other units are necessary for clarity or in quoting descriptions or official regulations. The tables which follow give (1) conversion factors between the different units and (2) equivalents in the other units for pressures in bars up to 3.6 bar.

5.2.1.1 Conversion Tables

Table 1 Conversion factors for principal units

	bar = N/m^2 x 10^5	atm	psi = lbf/in^2	kg/cm^2	Fresh Water		Sea Water	
					ft	m	ft	m
bar	1	0.987	14.504	1.0197	33.46	10.20	32.64	9.95
atm	1.01324	1	14.696	1.0332	33.90	10.33	33.07	10.08
psi	0.06895	0.06805	1	.0703	2.307	0.709	2.250	0.686
kg/cm^2	0.981	0.968	14.224	1	32.81	10.00	32.00	9.76
Water— fresh ft	0.0299	.0295	.433	.0305	1	0.305	0.975	0.297
m	0.0981	.0968	1.422	0.100	3.28	1	3.20	0.975
sea ft	0.0306	.0302	0.444	0.312	1.025	0.313	1	.305
m	0.1005	.0992	1.458	0.102	3.36	1.025	3.28	1

Table 2 Conversion table 0.1–3.6 bar

bar	atm	psi	kg/cm^2	Fresh Water		Sea Water	
				ft	m	ft	m
.1	0.10	1.5	0.10	3.3	1.0	3.3	1.0
.2	0.20	2.9	0.20	6.7	2.0	6.5	2.0
.3	0.30	4.4	0.31	10.0	3.1	9.8	3.0
.4	0.39	5.8	0.41	13.4	4.1	13.1	4.0
.5	0.49	7.3	0.51	16.7	5.1	16.3	5.0
.6	0.59	8.7	0.61	20.1	6.1	19.6	6.0
.7	0.69	10.2	0.71	23.4	7.1	22.8	7.0
.8	0.79	11.6	0.82	26.8	8.2	26.1	8.0
.9	0.89	13.1	0.92	30.1	9.2	29.4	9.0
1.0	0.99	14.5	1.02	33.5	10.2	32.6	10.0
1.2	1.18	17.4	1.22	40.2	12.2	39.2	11.9
1.4	1.38	20.3	1.43	46.8	14.3	45.7	13.9
1.6	1.58	23.2	1.63	53.5	16.3	52.2	15.9
1.8	1.78	26.1	1.84	60.2	18.4	58.8	17.9
2.0	1.97	29.0	2.04	66.9	20.4	65.3	19.9
2.2	2.17	31.9	2.24	73.6	22.4	71.8	21.9
2.4	2.37	34.8	2.45	80.3	24.5	78.3	23.9
2.6	2.57	37.7	2.65	87.0	26.5	84.9	25.9
2.8	2.76	40.6	2.86	93.7	28.6	91.4	27.9
3.0	2.96	43.5	3.06	100.4	30.6	97.9	29.9
3.2	3.16	46.4	3.26	107.1	32.6	104.4	31.8
3.4	3.36	49.3	3.47	113.8	34.7	111.0	33.8
3.6	3.55	52.2	3.67	120.5	36.7	117.5	35.8

5.2.2 Supply of Air

The first questions to be resolved in making use of compressed air for tunnelling are:

1. What is the maximum air pressure foreseeable?
2. What is the appropriate working pressure?
3. What volume of air must be provided?

From the answers follow the planning of bulkheads, air locks, compressor installations, and ancillary plant and equipment, and also appropriate medical precautions and procedures. Extra fire precautions are always necessary because of enhanced rates of combustion and difficulties of access.

The physical interactions of groundwater, compressed air and soil structure in the process of tunnelling are complex and must be examined in some detail. Pressure and volume of air have to be estimated initially with an ample allowance for possible contingencies, in order to equip the site with appropriate plant, but precise requirements can only be determined by practical experience in the progress of the work. Security of air supply in adequate volume is vital for safety wherever loss of air pressure can result in inundation or collapse of the tunnel. Not only must compressor capacity be ample for all foreseeable needs but independent standby power should be ensured.

It is usually relatively simple to fix a maximum for pressure, namely, the hydrostatic head resulting from a water column from lowest tunnel invert level to highest water level including allowance for tidal surges or flood waters where appropriate. There may however be an additional requirement if work must be done ahead of a shield in liquid mud whose density is of course greater than that of water.

The appropriate working pressure is discussed below, but as a starting point a hydrostatic balance level about two thirds of the height up the exposed tunnel face may usually be taken.

The quantity of air to be supplied is much more difficult to determine. The first requirement is to supply at least a minimum for each man working in the chamber. The figure in current British practice is 10 ft^3/min (5 l/s) measured at the working pressure. Compressor capacity is usually measured as the volume of free air per minute and therefore in defining the compressor capacity the above figure will be increased in proportion to the absolute pressure. This air volume should of course be delivered at a point sufficiently close to the face to ensure that men working there have an adequate supply.

In clay, or other ground of low permeability, there may be very little loss of air from the working chamber except through use of the air locks, and an exhaust pipe may be necessary, but if the ground is at all open there will be substantial leakages through the face and through the joints of the completed lining. A figure of 60 to 100 l/s per square metre of the tunnel cross section is suggested for moderately open ground. More may be required if the face is very open, and if the lining of the completed tunnel is not adequately sealed by grouting and caulking. This requirement, plus air consumed in the use of the locks will be well in excess of the minimum man requirements.

At the first Dartford tunnel, low pressure compressor capacity provided on each side of the river was 7000 l/s for the main supply in three electrically driven compressors and 2800 l/s in six diesel-driven standby compressors. The total was thus 9800 l/s for a face area of 86.5 m^2 which is about 80 l/s/m^2 main supply plus 30 l/s/m^2 standby. This proved more than adequate in use.

5.2.2.1 Deoxygenated Air

In the context of air supply it may be appropriate to refer to the hazard of deoxygenated air. If air displaces the pore water from a stratum containing oxidisable material the oxygen may be wholly or largely absorbed leaving mainly nitrogen. If this gas is then drawn into the tunnel because of a drop in pressure, men may be in danger of asphyxiation. Several instances have been recorded, most commonly due to oxidation of an organic stratum but also of iron pyrites. In one instance of Metro station work adjacent chambers were being worked at different air pressures and deoxygenated air in an intervening stratum was displaced by the higher pressure air into the chamber operating at the lower pressure. The remedy is of course provision of adequate fresh air where work is being done, and particularly after a shut down.

5.3 EXCAVATION AND SUPPORT

5.3.1 Gravel and Sand

The case of tunnelling in gravel or sand beneath the water table may first be examined. It is assumed that the gravel is connected to an extensive source of water and cannot be dewatered satisfactorily by pumping.

A tunnel face completely sealed by a watertight diaphragm would be subjected to the full water pressure of the hydrostatic head from the level of the water table, which, of course, increases from top to bottom of the face. The application of air pressure in the tunnel equal to the water pressure at mid level would produce an overall equality of thrust, but with excess pressure of water externally in the bottom half and excess air pressure internally in the upper half. Opening up of the face then produces a tendency for air to escape in the upper half and water to flow in below as shown in Fig. 5.1.

The air pressure effectively reduces the water pressure acting at the face but does not reduce the pressure of the gravel itself or its tendency to slip in, or to be washed in where the water is still flowing.

The air will escape all over the upper half of the face but more particularly so at the top where the pressure difference is greatest. In escaping it expands and displaces water and fine material and may well develop and enlarge a channel or

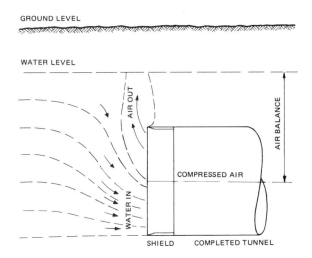

Fig. 5.1 – Air balance in tunnel.

pipe up to the surface, through which large volumes can escape, perhaps catastrophically. Such a sudden catastrophic escape constitutes a 'blow'; air pressure is lost and the tunnel is inundated until the channel chokes and pressure can be restored. On the other hand, the displacement of the pore water changes the soil from a saturated to a moist condition in which capillary forces provide a little cohesion and the stability of the mass is improved. The shield is designed to minimise the risk of catastrophic failure, and may incorporate devices such as a 'hood' at the cutting edge kept buried in the ground ahead, and shutters at the face or safety doors through a diaphragm.

The choice of air pressure for practical use is a matter of judgement. The level in the face at which the selected air pressure balances the hydrostatic head is a convenient measure to define pressure at any time. If the balance level is low in the face, the tunnel is kept drier but the risk of a blow is greater, the air consumption is higher and men are subjected to a higher pressure.

If the balance level is high in the face, the tunnel will be wetter with more danger of ground washing in and it may become more difficult to excavate and line the invert.

As already suggested, a balance level about two thirds of the way up the face is usually suitable as a starting point but will almost inevitably need to be adjusted to suit the particular tunnel. On general grounds of reducing risk of a blow and exposure of men, the lowest practicable pressure is to be preferred, but increased pressure may be needed for limited periods as when high tidal levels are significant, or perhaps for the invert construction.

It is not unknown for tunnel miners to ask for higher air pressure to get drier working conditions, but such increases should be carefully controlled. The drying up effect may be short lived because although the extra air pressure initially pushes back the ground water, a new pattern of flow may soon establish itself with little gain. Increased air consumption with enhanced ground disturbance and longer decompression times must be taken into account if the working pressure is increased.

5.3.2 Silt
For finer grained silty soil the principles of balance are the same but the lower permeability to water and air and the sensitivity of the soil structure to pore water content change the immediate problems. Inflow of water and escape of air will be less, but close support to the exposed ground surface will be required. Any loosening of the grain structure of the silt will immediately reduce its shear strength and increase its permeability so that collapse of the ground becomes possible, the water-bearing silt flowing like a viscous liquid. In major inundations water-borne sand and gravel can also flow similarly and a long length of tunnel can be filled.

The first use of compressed air without any shield in the Hudson river tunnel was originally thought to have solved the problem of tunnelling in river silt by regulating air pressure to a nicety so that the silt was maintained in a surface dry condition retaining its cohesion. The equilibrium was much too unstable for safe working until the Greathead shield in combination with cast-iron segmental lining was introduced, whereby exposed surfaces of ground were kept to a minimum and were provided with immediate support.

Silt continues to be the most unpredictable type of soil and its presence in a tunnel face always calls for caution. Its cohesive properties are unreliable and it cannot be readily strengthened by injection grouting because of its fine grain and low permeability. Very fluid resin grouts can be used but injection is necessarily slow and costly and it may be difficult to confine the material to the required stratum.

5.3.3 Clay
A characteristic of clay is that it is nearly impermeable and, except through fissures, there will neither be inflow of water nor escape of air through a homogeneous stratum. Nevertheless, use of compressed air can contribute greatly to safety in subaqueous tunnelling.

Even if the clay is stiff and unfissured and of sufficient thickness to provide adequate cover above the tunnel, compressed air may properly be employed both to provide continuous support to the roof of the tunnel and to be immediately available if the protecting layer above the excavation is unexpectedly lost, being breached by a slip or a fissure, or by a sudden dip locally in the clay surface because of erosion of an ancient surface by a stream or by weathering. Where the provision of compressed air is precautionary the tunnel may be worked at a nominal pressure of 0.3–0.5 bar unless and until an actual or anticipated emergency requires an increase.

If the clay is soft, silty or fissured or the stratum is of uncertain extent and thickness the use of compressed air may be the only practicable means of tunnelling safely. It cannot, however, be relied upon to support blocks of clay exposed in the top or face because air pressure will permeate fissures and may even assist in dislodging such blocks of clay. The air pressure will, of course, continue to act in relieving the thrust from deeper in the ground, but proper timbering of the face and top is essential to avoid this hazard.

In clay, escape of air at the face is normally very small and ventilation for the miners must be provided as discussed earlier.

5.3.4 Chalk

Chalk is a relatively soft limestone of Cretaceous age. Its properties range widely and its variations along with length of a tunnel are not always predictable. It is of low permeability but is frequently much jointed and fissured, particularly at shallow depths. It may contain cavities formed by solution action and 'pipes' leading down from its surface filled up with gravel or clay from an old land surface. These features were the cause of many difficulties in Stephenson's Watford railway tunnel in 1834-37, when, of course, compressed air working had not been developed.

The water which is to be controlled by compressed air enters through fissures and joints. It most usually comes from above but may sometimes be artesian. The usefulness of compressed air depends very much on the particular circumstances of the tunnel as may be exemplified by three instances.

The first Dartford tunnel was driven under the River Thames using shields and compressed air, The under-river drive was mainly through chalk, but with limited overhead cover; the under-land approaches from the portals descending towards the river banks exposed gravel, silty clay and peat above the chalk. The character of the chalk varied from very soft 'putty' chalk, probably caused by surface weathering in glacial times, to soft but coherent rock at greater depths but with numerous joints and fissures and bands of flint nodules. Conditions were wet, but controllable by moderate air pressure; generally speaking the hydrostatic balance level in the main tunnel was near or above the crown (maximum about 2 bar). Injection of grouts was used to minimise air losses through the gravel and reduce permeability.

In contrast, the Channel tunnel (further described in Chapter 10) was not to use compressed air although also in chalk, because the depth was much too great for appropriate pressures to be acceptable for men to work in, and because a suitable stratum was located in which the chalk was almost impervious and largely free from open joints and fissures, having a large clay content and in fact resembling in character an extremely stiff homogeneous clay.

Another contrasting tunnel in chalk was the cable tunnel under the River Thames at Tilbury which was sited at a depth of over 50 m in the hope of driving through better chalk with greater freedom from water-bearing fissures. The work was executed in free air, but a few large fissures were encountered requiring extensive grouting.

5.4 PHYSIOLOGICAL EFFECTS

Men are quite capable of hard physical work in compressed air at moderate pressures which in tunnelling are normally limited to about 3½ bar. In deep diving below 35 m, pressures are higher and different problems develop, both by reason of pressure and the marine environment. In tunnelling men enter through an air lock in which air pressure is gradually raised to that of the working chamber and they leave through the same lock. The principal physiological effect observed by a man entering is the equalisation of pressure in the ears. The inner ear is brought up to pressure through the narrow Eustachian tubes and if these passages are clear and unobstructed, no discomfort will be felt. If the passage is restricted, or is obstructed as when suffering from catarrh, it may be necessary to raise the pressure very slowly or it may prove impossible for the individual to enter without severe pain in the ears or ultimately a damaged ear drum. Various aids to opening the passages and permitting equalisation of pressure are useful: the act of swallowing can help, or nose blowing with the nostrils held. It must be recognised, however, that personal idiosyncrasies have to be respected and that for some individuals entry may not be possible.

Once the working pressure is attained without damage to ears a man can operate quite normally under pressure. It is sometimes suggested that the extra oxygen supply enhances his physical capacity.

The major physiological problems arise during and after decompression, and may not be immediately obvious. Under pressure additional atmospheric nitrogen, which constitutes four fifths of the atmospheric air, dissolves in the blood stream and progressively in the various tissues to which blood is fed. Nitrogen is particularly soluble in fatty tissue. Some tissues quickly approach saturation but others continue to take up further nitrogen for several hours.

On decompression the excess nitrogen must be discharged again. If decompression is sufficiently slow the emerging nitrogen will be carried to the lungs by the blood and there will be discharged without ill effects. Decompression may result in the formation of bubbles in the blood or tissues and if these bubbles are not harmlessly carried to the lungs by the blood stream, they may lodge in the blood vessels or tissues with painful and possibly serious consequences. There is still much debate on the precise details of the physics and chemistry and physiology of compressed air sickness. Decompression rules and timetables necessarily continue to be formulated empirically, guided by theories but evaluated by practical experience.

The most common phenomena are 'the bends', when a bubble lodges near a joint and exerts painful pressure on a nerve, and 'the niggles', minor irritations of a similar nature. These may occur during decompression, but more often may not be apparent for an hour or more afterwards. They can usually be relieved quite readily by recompression. The original working pressure, or a little more, may be necessary but often a lower pressure gives relief. Slow controlled decompression again, under medical supervision, usually resolves the problem.

More serious cases of decompression sickness, the so-called 'Type 2', occur when a bubble forms in the viscera, lungs, spinal chord or brain. Unless treated, paralysis or death may follow, and frequently did in the past, Again, recompression almost invariably relieves the symptoms, but decompression may have to be extremely slow, possibly extending over several days with reversals if symptoms reappear, to ensure that there is no recurrence.

There is a third form of illness which only develops over a period of months, namely aseptic bone necrosis, in which a bone, most often in hip or shoulder, is attacked and its structure damaged. If the attack is near a joint surface it may eventually interfere with the use of the joint and become painful and may require major surgery. If remote from a joint no ill effects may be noticeable. Diagnosis is by radiography but is difficult in the earlier stages.

Correlation with exposure to compressed air working was slowly established from about 1942 onwards. There was a medical study in New York State, but despite care in formulating and operating decompression rules a substantial number of cases were diagnosed in the construction of the third Lincoln tunnels (1953-57), in most of which the men affected had long records of past exposure to compressed air. Heavy compensation costs were incurred.

Medical records initiated at Dartford tunnel (1957-59) and elaborated at Clyde tunnel (1958-62) and subsequently were studied under the control of the Decompression Sickness Panel of the Medical Research Council and established clearly that aseptic bone necrosis is a form of compressed air sickness. The detailed study is particularly difficult because of the lengthy period of observation necessary and the problems of obtaining, maintaining and diagnosing X-ray records of the changing work force, whose employment in compressed air may be occasional and intermittent.

It is thought that extended decompression times should reduce the incidence. New tables have been devised accordingly and show promising improvement.

5.5 DECOMPRESSION TABLES

Pioneer work on the subject of decompression sickness was done by J. S. Haldane before 1908, for an Admiralty Committee concerned primarily with diving. As a basis for decompression tables he used a pattern of saturation times for different tissues, with corresponding rates of release of dissolved gas. He found that rapid decompression from a level of 2.3 atm absolute appeared safe, that is to say from

1.3 bar (19 psig). He adopted a ratio of 2 : 1 for the absolute pressure drop but expressed doubts as to the applicability of this ratio at very high pressures. Thus from a pressure of 1 atm rapid decompression to atmospheric pressure was permitted, from 2 atm the immediate drop was to ½ atm, and from 3 atm to 1 atm. Thereafter pressure had to be released very slowly, the rate depending on pressure and length of exposure. This formulation of the problem has been used ever since in the preparation of many tables, but details have been modified and assumptions as to tissue saturation times have been varied. There are other theoretical approaches. It is now clear that the 2 : 1 ratio does not ensure freedom from bubble formation in all conditions and that the initial rapid drop should not be so great.

In 1936 when the construction of the Dartford tunnel was under consideration, a committee of the Institution of Civil Engineers recommended rules for decompression based on Haldane's studies and on practical experience. Pressures up to 1.5 bar were considered not to require slow decompression, but for higher pressures tables were provided defining the amount of the first stage rapid decompression and a uniform rate for the succeeding slow decompression. The time of exposure to compressed air is relevant because it takes 4 hours or more for saturation of 'slow' tissues, which are likewise slow in releasing nitrogen. Accordingly, the tables permitted speedier decompression for short exposures. The main table set out, for pressures of 22 psi (1.5 bar) and over, the initial drop permissible in two minutes and the times for further uniform slow reduction to zero for times of exposures of: 6 hours or more, 4 hours, 3 hours, 2 hours, 1 hour, ½ hour. A revision of these tables was formulated in 1951 and incorporated in new Statutory Regulations in 1958; the decompression times were extended somewhat and the threshold for timed decompression was reduced to 1.24 bar (18 psi). It was not expected that these tables would eliminate 'bends' but it was considered that an incidence rate of 2% of compressions would be acceptable, because, except for unusual Type 2 cases which form a very small proportion of the whole, there appeared to be no permanent damage.

5.5.1 Blackpool Tables

When the statutory tables were worked to over a period cases of illness were encountered even below the 1.24 bar threshold and the incidence of bone necrosis was found to be widespread. Following Decompression Sickness Panel Studies a committee of the Construction Industry Research and Information Association re-examined the subject and published a report in 1973 recommending a new Code of Practice. It incorporated new tables with longer decompression times and with the threshold level reduced from 1.24 bar to 1 bar. There were also proposals for various other medical precautions and organisational arrangements, including X-ray examinations to be reported to a central register. The new tables are known as the 'Blackpool Tables' from the site of their first experimental use and have been widely adopted in Great Britain. At the maximum pressure of 3.4 bar, exposure exceeding 4 hours requires to be followed by 6 hr. 35 min. decompression time to follow. As a 12 hours limit for shift working is imposed on exposure time plus decompression time, this allows a maximum working shift time of 5 hrs. 25 min. at this pressure. Apart from this limitation, which takes effect above 2.8 bar, the Code permits the working of a full 8 hour shift, the assumption being that saturation is reached after 4 hours and that further exposure adds nothing to hazards.

5.5.2 New York split shifts
In New York very extensive tunnelling experience in the East River railway tunnels and elsewhere in the period 1904-21 and subsequently, led to the adoption of the split shift system in which working time at higher pressures was severely limited, a substantial intermediate period in free air being required.

Prior to 1909 shifts of 3 hrs. in, 3 hrs. out, 3 hrs. in for pressures exceeding 2.2 bar (32 psi) were worked and this pattern was progressively developed so that in the Lincoln tunnel (1953-57) the permissible shifts were typically:

Up to 1 bar (14 psi):   3 hrs. in, 2½ hrs. out, 3 hrs. in
At 3.4 bar (50 psi):   ½   5   ½
Decompression times were: 1 bar: 6 min.
                             3.4 bar: 37 min.

In 1960 these decompression times were increased for the second period to 9 mins. and 62 mins. respectively.

The limitations make impracticable substantial work in compressed air above 2.4 bar.

5.5.3 Washington State tables
In 1963 after further studies, Washington State adopted new standards which have been adopted with modifications in other states and countries. They are based on a single working period restricted progressively as pressure is increased but can be adapted to split shifts. Eight hours is allowed below 1.25 bar (18 psi) reducing to 3 hours above 3.31 bar (48 psi). The decompression is operated in 3 or 4 stages, the total time ranging from 16 mins. after 8 hours exposure at 1.0 bar (14 psi) to 249 mins. after 3 hours at 3.4 bar (50 psi). For comparison the Blackpool tables require 20 mins. and 200 mins. respectively.

The split shift system is now generally considered undesirable as actually increasing the hazards by doubling the number of decompressions. Complete desaturation is not achieved in the rest interval.

5.5.4 Comparison

A comparison of decompression sickness rates at various pressures using the Blackpool and Washington tables showed significantly lower 'bends' rates for the former despite restrictions on shift length in the latter.

There is a possibility that the limitation of exposure time at the higher pressures provided for in the Washington tables may be effective in minimising bone lesions in comparison with the longer exposures permitted in the Blackpool tables.

An interesting aspect of the Blackpool tables is the adoption of staged decompression, the pressure being held at each step of 0.2 bar (or 4 psi) for the number of minutes tabulated. An advantage is that it is easier to be precise in holding at a level than in operating a prescribed rate of drop between levels. The last step from 0.2 bar to atmosphere eliminates the uncertainty arising from leakages as the pressure helping to retain the lock drops to zero and the tightness of its seal is lost.

5.6 INCIDENCE OF ILLNESS

The physiological hazards arising from working in compressed air have not been eliminated but have been brought under control. Type 1 illness is accepted by those choosing to work in compressed air as an occupational risk with no long-term consequences. Individuals appear to differ considerably in their susceptibility and on any job there is likely to be a progressive elimination of the more susceptible. Some acclimatisation of men is observed over a few days if work continues at a steady pressure, but this is lost after absence of a week or ten days, and in any case, does not appear to provide any protection against an increased pressure.

Type 2 illness is rare but potentially dangerous; immediate and properly controlled treatment by recompression appears to be almost invariably effective. The recorded incidence is about 0.05% of decompressions.

The third hazard, that of bone necrosis, has been found by X-ray examination in a substantial proportion of compressed air tunnellers and in a smaller proportion of divers. Only about a quarter of the cases detected are in joint surfaces and produce symptoms. Because of its slow development and the difficulty of diagnosis a centralised system of records has been developed at Newcastle-on-Tyne to assist research into elimination of causes. Strict observance of improved decompression tables with accurate records is the most hopeful action.

5.7 MEDICAL CONTROL

In many countries regulations provide for the health and safety of men employed in compressed air. The precise official regulations applicable must of course be ascertained and worked to as a minimum, but additional safeguards may be specified or adopted for a particular project.

The rules become progressively more restrictive above a pressure of 1 bar or thereabouts, and may include the following requirements:

1. Medical examinations of workers before employment and periodically during employment including radiographic records if practicable.
2. Issue of identification discs to ensure proper treatment (by recompression) in the event of collapse away from site.
3. Strict control of entry and all decompressions by reliable lock keepers and proper detailed documentation of all exposures and decompressions.
4. Provision of changing and working facilities and rest rooms to enable men to remain on site for an hour or more after exposures over 1 bar.
5. Provision of a medical lock solely for therapeutic use and in charge of a trained medical attendant working under the direction of a doctor.

5.8 PLANT AND EQUIPMENT

The physical effects of compressed air working have been described above and the principal items of plant and equipment have been listed but are now described in more detail.

5.8.1 Bulkheads

The first essential is to seal off the working space from the outside air, closing off all openings. If the tunnel is worked from a single shaft the seal may be effected by an air deck across the shaft or by a bulkhead within the tunnel. If other shafts or adits lead into the working space they must likewise be sealed. Air locks provide passage through the bulkhead or air deck for men and materials.

The placing of the main bulkhead will be chosen to suit the particular project. It may be advantageous to provide initially an air deck and airlock in or at the top of an access shaft and to replace or supplement these later, when the tunnelling is sufficiently far advanced, by a bulkhead across the tunnel and two or more air locks through it. Unless the tunnel is small and pressures low it is essential to have separate man locks and muck locks to avoid mutual interference. Very careful planning of the lock arrangements is necessary to ensure that progress is not unnecessarily restricted by inadequate locking facilities.

A tunnel bulkhead must be a substantial and well built structure because very large forces are involved in a tunnel of large cross sectional area. For example, a 9 m diameter tunnel has a cross sectional area of 63.6 m^2; with a pressure as low as 1 bar the thrust on this area will be about 650 tonnes force.

Mass concrete is the most usual material for construction and a thickness of 0.4 to 0.6 times diameter is usual. Calculations of strength appropriate to the maximum possible air pressure should take account of the large holes required for air locks, but may usually assume arching action within the thickness. The whole thrust has to be transmitted by shear or otherwise into the tunnel lining behind the bulkhead and from the lining into the ground. A sufficient length of completed lining or other structural arrangement must therefore be ensured to distribute this thrust.

In addition to the air lock passages all services into the tunnel have to pass through the bulkhead including low pressure and high pressure air pipes, water supply, electric power, light and control cables, telephone cables, pumping mains and possibly such special services as hydraulic power, slurry discharge pumping or bentonite slurry supply. These have to be planned in advance and built in during construction of the bulkhead. As there is no reasonable possibility of making additional provision once the bulkhead is in use, ample spare capacity is advisable ensured by including a number of spare pipes blanked off until required. See Fig. 5.2.

Special care is necessary in concreting such a bulkhead to ram the concrete tightly round each service pipe, leaving no voids for escape of air and also to ensure careful sealing and grouting into the tunnel lining all round with particular attention at the soffit where the concrete may shrink away from the lining.

The bulkhead is ultimately demolished to clear the finished tunnel and this must be done without damage to the permanent lining into which it is anchored. Steel structures have been used for air bulkheads but are less easily adaptable to site requirements, and present the same problems of shear anchorage into the lining, and of providing for the passage of services.

An alternative to use of a bulkhead is the construction of an air deck in an access shaft if there are no other openings into the tunnel or if all are sealed off. The problems of making the deck airtight, and providing for the passage of services are much the same as for a bulkhead. Special care is necessary in dealing with the thrust upwards from the air pressure acting on the underside of the deck. Part will be taken safely by the dead weight of the deck itself, but any part transferred to the shaft lining needs to be examined critically against possible failure from breakage of the shaft lining in tension or shear, or loss of ground friction by reason of excavation or penetration of water or escaping air.

5.8.2 Air Locks
An air lock is an intermediate chamber between the open air and the working chamber through which passage may be effected between the spaces maintained at differing pressures. In tunnelling a lock functions to provide controlled entry to compressed air workings and exit therefrom. The lock is provided with two doors hinged to open respectively from atmosphere into lock chamber and from lock chamber to working chamber. It must be airtight and capable of withstanding the maximum pressure to which it may be subjected. The doors should be of steel accurately fitted and furnished with rubber or other sealing strips to ensure

Fig. 5.2 — Services into tunnel through bulkhead at air lock.

airtight closure and should be hinged as shown in the figures to allow even bearing all round, assisted by differential air pressure.

The principle of operation of an air lock is simple. In order to pass into the working chamber, which is at a pressure higher than atmospheric, the inner door of the lock is closed and the lock chamber is at normal atmospheric pressure while the outer door is open to the free air. A man enters the lock chamber, closes the outer door behind him, and compressed air is fed into the lock chamber through a control valve until the pressure is the same as that in the workings. The inner door is then free to open and entry to the tunnel is possible. In order to come out of the tunnel into free air the operation is reversed, compressed air being released from the air lock chamber to the atmosphere until the outer door can be opened.

Locks are required for the passage of men and materials, and although the principles are the same, there are important differences in detail. Locks are almost always cylindrical and the internal diameter is preferably 2 m or more. For men, decompression rates must be precisely regulated and from high pressures the time required may be a matter of hours, during which the lock is not available for other use. Dimensions of the lock must be such as to accommodate comfortably on seats the full numbers of shift workers and others who may be emerging at one time. The door dimensions (say 0.8 m x 1.2 m) need only be such as to allow a man to pass, or in an emergency a stretcher but should preferably be larger. The air feed and discharge pipes are usually limited to 25 mm diameter and may be fitted with automatic valve control to accord with the appropriate decompression tables. The rapid stage of decompression produces sharp cooling of the contained air and formation of fog which should be counteracted by heating during that stage. The lock is normally under the control of an external lock keeper who must have a window opening to see into the lock and telephone communication with the interior of the lock and the working chamber. Fig. 5.3.

For materials, not accompanied by men, the lock dimensions must accommodate the required number of waggons or skips being used, and must be long enough to take the longest timber, pipe or steel member likely to be required. In addition adequate clear space must be allowed for the door at the outer end to swing into the lock. A separate 'timber lock' comprising a long pipe with air doors is possible, but not often found advantageous. The door dimensions of a materials or 'muck' lock will be governed by the cross section of the loaded skips, but are of course limited by the diameter of the lock: 1.2 m wide x 1.4 m high is practicable in a lock of 2 m diameter.

For a materials lock, restricted solely to that use and never used for men, the air supply and exhaust pipes may be much larger: 100 mm diameter is common, to give the quickest practicable compression and decompression. Visibility is not important and heating is unnecessary.

In practice most materials locks, even if primarily used for their single

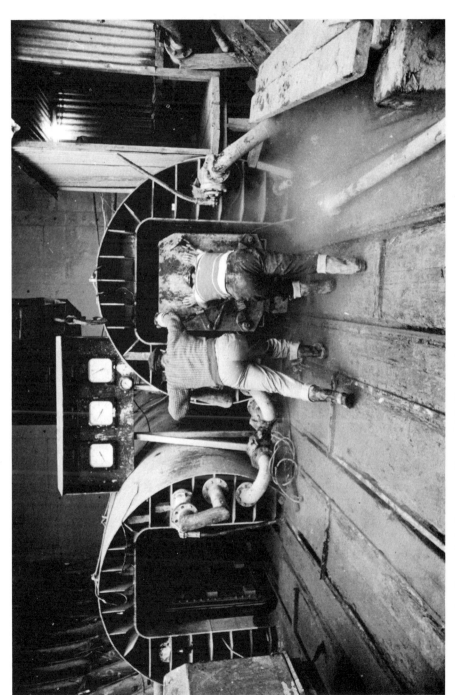

Fig. 5.3 — Two air locks for men and/or materials. Note: bulkhead in background, doors opening inwards, pressure gauges.

purpose, are equipped so that they can be utilised in emergency as man locks. They must then have small diameter air supply and discharge pipes, windows, gauges, telephones, seats, etc.

In addition to separate man and materials locks, consideration must be given to provision of an emergency man escape lock if the tunnel is liable to the hazard of complete inundation from the face. Such a lock will be sited as high up as possible in the tunnel to be above flood level. It should at all times be at working chamber pressure with its inner door open so that it can be entered without delay. It should be capable of accommodating the full number of men who may be in the working chamber at any time.

There is sometimes also a need for an engineer's survey lock for the work of carrying survey lines forward and for repeated checking as the tunnel face advances. These operations require lengthy occupation of a lock during which time neither men nor materials can pass through. It may be possible to utilise an existing lock if there is a weekend or other shutdown or if duplicate locks have been installed but the survey work is essential and time consuming, however costly interruption of passage may be. An engineer's lock has sometimes been installed in tandem with an emergency lock, extending the lock outwards so that the refuge of the emergency lock chamber remains open to the working shift even when survey operations are in progress. This can also serve for emergency access of a rescue gang into the tunnel.

The most common type of lock is the 'boiler lock' which comprises a cylindrical steel chamber riveted or welded of about 2 m or more in diameter and 5 m or more in length with steel end doors. It is normally installed so that the body of the lock is in free air while the end having the door opening outwards into the working chamber is built into a bulkhead if sited in the tunnel, or secured by a flanged connection if used at the top of a shaft (see figures). The cylinder is then in tension when the lock is under pressure. If the lock is in the open it is desirable to protect it against extremes of temperature by screening or insulation.

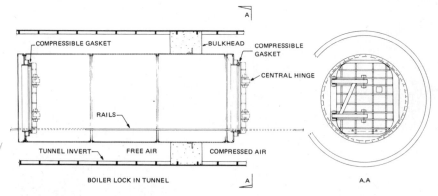

Fig. 5.4(a) — Boiler lock in tunnel.

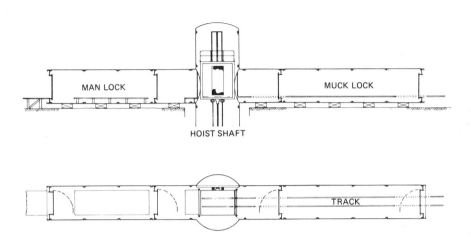

Fig. 5.4(b) – Section plan and elevation of T-locks at shaft head.

A lock used for materials is usually furnished with a rail track for passage of skips but there must be gaps in the track to allow the air doors to be closed, short lengths of rail being dropped into prepared seatings when the door is opened.

An alternative type of air lock is formed by constructing two bulkheads, with doors opening into the high pressure side, across a length of tunnel. This is suitable in a small diameter access tunnel, up to about 4 m diameter or so. In a larger diameter tunnel the volume of air used at each locking operation becomes excessive. Also, the provision of separate man and materials locks requires a duplicate adit.

Both types were used in the first Dartford tunnel. Initially, access on each bank of the river was through a vertical working shaft of 18 ft diameter sealed with an air deck. At each shaft boiler locks led horizontally through a T junction into a vertical winding shaft within which a hoist transported men or materials. The shaft was offset well clear of the tunnel and connected to it by two 4 m access headings. In each of these adits an air lock was constructed as described. The surface locks were used initially for sinking the shaft and constructing the pilot tunnel but the bulkhead locks were used for constructing the main tunnel, allowing the shaft to be used in free air. The tunnel was driven from both sides of the river simultaneously and these were connected by the completed pilot tunnel but had to operate at different pressures; therefore a mid-river air lock utilising two bulkheads across the pilot tunnel was necessary, fitted with four doors because the difference of pressure might operate in either direction.

Another type of air lock is the 'caisson lock' which is of limited capacity and not suitable for any extensive tunnel work. It comprises a vertical cylinder forming the materials lock and designed to accommodate a cylindrical bucket handled by a crane. The lower door of the lock is hinged to open downwards and is mechanically operated from outside, but the upper door is a separate circular lid which has a central rope gland and which lifts off with the bucket for discharge. When the bucket is returned and lowered into the shaft the lid is clamped down onto the top of the chamber. The man lock is a 'blister lock' on the side of the shaft immediately below the materials lock. It is necessarily of very limited capacity and quite unsuitable for use by large numbers or for lengthy decompressions.

5.8.2.1 Decanting

Where lock accommodation is so restricted but long decompressions are nevertheless necessary, a process known as 'decanting' can be used, subject to observance of supplementary regulations. The men are rapidly decompressed to atmospheric pressure in the small lock and go without delay into another more commodious lock in which they are recompressed as quickly as practicable to the original working pressure. Their decompression then follows the normal rules.

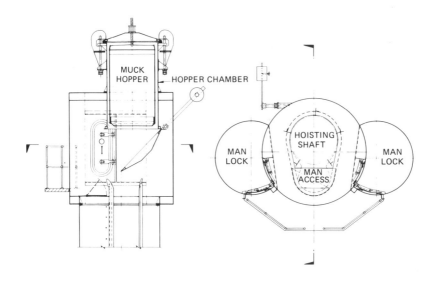

Fig. 5.4(c) – Sectional plan and elevation of Caisson locks.

Other types of lock may be adopted for particular circumstances but the principles are the same. It has sometimes been the practice in a long tunnel to construct a bulkhead part of the way along it and instal a second lock maintaining a lower pressure in the first section of the tunnel than at the face. This was considered helpful in providing an intermediate stage of decompression but it is not currently thought to be of any real advantage in that respect. It would certainly make it more difficult to ensure proper control of individual decompression times.

5.8.2.2 Medical Lock
Recompression is the necessary treatment for all Type 2 cases and many Type 1 cases of compressed air sickness. A separate medical lock at site becomes essential when such cases are to be expected.

It is normally of cylindrical form like a boiler lock, but the treatment chamber has its door at one end only, the other end being closed off. For entry and exit a small man lock is provided (see Figure 5.5). There is also a small lock for passing in meals or medical requirements quickly and easily.

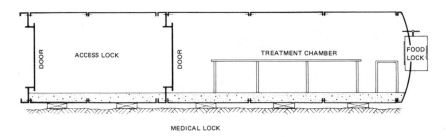

MEDICAL LOCK

Fig. 5.5 – Medical lock.

5.8.2.3 Equipment of Locks
The principal requirements have already been mentioned in describing the functioning of air locks. Little need be added in respect of materials locks unless they are required for occasional use by men, but for man locks a fuller description of operation, equipment and lock management is appropriate. In what follows a large tunnel using moderate air pressures is taken as the basis. Some simplification is possible in small tunnels at low pressures, while extra precautions are of course necessary if pressures are high.

A man lock must be operated under the control of an experienced lock keeper, who remains outside in free air and who is responsible for ensuring the proper regulation of all compressions and decompressions. Compression during entry may be delegated to a responsible and experienced man passing through the lock because the acceptable rate of pressure rise is a matter for each individual and does not involve hidden after effects. Decompression, however, must be controlled exactly in accordance with the prescribed tables and, except in emergency, should not be effected by anyone other than the responsible lock keeper.

There must be fixed in a place readily visible to the lock keeper and also to a man inside the lock, gauges showing accurately the pressure in the working chamber, and the current pressure in the lock and also a clock by which decompression can be timed. A bullseye window, in each door, is required so that the lock keeper can see those in the lock and take any necessary emergency action, and so that those in the lock can see gauges and clock when required. Telephones between lock keeper, lock chamber and working chamber are a most valuable provision.

The arrangement of air valves provides for normal operation by the lock keeper but also for emergency action by those in the lock. The piping is shown diagrammatically in Figure 5.6. Automatic control of the exhaust valve to the predetermined programme of decompression is sometimes employed. For a materials-only lock larger pipes can be used to operate more quickly and controls can be simplified.

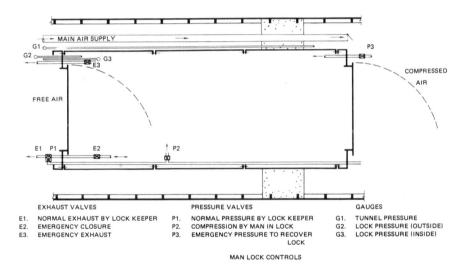

EXHAUST VALVES		PRESSURE VALVES		GAUGES	
E1.	NORMAL EXHAUST BY LOCK KEEPER	P1.	NORMAL PRESSURE BY LOCK KEEPER	G1.	TUNNEL PRESSURE
E2.	EMERGENCY CLOSURE	P2.	COMPRESSION BY MAN IN LOCK	G2.	LOCK PRESSURE (OUTSIDE)
E3.	EMERGENCY EXHAUST	P3.	EMERGENCY PRESSURE TO RECOVER LOCK	G3.	LOCK PRESSURE (INSIDE)

MAN LOCK CONTROLS

Fig. 5.6 – Controls in man lock.

Where men may have to spend an hour or longer in a lock, provision of relatively comfortable conditions becomes increasingly important. Adequate seating is essential with proper back support; at least 0.5 m and preferably 0.6 m width per man should be allowed and 1.3 m^3 of air space. This implies a diameter of at least 1.82 m. In a small lock with many men CO_2 levels may rise unacceptably during a long decompression and additional ventilating air will be required. This must be fed in at or above the lock pressure and preferably from a fresh air supply, and not from the working chamber, particularly in the event of a fire in the working chamber; the exhaust volume must of course be increased correspondingly.

Other requirements are a boarded floor, good lighting, heating for the rapid decompression stage, sanitary facilities and careful fireproofing against the enhanced hazard of fire in compressed air.

For a medical lock the requirements are more extensive. The compressed air supply should be fresh and always available at a pressure at least 0.7 bar above working pressure. An accurate recording gauge should show the pressure in the chamber to the medical attendant who should be responsible for controlling the pressure. Ventilation should be provided and properly regulated. Windows, telephone, lighting, thermostatically controlled heating, sanitary facilities and strict fire precautions are required. The chamber should be furnished with a full length bed and blankets.

As the medical lock will usually be sited on the surface it needs to be screened or adequately insulated against overheating from the sun and against cold. Most of these matters are more fully dealt with in the CIRIA Code referred to above.

5.8.3 Compressor Plant

In compressed air tunnelling the compressors supplying air to maintain the requisite pressure in the working chamber up to a normal maximum pressure of 3.5 bar, are described as the low pressure (L.P.) compressors. There are usually also high pressure (H.P.) compressors for power supply to air tools for excavation, drilling, air winches, and other purposes, which normally operate on a supply pressure of about 7 bar or more; in order to work efficiently in the pressurised working chamber the H.P. supply pressure must be increased correspondingly so that a differential of 7 bar is maintained.

The L.P. compressors are at the heart of the tunnelling installation. They will almost invariably be sited on the surface in a position where an ample supply of clean air is available. The compression of air has two immediate physical consequences: first, there is a substantial rise in temperature of the air; and secondly, there is an increase in humidity, because the compression increases the mass per unit volume of the water vapour present. Cooling of the air and removal of excess water are therefore required.

Accurate control of pressure is necessary and a quick response to any sudden demand for more air.

Figure 5.7 shows a plan of a compressor house on a large job.

Clean air supply is most important and filtration may be necessary in some situations. Siting of the intake should be such as to avoid fumes from any plant or traffic.

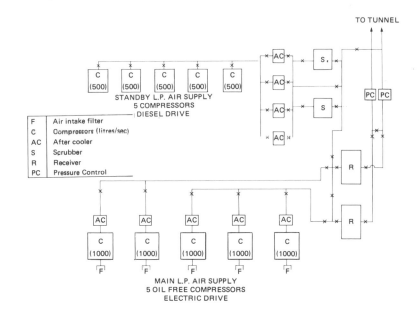

F	Air intake filter
C	Compressors (litres/sec)
AC	After cooler
S	Scrubber
R	Receiver
PC	Pressure Control

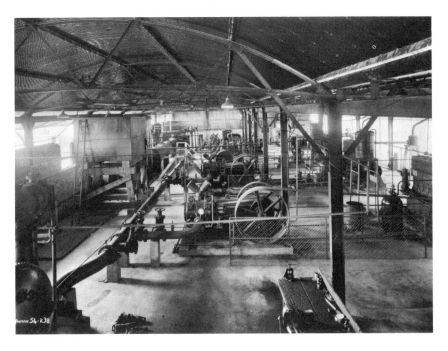

Fig. 5.7 – Compressor house.

5.8.3.1 Compressors

The quantity and pressure required have been discussed above. Except for small tunnels at low pressure the volume of air to be compressed is large and the plant is correspondingly large and heavy. It is advantageous to install a number of compressor units rather than a single one of the maximum capacity so that varying requirements may be met economically and the supply is not completely disrupted if one machine breaks down. Extra standby for emergencies has already been referred to.

L.P. compressor units are available for compression of about 150 l/s up to about 1500 l/s (say 300–3000 ft^3/min) and they may be electrically driven or diesel powered. It may be noted that to supply air at the rate of 60 l/s/m^2 in moderately open ground (see 5.2.2) a small tunnel of 2 m diameter would require 190 l/s and a large tunnel of 9 m diameter 3800 l/s.

(Note: 1 l/s = .001 m^3/s = 2.12 ft^3/min)

5.8.3.2 Cooling

The necessary cooling is effected according to the type of compressor and the temperature and quantity of heat to be extracted. There will be some cooling in the compressor itself, and if a two-stage compressor is employed there will be an intercooler incorporated, but in most tunnel installations there will also be an aftercooler through which the compressed air passes on its way to the tunnel supply main. Condensation of water vapour is to be expected in the aftercooler which must be drained effectively. Even after cooling the compressed air remains extremely humid as fed into the tunnel and as subaqueous tunnels are intrinsically wet the atmospheric humidity in the working chamber is usually 95–100%. Any lowering of pressure is likely to result in fog.

5.8.3.3 Oil separator

In most compressors some oil vapour or mist will be discharged with the compressed air, and should be removed by means of an oil separator, which may be a chamber packed with wood wool or other filtering medium, or a chamber utilising centrifugal action in the air stream, or may incorporate both devices. Oil free compressors are manufactured.

5.8.3.4 Receiver

The system may incorporate a receiver to act as a reservoir and regulator of compressed air and to smooth out fluctuations of pressure. Compressor output may be controlled automatically in accordance with the defined limits of receiver pressure. Silencers and pressure reducing valves may be useful additions to the circuit.

5.8.3.5 Air mains

The pipe lines to the tunnel are preferably in duplicate so that damage to one does not shut down the supply. They should be fitted with non-return valves as near as possible to the point of entry to the working chamber. Large diameter mains of 250 mm or more are to be preferred to ensure that air velocity at full capacity does not exceed about 10 m/s and thereby minimise loss of head.

5.8.3.6 Gauges
Gauges to indicate the pressure in the tunnel should be fitted in the compressor house and there should be telephonic communication between compressor house and working chamber.

5.8.3.7 H.P. Compressors
As already stated, higher output pressure is necessary for efficient operation of tools, that is up to about 10 bar. As with the main L.P. compressors, air as delivered into the tunnel should be clean and free from oil. Coolers with drainage and oil separators are therefore required in the delivery line.

5.8.4 Electrical Supply System
The principal aspects in which the electrical supply requirements for a compressed air tunnel differ from those for a wet tunnel in free air are the absolute dependence on compressor availability and the enhanced fire risk in the working chamber and air locks.

Supply of compressed air must be absolutely assured where there is any possibility of collapse or inundation. If compressors are electrically driven a completely independent duplicate supply is essential, or alternatively, diesel powered standby compressors of full capacity which can be quickly brought into use.

An independent emergency lighting circuit is even more important in compressed air workings than in free air and a telephone system independent of other circuits.

The greater fire risk in compressed air arises from the increased oxygen per unit volume of air. Oil filled electrical switchgear must therefore be fully safeguarded, or avoided altogether.

5.8.5 Pumping out water
The normal arrangements for removing water from a tunnel are dealt with elsewhere. In compressed air working it is common to utilise the air pressure to 'snore' out water. At the end of an armoured hose a filter to exclude stones is attached and the hose is connected through a cock to a pipe leading back to the free air side of a bulkhead. The filter is lowered into the water in the tunnel and, with the valve open, the compressed air, partly entrained with the water, drives and carries it through the pipe to discharge into a sump in free air. The 'snorer' is also sometimes a useful means of drawing fresh air forwards to improve ventilation at the face.

5.9 FIRE RISKS

Adequate supplies of water for fire fighting are important. The fact that outlets must discharge against the increased air pressure is not important if the supply is from the surface because the extra hydrostatic head will compensate.

Apart from the special risk to oil filled electrical plant, there is a greatly increased hazard from all combustible material. A major hazard can arise if heavy timbers supporting the face or elsewhere become ignited as combustion will be much more rapid than in free air and the site of the fire may be inaccessible. Lowering of air pressure to allow water to enter at the face may sometimes be a useful expedient, but with the disadvantage that the drop in pressure will generate fog and thereby add to the problems of fire fighting.

Fires in compressed air should therefore be fought by men familiar with the tunnel workings and with compression and decompression procedures in air locks, which may constitute a serious obstacle to ordinary fire brigades.

BIBLIOGRAPHY

The bibliography of compressed air working has two distinct aspects, the physical and the physiological. While the general pattern of a brief chapter bibliography followed (in Volume 2) by a more extensive and comprehensive main bibliography, is appropriate to the engineering aspects, much of the physiological material is so special to this chapter that the relevent section which follows will not be fully repeated.

Engineering aspects of work in compressed air are described in the old standard texts and others, supplemented extensively by Instn. Civ. Engrs. and other papers, a few of which are included below.

Greathead, J. H., 'The City and South London Railway; with some remarks upon subaqueous tunnelling by shield and compressed air', *Min. Proc. Inst. Civ. Engrs.*, 1895, **123**.
Hay, D. and Fitzmaurice, M., 'The Blackwall Tunnel', *ibid*, 1897, **130**.
Copperthwaite, *Tunnel Shields and the use of compressed air in subaqueous works*, Constable, 1906.
Hewett, B. H. M. and Johannesson, S., *Shield and compressed air tunneling*, McGraw-Hill, 1922.
Norrie, C. M., 'The River Hooghly Tunnel', *Min. Proc. Instn. Civ. Engrs.*, 1933, **235**.
Richardson, H. W. and Mayo, R. S., *Practical tunnel driving*, McGraw-Hill, 1941.
Groves, G. L., 'The Ilford Tube', *J. Instn. Civ. Engrs.*, 1946, **26** (Mar.).
Singstad, O., 'Historical development of subaqueous tunneling', *J. Boston Soc. Civ. Engrs.*, 1949, **36**.
Pequignot, C. A. (ed.), *Tunnels and tunnelling*, Hutchinson, 1963.

Kell, J., 'The Dartford Tunnel', *Proc. Instn. Civ. Engrs.*, 1963, **24** (Mar.). *See also* discussion, 1963, **26** (Dec.).

Haxton, A. F. and Whyte, H. E., 'Clyde Tunnel: constructional problems', *ibid*, 1965, **30** (Feb.). *See also* discussion, 1967, **37** (July).

Falkiner, R. H. and Tough, S. G., 'The Tyne Tunnel: construction of the main tunnel', *ibid*, 1968, **39** (Feb.). *See also* discussion, 1968, **41** (Nov.).

Glossop, R., 'The invention and early use of compressed air to exclude water from shafts and tunnels during construction', *Geotechnique*, 1976, **26** (June).

Physiological effects

Books and papers above are not repeated here:

Hill, L., *Caisson sickness and the physiology of work in compressed air*, E. Arnold, 1912.

Report of the Committee on regulations for the guidance of engineers and contractors for work carried out under compressed air, Institution of Civil Engineers, 1936.

Paton, W. D. M. and Walder, D. N., 'Compressed air illness: an investigation during the construction of the Tyne (Pedestrian and Cyclist) Tunnel, 1948-50', *Medical Research Council Special Report 281*, HMSO, 1954.

The Work in Compressed Air Special Regulations, S.I. 1958 No. 61, HMSO, 1958.

Golding F. C. and others, 'Decompression sickness during construction of the Dartford Tunnel', *Brit. J. Industr. Med.*, 1960, **17**, p. 167.

Duffner, G. J., *Decompression sickness and its prevention among compressed air workers*, Metropolitan Engineers Report, Seattle, 1962.

Safety standard for compressed air work, State of Washington, Department of Labour and Industries, 1963, Ch. 20, part 2.

McCallum, R. I., Walder, D. N. and others, 'Bone lesions in compressed air workers, with special reference to men who worked on the Clyde Tunnels 1958-1963', *J. Bone and Joint Surgery*, 1966, **48B** (May).

Compressed Air Safety Orders, State of California, Divison of Industrial Safety, 1966.

The problem of decompression sickness in diving and civil engineering, Annual Report 1965-66, Medical Research Council, HMSO.

McCallum, R. I. (ed.), *Decompression of compressed air workers in civil engineering*, Oriel Press, 1967.

Bennett, F. B. and Elliott, D. H. (eds.), *The physiology and medicine of diving and compressed air work*, Bailliere, 1969.

Medical Research Council Decompression Sickness Panel, 'Decompression sickness and aseptic necrosis of bone: investigations carried out during and after the construction of the Tyne Road Tunnel (1962-66), *Brit. J. industr. Med.*, 1971, **28**.

Walder, D. N. and McCallum, R. I., 'An objective appraisal of the Blackpool (U.K.) and Washington State (U.S.A.) Decompression Tables', *Proc. 5th Int. Hyberbaric Cong.*, Vancouver, 1973.

A Medical Code of Practice for work in compressed air, Report 44, Construction Industry Research and Information Association, London, 1973. 2nd edn. 1975, 3rd edn. in preparation.

Medical Research Council Decompression Sickness Panel, *Experience with a new decompression table for work in compressed air, Technical Note 59*, Construction Industry Research and Information Association, London, 1974.

Construction Industry Research and Information Association and British Tunnelling Society, discussion on 'The recommendations for work in compressed air and experience with the new decompression table', *Tunnels and Tunnelling*, 1974, **6** (Dec.) and 1975, **7** (Jan.).

Aseptic Bone Necrosis, (Proceedings of a symposium, Newcastle upon Tyne, 1976),*Technical Note 12*, CIRIA Underwater Engineering Group, London, 1977.

6

Rock Tunnelling

6.1 GENERAL REQUIREMENTS

In comparing rock with soft ground as a tunnelling medium the obvious contrasts are that rock is so much more difficult to break out that it usually requires drilling and blasting, and that the requirements for ground support call for a different approach. Of course, soft rock may be tunnelled using soft ground techniques, which indeed have also to be adopted with modifications for very heavy loadings encountered in squeezing rock, but in typical rock tunnelling long lengths can be excavated with such immediate ground support as is judged necessary, leaving the permanent lining as a separate and largely independent operation. If the excavation and ground support can be so executed as to develop effectively the arching action of stresses within the rock mass, the effect of the lining may be merely to seal in and secure that stress pattern, while providing additional strength to absorb long term changes resulting from relaxation in the rock, and also, of course, to provide a suitable interior finish.

Tunnelling in rock by drilling and blasting is unavoidably a cyclic operation and not continuous. A careful balance in the manning and equipment for the different phases is essential for efficient progress. The elements of the cycle are:

> Drill face to appropriate pattern and depth
> Withdraw drilling equipment
> Charge with explosives and withdraw all men
> Fire charges
> Ventilate to remove fumes
> Bar down loose rock and make safe
> Remove spoil
> Install immediate support

Where the tunnel is not driven full face but with top heading and bench, there will be a more complex dual cycle.

Machine tunnelling with a full face rotary boring machine is more nearly a continuous operation, as described in Chapter 7, but fixing of support may

Fig. 6.1 – A 7 m dia. tunnel excavated by drilling and blasting in hard rock. Note that rock is self-supporting, and provision of blowing

Fig. 6.2 — Trimming gantry in hard rock tunnel (Edmund Nuttall Limited).

impose a cyclic pattern in some degree. Methods of spoil disposal are discussed in general terms in Chapter 4. A factor of particular importance in rock tunnelling is the fragmentation of the rock which has considerable bearing on the suitability of handling machinery.

6.2 STRESSES

The stress patterns described in Chapter 4 for homogeneous ground uniformly stressed are equally valid for idealised rock, but in folded and faulted strata conditions can be very different. Residual geological forces may be heavy, and discontinuities in the rock may make the stress pattern far from uniform.

In tunnelling through rock the objective is so to construct the tunnel that the stresses and deformations in the ground and in the temporary and permanent supports are at all times kept within safe and acceptable limits. As operations proceed stresses are progressively redistributed, with relaxation in some areas and intensification in others. In particular the tunnel roof near the face is usually supported by transverse arching action bearing on the sides and by longitudinal arching bearing on the strata at the face and on the completed and supported roof behind. Advance of the face withdraws the front support and lengthens the effective span of the longitudinal arch, imposing added load on the rear supports as shown diagrammatically in Figure. 6.3. In this situation timing can be of vital importance. Where the work is advancing quickly and supports are provided close to the face all may be well, but any delay may allow serious increase of load and disturbance of rock structure to initiate overstressing or collapse.

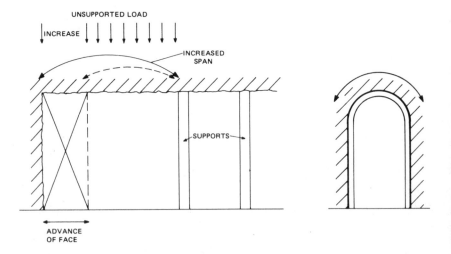

Fig. 6.3 – Increase of load as face is advanced.

The magnitude and pattern of the redistribution of stresses depend on various factors, including:

Rock type
Strength and other properties of the rock
Jointing and other discontinuities
Stresses existing in the rock
Size and shape of tunnel section
Type and strength of immediate support
Permanent lining
Construction methods and procedures

Stresses may be assessed empirically, or by mathematical and laboratory analyses, including the use of the finite element method, practicable with computers. The accuracy of results cannot be better than the accuracy with which the factors above can be ascertained, and some of those factors will vary unpredictably within the rock mass. However careful and elaborate the calculations, experienced judgement at site is absolutely essential.

In the actual construction progressive adjustment of stress occurs as some of the rock around the tunnel fails locally or moves along joint planes relieving stress concentrations. A final equilibrium is attained when peak stresses, no greater than confined rock strength, redistribute further back into the surrounding rock mass. Zones of failed rock may then remain in such areas as the springline and the crown, but needing only minor local support or containment.

6.3 ROCK CHARACTERISTICS

Rock structure is discussed in Volume 2, but the following notes outline rock characteristics in the context of drilling and blasting. Rock type is a very general term embracing a wide variety of geological factors ranging from basic formation—igneous, sedimentary, metamorphic—to specific properties such as texture, mineralogical and chemical composition, age and origin, anisotropy, degree of alteration, hardness. The term can usefully indicate the approximate grouping of such properties as compressive strength and modulus of elasticity, and can further be qualified by description as 'hard', 'medium', 'soft', used as a relative term appropriate to the rock type. Thus a 'hard' quartzite may have a compressive strength of over 210 N/sq mm, whereas a 'hard' sandstone may be about 120 N/sq mm.

Rock quality has to be assessed in the context of drilling and blasting. Very few rocks are too hard to be drilled with ordinary tungsten carbide tipped drills; some weak clay-like rocks tend to choke the drills, and also may shatter locally not pulling the round clearly. Fragmentation to a suitable size for handling may require study. Rock hardness controls the drilling rate but is not a well defined quantity and is not to be equated to compressive strength, or abrasiveness. Uniformity, texture, toughness to impact are all relevant to drill performance.

An important characteristic of excavation by drilling and blasting is the profile produced. Although the drilling pattern is chosen with this in mind, the geological features are dominant. In a strongly jointed blocky mass overbreak must be expected. Preferential failure on the weakest plane cannot be avoided.

6.4 DRILLING EQUIPMENT

Pneumatic rock drills are the most widely used type in mining, quarrying and civil engineering generally. They are operated by compressed air at pressures of about 7 bar (100 psi) and may be percussion or rotary or a combination of both actions. They range from hand-held units to heavy boom mounted 'drifters' fitted on 'Jumbos' which are mobile gantries of robust construction capable of being advanced to the face for drilling and withdrawn clear of the firing and spoil removal until the next cycle. Screw or chain feed mechanisms may be used to advance the drill in the hole. This equipment is particularly suited to large and long tunnels through reasonably uniform rock, where technique need not be varied greatly.

Hydraulic drill systems are coming into favour again in some tunnelling applications. Electric power drives an internal hydraulic motor. The advantages claimed are higher power output, lighter weight, reduced noise, reduced fogging, absence of compressed air lines. Higher production rates and lower operating costs are also claimed, but initial costs are higher and specialised maintenance is required.

For smaller tunnels the preferred tool is the lightweight drill which can be lifted, handled and operated by one man, and which is usually operated with the support of an 'air leg'. Since the invention and development of the tungsten carbide tipped bit in recent years, drilling speeds have advanced greatly.

6.4.1 Drilling Pattern

The number, arrangement and depth of holes and the charge weights and firing sequence are decided to suit the size, shape, and particular conditions of the tunnel, the available equipment and the blasting characteristics of the rock.

The basic drill pattern consists of:

1. Cut holes
2. Cut spreader holes
3. Outer rows and perimeter holes
4. Lifters or floor holes
5. Easer holes

Fig. 6.5 illustrates by way of example burn cut and angle cut patterns.

Fig. 6.4(a) – Twin boom drilling rig (Compair Ltd., formerly Holman Bros. Ltd.).

Fig. 6.4(b) – Lightweight hydraulic drill with telescopic leg (Torque Tension Ltd.)

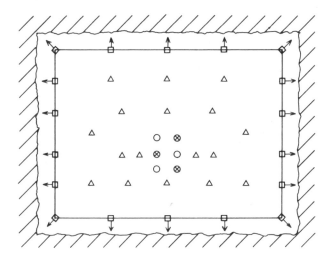

BOX TYPE BURN CUT

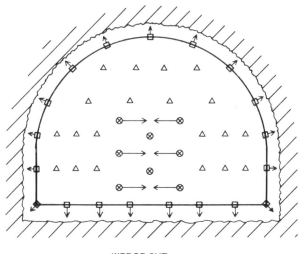

WEDGE CUT

○ UNCHARGED   ⊗ CUT HOLES   △ CUT SPREADER HOLES

⊗→ DO. INCLINED   ◁▫ PERIMETER HOLES AND LIFTER HOLES

Fig. 6.5 – Drilling patterns.

1. *Cut holes.* The pattern is developed around the chosen cut with the aim of ensuring fragmentation suited to the mucking and disposal equipment. The cut holes are intended to provide first a cavity into which the remainder of the face may break. Accuracy of drilling can be extremely important.

(a) *Burn cuts* (or parallel hole cuts) are favoured for hard, brittle, homogeneous rocks such as sandstones and igneous rocks. They are also suitable in small drives using heavy drilling plant, but are not so effective in laminated weathered or faulted rock. The typical cut comprises at least four heavily charged small diameter holes surrounding a central uncharged hole. Depending on the drilling plant available additional charged and uncharged holes may be incorporated. The uncharged holes assist in weakening the intervening rock between charged holes.

(b) *Angle cuts* cut out a wedge or pyramid from the face, but their drilling at a suitable angle depends on sufficient room in the tunnel for an economic length to be taken out. The included angle formed by the wedge may be 90° to 60° but the more acute the angle the more intense the charge required, and a double wedge cut may be needed.

In the pyramid cut the holes are drilled along the sides and angles of a pyramid, charged at the apex. The drag or fan cut is half of a wedge cut, to drag from floor or sides or from a fault or weakness in the face. It is favoured in sedimentary or laminated rock but requires more holes. In dense rock it is less effective than wedge or pyramid cut.

Burn cuts are favoured for rapid advance and high speed drilling. They are not restricted by size of tunnel. Angle cuts are considered more reliable, giving less vibration, and using less explosive, as well as being suitable for a wider range of conditions.

2. *Cut spreader holes* are intermediate between cut holes and perimeter holes.

3. *Perimeter holes* delineate the required tunnel profile, usually angled slightly outward to minimise incidence of tight spots.

4. *Lifters or floor holes* are one or two rows immediately above floor level, usually angled slightly downwards.

5. *Easer holes* are additional uncharged holes to influence breakage between charged holes and to assist in limiting overbreak.

In making the final choice the important aspects to be considered are: fragmentation—to be co-ordinated with mucking plant; overbreak control—particularly important where lining involves backfilling; vibration and noise—of increasing importance, more especially in urban areas, both in respect of damage to structures and environmental amenity; economics—in the absence of other restrictions the fastest sustained advance is likely to result from the longest practicable rounds, and fewest holes per round, but the drilling and mucking cycles must be compatible within the shift time.

6.5 EXPLOSIVES

There are two main categories of authorised explosives: 'permitted explosives' approved for use in gassy conditions, more particularly where the presence of methane is possible, as in coal measures; and those for general use in non-gassy conditions. They are further classified as gelatinous, semi-gelatinous and non-gelatinous, and slurried explosives. For tunnelling, gelatinous and semi-gelatinous explosives are almost always employed, having high water resistance and high density (in the sense of concentration of explosive energy). They have to be used in long small diameter holes and must therefore be sufficiently sensitive for the detonation to travel without fail the whole length of the long narrow column. The choice of the particular grade of explosive will depend in part on the hardness of the rock and on the wetness at the face.

The handling, storage and use of explosives in a tunnel requires particular care. Every stage of the process from delivery at site to ultimate use should be most strictly regulated and should at all times be under the control of named responsible persons, who will ensure compliance with statutory requirements, safety codes, and other rules and procedures special to the project. When a tunnel is advancing steadily a very regular routine will usually be established for each shift and it becomes very important that the hand-over from one shift to the next is properly organised and that there is no laxity in observing safety rules.

6.5.1 Detonators

Electrically activated delay detonators are normally used. There is debate over the relative merits of half-second or milli-second detonators (.025 to .075 sec). The half-second delays have advantages in allowing the successive 'pulling' on the face to develop more fully, and in lessened shattering at the perimeter, but they increase the possibility of sympathetic detonation. A combination of milli-second and half-second detonators may offer advantages on large faces with complex patterns.

6.5.2 Charging procedures

Column loading, following thorough clearing out of the hole, is the feeding of the primer charge and then the other charges down the hole end to end until the required total charge is placed, leaving uncharged perhaps 300 mm at the top. In spaced loading where a maximum charge was not required it was the practice to space out the charges with short pieces of timber, but it is now better practice to employ low density semi-gelatinous charges. Stemming with clay cartridges at the top to confine the explosive charges adds to the efficiency of the blast but because of time and cost is not always practised. Gelatinous explosives are always tamped into the hole with a wooden rod. ANFO, which is a mixture of ammonium nitrate and hydrocarbon oil, is sometimes used, but not in wet areas, as are explosives of lower density. It can be charged into the hole by means of special pneumatic equipment comprising a pipe and pressure vessel, safeguarded against build-up of static electricity.

6.5.3 Firing arrangements

Standard precautions prior to charging at the face include the disconnection of all electric power from the jumbo or other plant and the removal of all power leads to a distance of 70 m or so from the face.

Firing circuits may be coupled to the mains or may be operated from magnetic-type exploders having a capacity of 100 detonators.

Series or parallel circuits are used, the latter being the more usual in complex tunnel work. The series circuit can be more simply tested; with a parallel circuit additional care with detonators is necessary. The firing line consists of twin insulated cables connecting to a firing switch up to 300 m from the face. They should be located on the opposite side of the tunnel from lighting, power and other services, and should be inspected and tested to ensure that they are undamaged and are properly insulated prior to firing. Detailed safety rules should be made and observed.

Having fired a round the first essential is to ensure that the air is cleared of poisonous nitrogen oxide fumes and that no misfires remain unexploded. Watering down of the muck pile is likely to be the first operation, followed by clearing up of the floor and scaling down of the sides and roof to remove all loose rock which might fall. Mucking plant for disposal to the conveying or transporting plant should have output compatible with the rest of the cycle of operations. It should have a good command of the face area so that it can scale the sides and face and clear the corners all without excessive manoeuvring. It may be rubber tyred, crawler mounted, or rail track mounted. Although the independent machines are more versatile they may be liable to heavy repair and maintenance costs, so that the rail mounted equipment may be the more robust and economical if chosen to suit the job.

The main types of plant are: face shovel, with built-in chain conveyor; throw over shovel loaders emptying direct into trucks or skips; side tipping loaders. The latter two have the disadvantage of requiring forward and reverse movements for each bucket load.

6.6 VENTILATION

6.6.1 Methane

The properties of methane gas have been described in Chapter 3. Its presence in a tunnel constitutes a hazard because it forms an explosive mixture with air at a dilution of about 20 times by volume. The use of 'permitted explosives' has been mentioned above, but the continuing presence of methane may impose the need for extensive precautions. Mining regulations on the subject are detailed and strict. The gas commonly originates in carbonaceous rocks, more particularly in coal seams and oil-bearing strata, but also in peat and other organic deposits. It can travel laterally for considerable distances through joints and fissures, and can be transported in solution by water. It may appear in a tunnel as a steady infiltration or suddenly when a pocket is penetrated by a drill.

Sampling and testing to detect its presence where there is reason to suspect it, and routine monitoring when identified may be vital to safety. A supply of air adequate to dilute and remove the methane is required. Concentration exceeding 1% is considered highly dangerous, and at one quarter of that level precautionary measures are likely to be essential, particularly against possible ignition by any flame or spark or hot spot. The installation of flameproof electrical equipment in such conditions may be obligatory. Obviously, even the use of 'permitted' explosives must be regulated accordingly.

6.6.2 Removal of fumes

Forced ventilation is necessary to remove fumes, heat, and dust from the working areas. There is a choice between systems feeding fresh air to the vicinity of the face, from which the contaminated air flows back along the tunnel, and systems extracting contaminated air at the face, thereby drawing fresh air in along the tunnel. Combined or alternating systems are also possible. The most suitable system depends on the project as a whole. If the vicinity of the face is the only work area it may be advantageous to make it habitable as soon as possible after blasting by direct supply of fresh air, but if follow-up work on supports and lining occupies the excavated tunnel, the blowing back after firing at regular intervals of a cloud of fumes and dust could be unacceptable, and might make an extract system preferable. Another factor is that firing might be timed at a change of shift when time for clearance of the air could be made available. The problem can be even more complex if a network of interconnecting tunnels is under construction. The whole problem of ventilation is one of great importance to be studied carefully in advance. In addition to methane if present and fume clearance, ventilation must deal with vehicle and plant exhaust fumes, drilling dust, blasting dust, vehicle and plant heat generation, geothermal heat, and body heat. Dust suppression is usually managed satisfactorily by water spraying, but there are usually regulations relating to the danger of silicosis which must be strictly observed.

6.7 DRAINAGE AND PUMPING

The volume of water entering a rock tunnel may vary from no more than that introduced for hosing down and dust suppression to the volumes encountered in subaqueous tunnels short of catastrophic inundation. In mountain tunnels springs of very hot water may be experienced, and jets of water at high pressure.

It is not proposed to generalise about these exceptional major inflows at this stage except to suggest that where the possibility exists contingency planning in advance is prudent, with particular attention to the safety of men underground. Inundation is not instantaneous and practical escape ways and methods can be devised.

Where inflows are normal the risks of washout in rock are much less than in soft ground tunnels, although soft filling and pulverised rock may be washed out of a fault zone, or a bed of weakly cemented or uncemented sandstone may be encountered, for which soft ground techniques are appropriate.

If the tunnel is driven on a rising gradient water entering can usually be drained under gravity back to and out of the portal, presenting few problems. On a falling gradient, as necessarily in a subaqueous tunnel, gravity will drain all water towards the face and collecting and pumping sumps are necessary. Fixed pumping mains will be installed to carry the water back to a main collecting sump near the portal, or at a working shaft, from which the water must be lifted to the surface and discharged.

The selection of pumps will be governed as to size and number by the expected inflow, preferably with a large contingency margin in addition to maintenance and repair requirements, to cover unexpected flows. The type will depend in part on the solids content of the water and the working head. Small readily portable pumps are required at the face and other working areas, with larger fixed installations to the rear. Abrasive and corrosive action from the solids and from saline content may impose very severe wear on pump impellers and bearings.

Waterproofing problems are discussed in Chapter 8.

6.8 IMMEDIATE SUPPORT

The general problem of stress in the rock during tunnelling has already been discussed. The need for immediate support, that is, support prior to the permanent lining, will depend on the geological detail, namely: rock type, joint pattern, dip and strike, discontinuities, ground water, rock material properties, state of weathering or alteration of rock mass. The need for support will further depend on construction factors, namely: size and shape of tunnel, direction of drive relative to dip, excavation method and procedure. Immediate ground support has two objectives: first, to give local support to rock which might fall out or be seriously displaced, and second (and perhaps most important), to guide the development of the natural arching action and to preserve it.

The degree and quality of this arch depends on the state and nature of the rock and particularly its competence. The simple picture, greatly modified by rock structure, is that an arch forms above the excavated roof leaving a roughly triangular zone which may need added support. If it is allowed to relax the weakness may spread upwards to a greater height and heavier support becomes necessary. The choice of method of arch preservation depends on the factors listed above and also on other factors such as permissible ground subsidence, permanence of opening, economics of lining.

6.8.1 Arch ribs

The traditional timbering has been largely replaced by steel supports, but does have the advantage of being more easily cut to length and shape, and perhaps of giving more warning of subsequent movement. It can also be adapted more readily to varied cross sections and special requirements. Where timber is plentiful and steel scarce and costly it may be the right and obvious choice. Timber which has to be left in, however, is to be avoided because of its eventual decay.

The most generally useful support is the arched steel rib shaped to conform to the intended cross section of the tunnel. A rolled steel channel or H-section is usual. It is designed to carry in the first place the loosened rock beneath the natural arch by means of blocks and wedges which should be spaced as closely as practicable to get even bearing and minimise bending movements in the rib. At the same time adequate footblocks or sills are provided and wedged to take the vertical loading, and strutted apart or otherwise secured against horizontal displacement.

Where there is loose incompetent rock between ribs, laggings spanning between ribs may be added, open spaced or close-boarded as circumstances dictate, and packed up to the rock as necessary. The laggings are preferably of steel for permanent work but may be of timber in temporary pilot headings. See Fig. 6.6.

The system is adaptable to a wide range of excavation procedures. A tunnel boring machine should produce a smooth circular cavity and, if ribs are employed, they will be fully circular with suitable facilities in the machine for their handling and erection. It may well be, however, that the immediate erection of a segmental precast concrete lining is to be preferred in such a case.

A circular invert is not favoured for other methods of rock excavation because it is time-consuming to trim to shape and makes vehicle access difficult. The preferred shapes are a semi-circular arch in the top and a straight or horse-shoe shaped lower half.

Such a tunnel may be excavated full face, or in two stages with a top heading and bench initially, followed by bench excavation to invert. In the latter case semi-circular ribs are fixed in the top half, supported at springing on sill beams, which in turn are underpinned by the ribs for the lower half. During the transition period relaxation of the top rib support must be prevented, possibly by use of hydraulic jacks and folding steel wedges.

Close monitoring of progressive increases in loading of ribs as the face advances may allow support requirements to be more accurately assessed. Early

and efficient installation of ribs and better natural arching may suggest a wider spacing between ribs, or conversely unexpectedly heavy loading may require added strength in support. Steel ribs may ultimately be incorporated in the final permanent lining, being taken account of in the design, or in some cases may be dismantled for re-use.

6.8.2 Liner plates
These are steel plates generally flanged for bolting together, which can be used to cover and support the excavation, in combination with, or independent of, steel ribs. They are generally similar to a cast-iron lining, but normally lack the strength and corrosion resistance requisite for a permanent lining, and are ultimately superseded by a concrete lining cast *in situ*.

6.8.3 Rock bolting
This is a system for strengthening and supporting the rock surrounding the excavation by means of bolts anchored deep in the rock and stressed to compress it from the face. The term is also used to cover untensioned dowels grouted in as reinforcement, further described below.

The primary function of rock bolting is to maintain the integrity of the stressed rock so that it acts more effectively as an arch or beam spanning across the excavation, or so that it secures any loose rock or thin stratum at the surface of the cavity by anchoring it at depth. The relative importance of these aspects depends on the particular circumstances in the tunnel.

The object of rock bolting in the case of circular or arched openings is to create a zone of radial compression in the rock and to reinforce the zone of highly stressed rock round the cavity. In the roof of a rectangular heading the bolts should bind together the rock layers to form a fixed beam stronger than the sum of the individual layers, and to suspend weaker strata from a stronger zone above.

For these purposes the bolts should be installed as soon as possible to secure the ground before bed separation or joint movement takes place. Secure anchorage of the bolts must be effected.

The life of the bolt system must be adequate for its function. If it is merely to give temporary support until a permanent lining is installed, or until a pilot heading is enlarged, corrosion is unlikely to be important, but loss of tension due to slip at the anchorage or yield at the face must be minimised. Where the bolts have a permanent or a long-term function protection against corrosion becomes important. Corrosion resistant alloys may be used and protection by grouting can be specified. Resin grouts with the dual functions of anchoring the bolts and protecting against corrosion are used.

Anchors are of three main types: the expansion shell, the slot and wedge, and the chemical grout socket. The expansion shell consists of a wedge-shaped plug, screwing on to the end of the bolt and thereby pulled out against outer wedges, or leaves, which are forced outwards against the sides of the hole. Slot-and-wedge bolts are anchored by driving the slotted end of the bolt against a wedge at the end of the hole, thereby expanding the end of the bolt against the sides of the hole. The hole in this case requires to be drilled to depth precisely. The rock must be sufficiently strong to stand the local stresses imposed by the driving and wedging actions. Chemical anchorage is by filling of the space between bolt and hole with polyester resin grout, either locally at the anchorage or throughout its length. Resin and catalyst accelerator are prepared in cartridge form and after insertion in the hole are mixed by insertion and rotation of the bolt. Devices to retain the grout in an upward inclined hole are necessary until the grout sets and develops its strength. Fig. 6.7(a), (b), (c).

Point anchor bolts may be converted to column grouted bolts to improve anchorage in soft ground and to provide protection against corrosion. Cement grout is usual but resin grouts may be preferred. An injection pipe through the washer is used and an air release pipe from the back of the cavity, which must be sealed off at the rock face. Resin grout cartridge systems are also available.

Untensioned column grouted dowels placed in a regular pattern in a rock mass may provide suitable reinforcement to maintain stability or absorb peak stresses. They may be deformed steel bars encased in cement or resin grout or timber dowels in resin grout. The latter are useful where the rock is to be mechanically excavated later. They were used in the form of hollow bamboo rods in conjunction with advance grouting from the Mersey Kingsway tunnel pilot, before its enlargement by machine.

Bolts are usually of medium tensile steel bar up to about 30 mm diameter with one end threaded for nut and washer and the other adapted to the chosen type of anchor. The washers are flat plates to bear against the rock surface, drilled for grouting if required. Washers profiled to deform at the specified tension can be obtained. A swivel hemispherical washer to assist in getting uniform bearing can be provided. Fig. 6.7(d).

Accuracy in the diameter of the hole is important, wide enough to give clear passage to the bolt assembly, but tight enough to fit the anchor without excessive clearance. Precise depth is important for wedge anchors and for resin capsules.

Tensioning by torque wrench is usual, but direct hydraulic tensioners are better. Rock bolting machines have been developed for use in mines.

The bolting system has to be designed to suit the tunnel, the rock and the method of tunnelling. Bolts should normally cut across the rock stratification and always should be anchored in competent rock, but variation of length so that all anchors are not in one horizon is advantageous.

Tunnel dimensions and drilling equipment may impose limitations on length, but there is usually little to be gained beyond a depth of twice the radius of the tunnel. Another guide for length is that in jointed rock it should be not less than three times the width of joint blocks, to ensure anchorage in layers at least two

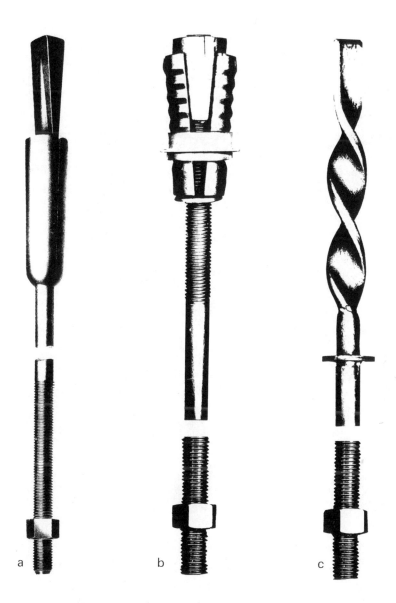

Fig. 6.7 – Rock bolts: (a) Slot and wedge; (b) Expansion shell; (c) Chemical grout (b and c: Torque Tension Ltd.).

Fig. 6.7(d) — Examples of various types of rock bolts and washer plates (Torque Tension Ltd.)

blocks behind the surface. Spacing should be regular and preferably about half the bolt length or less. Practice in Australia based on work by the Snowy Mountain Authority aims in arched openings at creating a compression of 70 kN/sq m (10 psi) in the zone of uniform compression.

In large cavern excavations long rope anchors may be used.

6.8.4 Sprayed concrete
Sprayed concrete or Shotcrete, can be used to assist in providing effective immediate support. It is more fully discussed in Chapter 8, as contributing to the permanent lining. If used near the face in conjunction with drill and blast excavation high early strength is essential to resist blast damage and allow build-up of the desired thickness. Accelerating agents are commonly added, aiming at an initial set after about 30 s and a final set after about 120 s. Mesh reinforcement may be fixed close to the rock in advance. Steel fibre reinforcement improves flexural strength.

6.8.5 Segmental linings
In an accurately bored circular tunnel precast concrete segmental linings (described in Chapter 8) can be used in conjunction with grouting to provide immediate support behind the cutter head and shield. Expanded linings are not likely to be used for any but soft ground because of the danger of severe point loadings from high points and trapped fragments.

6.9 GROUTING

In rock tunnelling the function of grouting in the context of excavation and immediate support is primarily in sealing fissures in the rock and displacing water from sheared zones and generally improving the competence of the rock mass. Backfill grouting between an immediate support system and the rock can be utilised to increase contact area and preload the rock. Its subsequent use in conjunction with segmental linings has been mentioned. It also may be applied in sealing off leaks at a later stage.

Rock tunnels sometimes require extensive grouting operations to seal faults and fissures which would otherwise allow great quantities of water into the tunnel. There are obvious advantages in discovering the requirement for grouting by drilling ahead of the tunnel face and monitoring the flow of water encountered during drilling. The grouting operation can then be effected before the advancing tunnel encounters the fault and the flow of water.

BIBLIOGRAPHY
General books, see bibliography to Chapter 4; particular projects, see general bibliography in Volume 2.

Rankin, W. W. and Haslam, R., 'Modern blasting practice in tunnelling operations', *Civ. Engng. Publ. Wks. Rev.,* 1957, **52** (Feb., Mar. and Apr.).

Fish, B. G. and Westwater, R., 'Blasting practice in shaft sinking and tunnelling', in *Symposium on shaft sinking and tunnelling,* London, 1959.

Lang, T. A., 'Theory and practice of rock bolting', *Trans. Soc. Min. Engrs. AIME,* 1961, **220**, 333.

Deere, D. U., 'Technical description of rock cores for engineering purposes', *Rock. Mech. Engng. Geol.,* 1963, **1**, 18.

Fogden, C. A. and Garrod, A. D., 'Hazards from blasting fumes in normal rock tunnelling with particular reference to nitrogen dioxide', *Proc. Instn. Civ. Engrs.,* 1965, **31** (July). *See also* discussion, 1966, **34** (Aug.).

McGregor, K., *The drilling of rock,* C. R. Books, 1967.

Proctor, R. V. and White, T. L., *Rock tunneling with steel supports* (including K. Terzaghi, *Rock defects and loads on tunnel support, an introduction to tunnel geology*), Commercial Shearing & Stamping Co., Ohio, 2nd edn., 1968

Stagg, K. G. and Zienkiewicz, O. C., *Rock mechanics in engineering practice,* J. Wiley, 1968.

Deere, D. U. and others, *Design of tunnel liners and support systems,* U.S. Department of Transportation (NTIS, PB 183799), 1969.

I.C.I. Blasting Practice, Nobel's Explosives Co. Ltd., Scotland, 4th edn., 1972.

Barton, N. and others, 'Engineering classification of rock masses for the design of tunnel support, *Rock Mech.,* 1974, **6**, 189.

Jacobs Associates, *Ground support prediction model (R.S.R. concept),* U.S. Bureau of Mines (NTIS, AD 773018), 1974.

Bieniawski, Z. T., 'Rock mass classifications in rock engineering', in *Proc. Symposium on exploration for rock engineering,* Johannesburg, 1976.

Langefors, U. and Kihlstrom, B., *The modern technique of rock blasting,* J. Wiley, 3rd edn. 1978.

Schach, R. and others, *Rock bolting, a practical handbook,* Pergamon, 1979.

Hoek, E. and Brown, E. T., *Underground excavations in rock,* Institution of Mining and Metallurgy, London, 1980.

7

Tunnelling Machines for Soft Ground and Rock

Twenty five years ago a separate chapter would not have been necessary to cover the use of excavating machinery in tunnelling work. In recent years, however, progress has been so rapid that a survey of current plant is likely to be out of date before it is published. Better then to emphasise the important principles rather than catalogue the current solutions. It is convenient to deal separately with soft ground and rock machines, but they have much in common.

7.1 HISTORICAL DEVELOPMENT

7.1.1 Soft Ground

The circular Greathead shield of 1869, in which excavation was manual, forms the basis for all subsequent tunnelling machines for soft ground. They are in essence shields with mechanised excavation devices built in, or excavators adapted for use within the protection of a shield.

The tube railway developments in London clay disclosed conditions which encouraged the use of mechanical excavation in the 1890's. On the Central London Railway two mechanical methods of excavating the clay were tried in conjunction with the Greathead shield in 4 m diameter tunnels.

First was the Thompson ladder excavator which was a track mounted pick and bucket ladder, as its name implies, based on the same principles as the ladder dredger. This machine proved indifferent; apart from its predictable tendency to leave its rails, it could not excavate the whole face, and the mounting of the tools on an endless chain was vulnerable. The second method, the 'Price digger' of 1897, introduced the full face rotating cutting head, with picks (including gauge cutters) mounted on the head. The first models were electrically driven through an axle which proved to be a weakness, and on the subsequent Hampstead and Piccadilly tubes the cutting head, still electrically powered, was driven through gears and a pinion and large diameter internally toothed ring well forward in the shield, greatly reducing the bearing and torsional problems encountered in the first layout.

Fig. 7.1 — Thomson's Digger, January 11th 1898

Under favourable conditions the 'Price diggers' progressed much faster than the Greathead shields, especially when efficient belt conveyors were introduced, but they were initially difficult to steer. With care and experience in driving quality of work improved, but the Greathead shield was considered more satisfactory in respect of accurate alignment and freedom from subsidence of the lining.

Fig. 7.2 – Markham Digger Shield as developed from Price Rotary Excavator in 1936. Average speeds of over 50 m were sustained.

In 1903 Price digger shields were driving up to 80 rings (41 m) of 4 m diameter cast-iron segments per week with a record of 56 m.

Between the wars 'digger shields' (or soft ground tunnel borers as they were termed in the U.S.A.) were developed gradually, always working on the rotating cutting head principle and always within a Greathead shield with the exception of an occasional machine for hard dry self-supporting clay.

7.1.2 Rock

In rock, drill and blast excavation was commonplace in mines in the 18th century, but a major advance took place with invention and development of pneumatic and steam powered percussion rock drills in the first half of the 19th century, and the invention and application of dynamite in the 1860's (used in the St. Gotthard tunnel 1870 onwards).

The development of drill and blast methods has been continuous since then, and accounts for the vast preponderance of rock mining and rock tunnelling excavation to this day.

The removal of the debris after blasting, whether by rail, truck or belt conveyor, has also developed over the years, with considerable ingenuity in design to enable powerful plant to operate in confined spaces.

The drill and blast methods and the associated spoil removal are covered elsewhere in this book and more comprehensively by mining literature and are not considered further in this chapter.

The one early and splendid example of the rock tunnel borer is Colonel Beaumont's machine built by John Fowler & Co. in 1881, used 1881-2 on a pilot bore for the Channel tunnel at Folkestone working in chalk, and in 1883-4 to drive pilot and ventilation headings (some of them still visible) through Bunter sandstone for the Mersey railway tunnel.

Whilst coal-cutting machinery, and other mining plant not discussed here, were occasionally adapted for use in tunnels, no remarkable developments in tunnel boring machines took place until the 1950's. By that time the advances in metallurgy, hydraulics, the technology of lubrication, bearings and other branches of mechanical engineering were sufficient to allow machine excavation to be considered seriously, and the rising cost of labour gave an extra incentive to development.

Until the 1950's, no tunnelling machine had been produced capable of excavating hard rock. Soon thereafter the race was on to produce tunnel boring machines (often referred to as 'TBMs') which would cope with an ever wider range of rocks.

7.2 SOFT GROUND TUNNELLING MACHINE TYPES

7.2.1 Full face machines

A rotating cutting head is mounted at the front of a Greathead shield. It can be carried either on a central shaft or on peripheral roller bearings. Occasionally it is driven by powering the central shaft, but more usually by an annular gear; some of the configurations have been developed at least partly to avoid the patents of others. Radial hydraulic motors have become a clear favourite for powering the head, and a number of compact motors (depending on the diameter of the tunnel) are mounted around the head. Typical speeds of rotation are in the range 2-6 revs. per minute.

The cutting head has usually four to six spokes, radiating from the centre of the head at its front, and on it is mounted an array of cutting tools, normally picks, which scrape material from the working face as the head rotates. Behind or between the spokes are buckets or scoops which carry the spoil upwards so that gravity deposits it on a conveyor for removal to the rear of the machine.

The spokes are normally disposed so that the centre of the cut face is slightly in advance of the periphery. Thus the cut face forms a shallow cone with its apex at the centre. This gives some directional stability as the tunnelling machine is jacked forward, and also allows the spoil conveyor to be well forward.

The cutting tools at the centre naturally have very limited travel and an interesting series of designs has resulted. Some have favoured an embryo auger at this point, known as a 'stinger', which must give some additional marginal stability although it is vulnerable to damage when directional changes are made,

Fig. 7.3 – 'Open Wheel' Machine. Typical specification for 3 m dia. machine with reversible cutting action: Power 130 kW; Wheel torque 15500 kg m; Thrust 1200 T; Weight of shield and wheel 25 T (Zokor).

either to negotiate intentional curves in the tunnel or more particularly when sharp corrections have to be made to keep the tunnel on the desired line and level.

The diameter of the excavation is determined by the outside, or 'gauge', cutters. In very soft ground it has occasionally been the practice for the cut diameter to be slightly less than the diameter of the cutting edge of the Greathead shield, leaving a thin slice to be trimmed off by the cutting edge. Normally, however, the cut diameter is marginally greater than the shield diameter to reduce the friction on the skin of the shield during driving. The gauge cutters, of course, travel further than any of the other tools and are subject to greater wear. The wear on the cutters and the consequent reduction of the cut diameter may cause increasing difficulty in jacking the tunnel machine forward.

The direction of rotation of the cutting head is generally reversible, so that any tendency for the shield itself to contra-rotate can be corrected. Sometimes retractable fins are fitted which, when extended out into the ground, act to prevent or correct rotation of the shield. Fins leave a disturbed path in the ground which is often undesirable.

7.2.1.1 Oscillating cutting head

This tendency of the shield to rotate may first have led to the idea of having an oscillating as opposed to a rotating cutting head. Several soft ground machines have been used in which the cutting head oscillates through 45° or more, driven by hydraulic jacks, so that each spoke of the cutting head with its tools scans the face like a windscreen wiper.

The drive jack mechanism for an oscillating head is mechanically simpler and therefore should be cheaper and more reliable than a number of hydraulic motors. In practice, the motors, which have a multitude of other applications in mining and industry, are competitively priced, very reliable, and easily replaced as a standard unit.

One disadvantage of an oscillating head is that each 'spoke' has to carry a full array of cutting tools and if any fail the gap is more serious than on a rotating head. Nevertheless, oscillating heads have given very satisfactory results.

7.2.1.2 Variations to suit ground conditions

The basic machines, just described, operate within a Greathead shield having a circular cutting edge, a steel tail (within which segmental linings are erected) and hydraulic jacks for pushing the machine forward off the completed tunnel linings. Such machines can operate in stiff clay, cemented sands, or dry silts with adequate 'stand-up' ability.

If ground conditions are sufficiently favourable, it is possible to dispense with the tail, and to build flexible jointed segmental linings as described in Chapter 8.

If, on the other hand, the soil has a tendency to move in at the cutting face— either a very soft clay squeezing in or a less cohesive soil running in—then with

Fig. 7.4 — Kinnear Moddie Drum Digger as used on Victoria Line. 4 m dia.

such a machine the spaces between the spokes can be plated over at the face, leaving slots (possibly of adjustable size) to reduce the ingress of soil. It is hoped thus to ensure that just the right amount of spoil is removed per unit of tunnel advance so that subsidence above the tunnel is negligible, but, in practice, that can only be achieved in homogeneous ground, and the method is unsatisfactory when, for instance, most of the face is in stiff clay, but includes a stratum of dry sand or soft mud which flows freely through the slots however narrow they may be. The thrust applied in supporting the face adds to the frictional load on the cutter motors.

Various machines have been designed to allow the cutting head to move forward independent of the shield itself. This is advocated partly to allow excavation to proceed constantly, even while a ring of lining is being erected, and partly to improve the steering characteristics of the machine. If the cutting head is adjustable relative to the axis of the shield, then it can excavate ahead of the shield in the most desirable direction irrespective of the actual attitude of the shield, and when the shield is jacked forward it will tend to move into the excavated hole rather than drive perhaps further off line or level. This arrangement has not been widely favoured perhaps because it makes for more mechanical complications in the already congested shield, and if the ground is good enough to allow such unsupported excavation in front of the shield, then steering and other problems tend not to be important. On the other hand, the ability to retract a stalled cutting head a few centimetres has obvious advantages.

Another variation is the articulated machine. The front shield unit, with cutting head, is as previously described but in place of the integral tail is another short length of shield comprising a thrust ring, which is separate from the shield proper and which can be expanded to grip the surrounding ground. The machine moves in pulses by successively pushing off the expanded thrust ring whilst excavating, then relaxing the grip of the thrust ring and pulling it forward, to be re-expanded against the ground. This modification is believed to have originated in the United States where it is common practice, even in soft ground, to use steel ribs, or rings, with laggings for immediate ground support. Such lining cannot normally accept the thrust of the shield rams, so the thrust ring or some other device is required. The articulated machine is able to negotiate tighter curves than a rigid shield, which can be an important advantage for sewer and water tunnels.

7.2.1.3 Subsidiary equipment
Full face machines, whether in soft ground or rock, require considerable service facilities behind the shield. These are either towed by the shield on sledges running on the invert of the completed tunnel, or rail mounted. Typically, a soft ground machine would require power cables and transformers, arrangements for unloading, storing and erection of tunnel segments, a control console,

electro-hydraulic power packs for shield rams and drive motors, grouting equipment, and an integral spoil removal system to transport spoil far enough to the rear for loading either into large shuttle cars or trains of skips or on to a main conveyor.

7.2.1.4 Economic utilisation

The full face tunnelling machines just described entail a major investment. They are unlikely to be efficient in ground conditions other than those for which they are designed, and can be a major source of delay and expense if they encounter unfavourable conditions.

The initial outlay includes not only the machine and subsidiary plant but also all the provisions and facilities at site, the layout of shield chambers, access tunnels, railways, shafts, winding and surface spoil disposal arrangements, all geared to deal with the special characteristics and high output of the machine. Such a machine, organised for a major drive, will have a long train of support plant behind it and cannot achieve its full potential until sufficient length of tunnel has been driven and lined to allow space and time for all the following plant to be installed and working.

For a full face tunnelling machine to justify itself economically there must be time and capital available for obtaining the machine and all its subsidiary requirements and setting it to work. It is unlikely to be advantageous unless the drive exceeds 1 km and is in reasonably uniform conditions.

7.2.2 Independent excavators

In contrast, simple Greathead shields can be launched from shield chambers close to the working shaft or even from the shaft bottom itself and can soon be working at full output. This advantage and others have led to the development of a family of excavating machines some of which can be brought in to work in conjunction with a basic Greathead shield and others of which are actually mounted on a modified shield structure, although normally removable. These machines increase the progress and reduce the labour of excavation without involving the delay and expense of setting up for and using a full face tunnelling machine.

7.2.2.1 Boom cutters

The boom cutter is one such development. The basic mechanism was originally developed as a tractor mounted road header machine for mining work. The boom of such a machine can be mounted within, or upon, the shield structure and operated so that a rotating cutting head on the front of the boom scans the working face. Spoil falls and is carried back by conveyors for disposal.

The boom may be telescopic, and incorporates the motor and drive shaft. The cutting head, which rotates about the boom axis, may be conical or flat faced, but carries cutting tools or picks to excavate the ground.

Other configurations of cutting head are available which may most easily be described as operating on the lawn-mower principle.

The type of cutting tool or pick mounted on the cutting head can be selected to suit the type of ground to be encountered, but large cutting heads have been found to be less susceptible to clogging in softer ground.

This type of excavator allows easy access to the face if support of the face or ground treatment is found necessary.

Another development for self-supporting ground, but giving at any time the option of reverting to hand excavation, is the claw-armed digger shield. Semi-circular cutter arms are mounted on pivots close to either side of the vertical (or the horizontal) axis at the front of a Greathead shield. When retracted they lie close to the cutting edges of the cylinder and from this position can be thrust forward and round so that they slice out a hemispherical cavity ahead, whose shape contributes to the stability of the excavation. The cutter profile can be designed to cut out other shapes of tunnel cross section.

7.2.2.2 Bucket excavators
In the same way that the boom cutters were introduced into the traditional Greathead shield, so were bucket excavators. Initially they consisted of a telescopic arm with fixed bucket which cut down the tunnel face and raked spoil back to a conveyor. Later developments utilise a jointed arm and variable angle bucket based on the tractor mounted back-actor principle. This method of excavation is often proposed for a mixed or broken face of gravel, clay or soft rock as the bucket can bring considerable force to bear to break out hard material, but full consideration must be given to methods for support of the face.

7.3 THE BENTONITE SHIELD
The difficulties of driving tunnels through cohesionless ground such as sands and gravels, especially below the water table, have been rehearsed elsewhere in this book (Chapters 4 and 5) together with the special measures such as compressed air, chemical treatment or freezing. These difficulties have had the dual effect of making such tunnels expensive and also of discouraging the driving of tunnels in such strata in the first place.

Since 1964 the authors have been concerned with the invention and development of methods of tunnelling which to some extent overcome the difficulties. The initial concept was very similar to an orthodox full-face TBM but with a pressure bulkhead so that the cutting head operated in a chamber filled with a thixotropic bentonite slurry kept at a pressure sufficient to support the face and keep back ground water.

The slurry from the chamber, carrying excavated spoil, is circulated through a control gate and pipe line to a separation plant whence the spoil is carried away to disposal. The slurry is reconditioned and returned to the chamber.

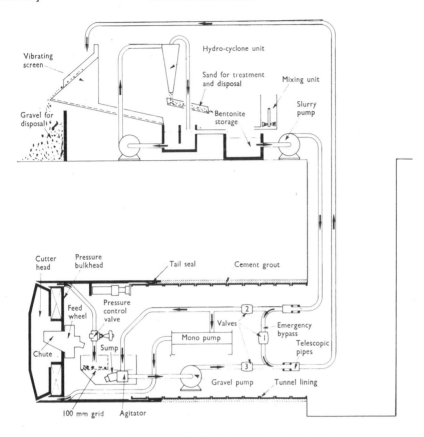

Fig. 7.5 – The Bentonite Shield – diagram of slurry circuit.

The first tunnel built by this method was successfully accomplished in 1971-3 on the proposed line of a new London tube railway near New Cross in south-east London.

7.3.1 Variations
Meanwhile in continental Europe and more especially in Japan, where a huge programme of public works was in progress in the 1970's, the bentonite shield or slurry shield method was developed on a large scale and in various forms. In 1979 it was reported that out of over one hundred tunnel machines at work in Japan, no fewer than thirty-five used the slurry shield principle.

The original machine in London used bentonite slurry in the belief (subsequently confirmed) that it would act as it does in 'slurry trench' or 'diaphragm wall' methods of construction. One important effect was that the settlement of overlying ground and buildings was greatly reduced to acceptable levels. The use of a potent thixotropic slurry is still to be recommended for work below vulnerable structures. Nevertheless, the experience gained on subsequent tunnel drives has produced a new slurry technology akin to that used in oil well drilling, and in some grounds the soil itself, with or without additives, will, in the course of excavation, provide an adequate clay slurry to support the face.

The beauty of using a fluid slurry rather than compressed air to support the working face is that the pressure in the slurry varies with depth just as does the ground water pressure, so the instability of air pressure on a vertical face is eliminated and excessive pressure need not be applied at the crown.

If bentonite is used, then a plant is required to recover the slurry from the spoil. The plant is sited on the surface except in large diameter tunnels. Stones can be removed by sieving, and other particles by centrifuge and hydrocyclone. Settling tanks have been used in some circumstances.

A variation, also using a full face machine, is to add only sufficient water at the working face to turn the spoil into the consistency of thick toothpaste so that it can be extruded behind the machine. Clearly such a system can only be used on cohesive soils such as clay or clayey silt, and there is cause for concern as to how well the working face is supported to prevent settlement of overlying buildings, etc. By plating in large areas of the cutting head or having adjustable slots through which the spoil comes back, and by maintaining but adjusting the forward thrust on the cutting head to suit varying conditions, there is no doubt that support of the working face can be achieved except in the worst conditions.

When a slurry shield is working well there are very great advantages. The number of men required is reduced even below that required for orthodox TBM operation, with the spoil being handled by pumping throughout. Conditions in the tunnel are greatly improved by the reduction in materials handling, and the absence of noise, dirt and dust. But things can go wrong, and if so, the presence of the full face machine and the pressure bulkhead complicate corrective measures. It is difficult to get at the working face (even to replace cutting tools). It is often necessary or prudent to make provision for pressurising the tunnel with compressed air when required to carry out various operations, such as repairing the seals around the tail of the machine. These seals gave much trouble in the early tunnel drives, and without them ground water, grout and slurry can escape into the tunnel.

Bentonite shield tunnelling is still a specialised and expensive business but the system can now offer substantial savings of time and money compared with earlier expedients.

7.4 OPERATION OF MACHINES

7.4.1 Hydraulic system
Soft ground machines, like Greathead shields, are normally advanced by thrusting off the tunnel lining built immediately behind the machine. The pistons of an

array of hydraulic rams around the perimeter of the machine extend backwards, transmitting the force to the lining through shoes designed to spread the load. Small machines operate on as few as six rams whereas the largest machines (over 10 m diameter) may have as many as forty. The maximum force per ram varies between 10 T and 160 T. The power is transmitted through an hydraulic system incorporating safety devices, pressure limiting switches and control valves from one electrically driven pump which can develop pressures of up to 35 or 40 N/sq mm but generally kept around the 15 N/sq mm level.

Industrial power packs of electric motors driving hydraulic pumps and hydraulic fluid reservoirs are installed to operate each major portion of the hydraulic system, the cutting head, the shove rams, and the erector mechanism for the tunnel lining, although in the smaller diameter tunnels a combined power pack system is usual. Power generation will obviously vary to suit the type of machine used, but typical of the 4 m diameter digger machines used on construction of the Victoria Line under London through clay was a 200 kW McAlpine machine, although power requirement can be as high as 450 kW.

7.4.2 Steering

Steering of the shield is effected by selective use of the thrust rams. Position and attitude of the shield must be ascertained relative to the specified alignment and to the actual position of the last completed rings. As discussed in Chapter 9, the required centre line may be defined by plumb lines and levelling rods, or a laser beam projected on to a target on the shield. Calculation of the appropriate corrective measures must not be delayed; a computer may be helpful, but experience of the responses of the shield is essential.

Modification of the attitude of the rings, whether for a specified curve or correction of errors, may be by packings in the circumferential joints or by introduction of special segments forming a tapered ring.

When a soft ground machine is excavating the rate of advance of the cutting head may be limited by the resistance at which it stalls or by clogging of the spoil handling system whether by excessive volume or stickiness or spillage at transfer points. Too slow a rate can waste time and power and on occasions can result in large coagulated masses of small debris, or on other occasions may exacerbate a dust problem.

Comparison of the steering characteristics of many shields and tunnelling machines has shown that steerability is dependent on the ratio of diameter : length of shield. If this exceeds 1.4 alignment control is usually satisfactory; below 1.1 it is almost always difficult.

7.4.3 Support at the face

The subject is discussed in Chapter 4 but certain aspects are particularly relevant to machine excavation. The normal action of taking a cut from the face precludes support for that area at that moment, whether the cut is by hand or machine, except so far as fluid pressure contributes to support as in the Bentonite Shield. Stand-up time is therefore very critical. Hand excavation allows support to be maintained over most of the face while a small part only is advanced, but with mechanical excavation on a larger scale the problem is rather different. The choice of machine obviously should take into account the expected behaviour of the ground, assuming that normally it will stand up throughout the cycle of operations. Abnormal, even if not unexpected, conditions may demand face support. The immediate problem is then that of access to secure the face, possibly followed by hand excavation over the critical length. Access may be very difficult with some types of full face rotary cutting heads, but those plated between spokes can give partial support even when cutting, and even if brought to a standstill may be manageable.

With boom cutters and other independent excavators the conditions more nearly resemble hand excavation on an enlarged scale, and the machine can usually be drawn back, or moved to one side to allow timbering or other free support. With such machines special supporting devices can be incorporated in

Fig. 7.6 — Bucket Excavator. The bucket is capable of 360° rotation and considerable break out force can be applied anywhere in the tunnel face. Note the 'poling plates' around the top of the shield which can be jacked forward independently, and the jack operated breasting plates which can be hinged back, or which can help to support the upper half of the tunnel face. This 9 m dia. machine was built for the Tehran Metro (Zokor).

the shield, such as the hydraulic face jacks of hand shields, or plates hinging out from the cutting edge as were used in the 6 m shields in the Washington, D.C., and Baltimore metro construction. Hydraulically operated platforms, or 'tables', at different levels in the face can provide a series of shelves limiting inflow of dry sandy material to its angle of repose. In the Hamburg metro such a system was adopted for the top half of a mixed face, the lower half being in free standing clay.

In another support system used in Frankfurt and Essen metros, the need for direct face support was minimised by using a 'blade shield', in which the periphery of the cutting edge is built as an array of blades which can be advanced individually, much as in 'piling' ahead of a face.

These devices, of increasing elaboration, are seen by some as a substitute for the traditional skills (now regrettably rare) of the soft ground tunnel miner. They are indeed an adaptation of his techniques, but there is less flexibility in their use and it is more difficult for those operating them to form a judgement of the response of the ground.

7.4.4 Special protection of plant

Mechanical and electrical plant working in a tunnel under construction is usually subjected to very severe conditions.

Water leaking or flowing into the excavation is usually unavoidable, but it may carry in solution corrosive salts. Fine dust particles of highly abrasive character may also arise from the breaking up of the rock or from deposits of sand and may be carried in the water, or as airborne dust, settling on damp surfaces and forming a grinding paste which can destroy bearings.

The need for careful waterproofing of all electrical equipment and connections is obvious, but additional screening should be provided wherever practicable.

Mechanical bearings, especially those near the working face, need very special protection; complex seals may be used, supplemented by automatic continuous grease injection. The surfaces on which the seals bear also need protection against wear and corrosion, as do moving surfaces in the hydraulic system, such as thrust rams and control valves where heavy chrome plating or use of special alloys may be thought necessary.

7.4.5 Grouting

The structural function of grouting is discussed in Chapter 4 and elsewhere, but its possible leakage from the back of the lining into the tail of the shield or outside the tailskin is particularly a hazard to proper progress of a machine. The tail may become 'grouted in' if it stands too long or grout may build up thickly on the outside of the tail and hamper movement by displacing excessive ground.

In the Bentonite Shield the tail seal is particularly important to avoid contamination of the grout by leaking bentonite slurry or of the bentonite slurry in the face by cement.

7.5 ROCK TUNNEL MACHINES

The development of modern rock tunnelling machines has been a feature of the last three decades, and followed swiftly in the wake of the production of reliable machinery for use in excavation of soft rock in the mining industry. By 1956 tunnelling machines were being used in medium rock conditions such as sandstone and limestone. Although they were not then considered to be economically successful, they provided the basis for future development.

Many of the problems encountered with the mechanics of these machines were similar to those met with on the soft ground machine development: but the main area of concern was with the cutting tools, the constant renewal of which, almost on a daily basis, was a considerable item of cost and prevented worthwhile rates of progress being achieved. The first successful hard rock borer was produced in 1957 by the Robbins Co. in America. The machine, about 3 m diameter, was more robust and powerful than previous models and, after various improvements and adaptations, was able to bore for days before disc-cutter replacement was necessary, the rock encountered (in a Toronto sewer tunnel) being inter-bedded siliceous limestone and shale with compressive strengths ranging up to 140 MN/sq m.

Whilst the success of this first machine led to some others being over ambitious and committing TBMs to drives beyond their powers, improvements and developments have been continuous in recent years.

The designers of TBMs now understand much of the nature and magnitude of the forces which the frameworks of their machines must endure; the mechanism for cutting rocks of an ever-widening range of types is understood reasonably well, and a range of cutting tools, especially disc cutters, of lengthening working life, is available. A major problem remains in the intrinsic variability of rock in texture, hardness, jointing, and fissuring, angle of dip, water content; a machine must be adaptable.

7.5.1 Full face cutters

The use of a full face TBM assumes the ability to cut in rock a cylindrical hole, self-supporting for a sufficient time. The machine typically comprises a fixed head, supported by jacks on shoes in the invert and at the sides, containing the drive motors and a rotating cutting head carried in a large and heavy thrust bearing. Behind, and attached to the fixed head, is a chassis on which are mounted electro hydraulic motors, conveyor, rear jack, and an expanding ring or series of pads which can grip the tunnel walls and against which forward thrust can be made. The whole mechanical system must transmit the torque and thrust necessary for boring, while remaining accurately on the centre line, and steerable.

One of the shortcomings of drill and blast tunnel construction is the heavy incidence of overbreak. Despite improved techniques, a very considerable (and unpredictable) quantity of rock is excavated outside the desired tunnel profile, and has to be replaced, generally with concrete, in the course of supporting and lining the tunnel. The operation also disturbs and weakens a further area of rock.

One of the great advantages of the TBM is that, unless the rock is so cracked and fissured that blocks fall into the tunnel, it cuts a smooth bore of the correct profile which not only gives a useful reduction in the amount of excavation but also makes the best use of the rock strength and facilitates the construction of any tunnel lining whether it be *in situ* concrete, or precast segmental lining.

It has been shown that a TBM can bore a smooth tunnel which will stand without temporary supports through rock which, if blasted, would require steel ribs and laggings or other support measures. It is interesting to observe that, with rotary boring, rock tunnel technique approaches that in soft ground, by adopting a circular form and that it also lends itself to use of precast segmental linings. Figs. 7.7(a) and 7.7(b).

If there is a danger of rock falling behind the cutting head, it is common practice to provide a steel canopy or hood on the fixed head to protect men and machinery in advance of tunnel support being installed, and a drilling platform for rock bolting overhead may also be provided.

If the rock is heavily fractured or unstable the machine may need to be mounted in a shield in which even the method of forward thrust may be similar to that for a soft ground machine.

7.5.1.1 Cutter head
The design of the cutting head varies for different types of rock. Drag bits on radial arms may be adequate for soft rock such as chalk. Disc cutters, multiple discs or roller cutters are necessary for harder rocks, so mounted on a strong cutting head that as the head rotates successive tools following circular paths cut and split the rock in the most economical manner, taking advantage of the configuration of the rock face left by the previous tool. Fig. 7.8.

7.5.1.2 Rotation
Rotation of the tunnel machine contrary to the direction of the head is resisted either by skin friction of the shield to the ground or by the side and vertical thrust rams pushing anchor shoes against the excavated sides of the tunnel. Unlike the soft ground machines, the head cannot be reversed to counteract this roll tendency without resetting the tools, as the cutting tools fixed to the head generally are only capable of effectively cutting the rock in one direction.

7.5.2 Boom cutters
An alternative excavating method is the use of boom cutters, which, as for the full-faced machines, may or may not be mounted within a protective shield.

Fig. 7.7(a) — Shielded full face machine 3.9 m dia. used for water supply tunnel in limestone in Italy. Machine provided with rear hood ... ... as ... ... Note the face support bars for use in unstable rock conditions (Robert Priestley Ltd.).

Fig. 7.7(b) — Rear view showing probe drill mounted on hydraulic arm within the machine body. One of the difficulties of machine tunnelling is to reconcile rapid progress with any necessary probing ahead to locate hazards (Robert Priestley Ltd.).

Fig. 7.8 – Full face hard rock machine. Note the massive construction of the cutter head and its roller discs (Thyssen (G.B.) Ltd.).

Fig. 7.9 — Track mounted boom tunnelling machine with spiral cutting head. Debris is swept back automatically through the machine on to the belt conveyor behind (Thyssen (G.B.) Ltd.).

The cutting head can take various forms, the design taking account of the strength of the rock and the loads imparted through the cutting tools. In self-supporting rock conditions the boom may be mounted on a crawler chassis, which may have a cover for protection of the operator from falling debris. Forward thrust is usually taken to the ground *via* the crawler tracks but some strutting to the side walls may be necessary. Fig. 7.9.

7.5.3 Excavators

Excavators working on the same principles as those for soft ground are also extensively used, being suitably more robust to deal with rock. Again they can be housed within a shield if ground conditions so dictate. The largest example of this type of machine is the 'Big-John' used on the 12 m diameter Huttegg Central Section of the Seelisberg Highway tunnel between Italy and Switzerland. This 450 T excavator rested on two runways mounted within a shield and was moved fore and aft by two 400 T hydraulic jacks. The telescopic boom was radially positioned by a 100 T jack whilst two 400 T jacks manipulated the digging action of the bucket upper teeth (weighing 0.6 T each) in removing the jointed and fractured shale, and drawing the excavated material back on to a conveyor. Final trimming of the tunnel shape was by the cutting edge action of the shield. This arrangement averaged 8 m per day advance.

Many modifications have been devised in an effort to improve the cutting efficiency of the machines and cutting tools. One such device to reduce the forward thrust required is by undercutting of the rock face. Separately driven cutter heads mounted at an angle to the main axis on a rotating head attack the face in a helical path following the perimeter like a screw thread.

Direct thrust of tools against the face is not required. The cutter tips act at some depth below the face which results in a groove being formed from which the major part of the rock breaks away towards the free face created during the previous pass of the head.

This radial undercutting action has been found to require as little as 30% of the thrust requirements of more conventional full face rotating machines. This obviously has the advantage of considerably reducing the load on the head's main bearings and the anchorage faces for forward movement of the machine.

Steering of the machine is claimed to be far easier, and tighter curves are possible, and by suitable arrangement and gearing of the individual cutter heads tunnels of other than circular cross-section are possible. The machine is obviously complex to manufacture and maintain and would appear likely to operate best in homogeneous rock.

The system has been further developed to produce the Mini full-facer. A single rotating cutter head is mounted on the end of an arm which can be manoeuvred vertically up and down. Cutting starts at the invert and the cutter head is swung upwards in an arc towards the crown. On completion the cutter head is lowered, the machine advanced a pre-determined distance governed by the strength of the rock and the process repeated. This configuration enables tunnels as narrow as 1.3 m and of 2.2 m height to be formed. Pressure pads grip the sides of the tunnel to resist any thrust and excavated material is moved backwards on to a conveyor system by the downward swinging cutter head.

7.6 OPERATION IN ROCK

7.6.1 Power requirements
Power requirements tend to be much greater for rock machines than for soft ground due both to the larger thrust forces required and to the greater expenditure of energy on cutting per unit volume. The power is transmitted by electro-hydraulic means and can be as high as 5000 kW as provided for the 'Big-John' excavator and supporting equipment, or as low as 400 kW on a Robbins full face machine of 3.5 m diameter used on the Kielder project in north-east England.

7.6.2 Protection
In rock tunnels immediate overhead protection in bad ground is mainly afforded by the provision of a shield above the tunnelling machinery. Some support of the excavated face, and shielding against falls, can be given by the cutter head of the machine, but any requirement for continuous general face support suggests the need for some change of techniques.

Access to the face suffers the same limitations as for soft ground machines and is easier when the cutting mechanism can be manoeuvred out of the way, as with boom cutters and excavators.

7.6.3 Linings
In situ concrete lining can be used where the cut rock stands without immediate support, or where temporary ground support is feasible by arch ribs or rock bolting and possibly sprayed concrete. The machine must be designed from the start with the necessary capability to accommodate such support.

Precast segments are a valuable alternative. They can readily be installed in a smooth cylindrical excavation, in contrast to the difficulties of erection in an irregular blasted profile.

7.6.4 Disposal
The excavated material has to be collected at the face and transported through the various types of machine on to a conveyor which may be of rubber belt, chain or plate type. Any size of material can be handled, depending on power drive available and adequate clearance, but problems arise if some of the fragments are too large, blocking passage, or perhaps worse, too fine. Dust,

or fine, gritty slurry can form a very abrasive mixture and can choke transfer points or accumulate obstructions. Some full face machines are designed with a diaphragm close behind the face to trap dust and provided with water spray damping.

7.7 MERSEY KINGSWAY TUNNEL MOLE

Many of these problems in rock TBMs can be exemplified by the experiences on the Mersey Kingsway Tunnels (1971, 1973). A highway tunnel having a bore of 9.6 m, it was unique in being machine driven beneath the estuary of the river Mersey through Triassic Bunter Sandstone. The water-bearing sandstone is generally medium grained, weakly cemented, and with occasional silty parting layers. The general dip, but with superimposed current bedding, is at about 7° in the line of the tunnel, but with faults across the line. The bed of the river was believed to be rocky without any bed of clay, and wet conditions were anticipated, as was confirmed by a central pilot tunnel driven by drilling and blasting. A tunnel 'Mole', originally designed and used to drive diversion tunnels at the Mangla Dam, was acquired and was modified extensively for the new conditions. The diameter had to be reduced from 11.2 m, central access into the pilot tunnel was provided, and a system for handling and erecting a heavy concrete segmental lining as close as possible behind the face was installed. Disc cutters projected about 300 mm ahead of the face of the very substantial cutting head, so that space was clear for broken material to fall into the invert, from which it was picked up by peripheral buckets, and discharged *via* a shute near the top to a conveyor system and ultimately to a point 30 m behind the face. Up to 500 tons of forward thrust was available from rams acting on thrust pads jacked out against the completed concrete lining. Ten 75 kW electric motors spaced round the circle drove the cutting head which ran in a 5 m diameter roller thrust bearing. Renewal of cutters was effected at intervals of about 100 m by means of a short cross heading out of the side of the pilot tunnel. Figs. 7.10(a) and 7.10(b).

In operation considerable difficulties were experienced, attributable in large degree to: (a) the very wet and saline conditions under the river; (b) the way that some of the rock broke down to fine abrasive sand, which tended to become re-cemented in the invert; while (c) some layers broke off at the face as lumps, jamming rotation; and (d) fractured rock, more particularly in fault zones. The practical importance of such features, although known, was certainly not fully appreciated in the machine design.

The drive started downhill from the end of an open cut, as a consequence of which the water accumulated in the invert at the face, from which it had to be lifted at least up to the central pilot tunnel. The expected slow start with new systems and equipment was made worse by considerable overbreak

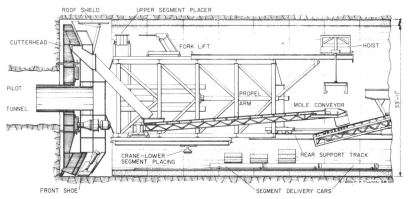

Fig. 7.10(a) – 'Mersey Mole' sectional elevation. Note the small cylindrical access into the pilot tunnel.

Fig. 7.10(b) – Plan view of Robbins machine preparing to drive into the Bunter Sandstone at the Wallasey portal in 1967.

in the crown, above which the depth to the top of the sandstone, overlain by boulder clay, was only about 6 m. The slow advance allowed time for overbreak to develop and spread and the shallow rock cover made less effective natural longitudinal arching. Another difficulty adding to delay was that the heavy machine, carrying also overbreak load in the crown, encountered silty strata in the invert and settled about 80 mm, making ring building even more difficult. Portal conditions nearly always present special hazards, and it might have been worth considering rock bolting from a top heading, but with all bolts and steel clear above the Mole cut.

A fault, known to be present, had been encountered in the pilot tunnel and secured with steel arches, timber and grouting, but when approached by the main drive it was found that water had eroded and was eroding seriously a filling of silty gouge in the fault gap which led up to the river bed. The rock on either side of the fault was more fissured than normal. The area was first extensively grouted from the pilot tunnel. As a safety measure the machine drive was stopped while a concrete hood 6 m x 2 m x 24 m reinforced with steel joists was constructed in three 2 m x 2 m headings driven successively side by side clear above the machine cut. After eight weeks' delay the drive was restarted and carried successfully through the fault zone. The emphasis here is again on the demand made by a machine for reasonable uniformity and on its lack of flexibility.

A further trouble, attributed in part to this delay in very wet conditions, was the failure of the 5 m diameter main bearing behind the cutting head. Water carrying grit had penetrated the bearing seals. The point at which the machine had stopped was fortunately in sound rock and was not abnormally wet. The machine could not be withdrawn through the completed tunnel because of the concrete lining, and the bold enterprise of replacement *in situ* was decided on. A spare bearing (in poor condition) was available, and was renovated and brought into the tunnel. The cutter head had to be drawn forwards from the fixed head so that the roller path might be pulled off and then the new bearing had to be fitted as a shrink fit in its place. All this is normally an operation requiring extremely clean dust-free conditions. Here, there was no danger of dry dust but water and grit were continuously and pervadingly present. A working chamber with an overhead runway beam was constructed by enlarging upwards with removal of two completed rings and some additional segments from the lined tunnel and the new bearing was suspended from the runway behind and above the cutting head. The cutting head was then anchored securely into the face of rock ahead and the Mole was withdrawn axially, for which an extraction force of 280 T was necessary. The new bearing was fitted to the Mole after heating to a temperature of 11°C above ambient to effect the necessary shrink fit. The Mole was then steered forward with great precision into the cutter head. After six weeks' delay the drive was successfully resumed.

Fig. 7.10(c) – 'Mersey Mole' breaking through on completion of its first drive to form a junction at the Liverpool side (March 1970).

The relevance of this to employment of such machines is to give emphasis to the need first for extreme precautions in protection and sealing machines against intrusion of abrasive grit and saline water, and second, for contingency planning for major repairs in any machine failure. Further severe damage to the Mole resulted a little later from a broken pinion tooth lodging in the ring gear, and extensive remedial work took about three weeks.

Duplication of the tunnel followed on completion of the first drive, with the machine modified in the light of experience. Handling and control of the spoil were improved. Slurry was drained and processed separately, as were blocks of rock. The overall tunnelling time was only half that for the first drive; 13 months against 27 months. It is of interest that a 3 m machine, designed, on the basis of experience in the first main drive, to cut a pilot tunnel for the duplication, had to be withdrawn because the volume and character of slurry generated could not be satisfactorily handled in the limited space available. The pilot was completed by drill and blast.

There is little doubt that machine tunnelling was the appropriate method for the project, and a recital of these difficulties simply points out the practical consequences of quite minor departures from the expected ground and water behaviour, and the necessity to have available engineering experience and resources to overcome them. The machine is not an automated answer to tunnelling but another tool to be adapted with skill and imagination to the conditions encountered.

7.8 EFFECTS OF MECHANIZATION

It is a truism that the design of tunnels must be closely integrated with the construction, and the advent of the TBM emphasises the need.

Unless the designer has a fully adequate understanding of the methods of construction and is competent to assess the suitability of the resources which can be made available, much time and money may be wasted. Contractors tendering for a tunnel in a period of a few weeks are in a very difficult situation if the promoter and designer have not taken every opportunity in the preceding months or years to collect and collate all possible information about geological and hydrological conditions, and have not so specified the project that the most economical method of construction, in time and cost, can be adopted.

Major schemes often require the design and construction of TBMs specially for the project. This process can take more than a year in itself and if the project is urgent and the other preparatory work is comparatively brief, then if machine tunnelling is considered to be the appropriate technique, earlier completion of the tunnels may be achieved if the promoter is prepared to order the design and manufacture of TBMs before signing a contract for the tunnel construction. Here is a situation which tests the confidence of the client in his engineers, and which tests his engineers' competence.

By close collaboration and carefully formulated contracts, advantages have been gained by ordering TBMs in advance, notably for London's Victoria Line tunnels, where the relative uniformity of the London clay and familiarity with machine performance and ultimate requirements simplified the complex relationships.

Another problem is introduced if a contractor already owns the only TBM apparently suitable for a proposed tunnel, and he is thus insulated against close competition from other contractors. This situation seldom, if ever, stifles competitive tendering, partly because it is generally necessary and quite costly to recondition and modify a machine for a new tunnel, partly because the fortunate owner of the TBM is usually acutely aware of its limitations, and partly because tunnel contractors are highly competitive and have an illogical desire to face the challenge of yet another tunnel.

7.9 CURRENT AND FUTURE DEVELOPMENT OF ROCK TUNNEL MACHINES

Some have dreamed of a machine capable of dealing with any stratum or combination of strata. Such a machine, if attainable, would be too expensive for normal use. It could only be done by fitting the ground to the device and not the device to any ground. Protective provision of a roof shield, a rock bolting platform, sprayed concrete, early erection of arch ribs, or of a segmental lining, all service special requirements but a choice must be made. It is more realistic to aim to make machines which are more adaptable either in the course of a single drive, or for use on subsequent tunnels. Fig. 7.11.

For the full face rotating head TBM, better disc cutters and picks are being developed all the time: mechanical and electrical components are being improved in strength and reliability and better protected from dust and water. Working conditions for the operators are meeting higher standards in terms of safety, noise, temperature and quality of air. Fig. 7.12.

In any particular case much of the machine design is dependent on expected geological and water conditions. It may often be valuable to give maximum access, and essential to give some access to the working face to deal with special problems. It has been found desirable in some types of rock to design machines which allow sprayed concrete to be applied to the rock close up behind the cutting head. Such an arrangement is likely to conflict with the precaution of having a protective hood over the machine. Similarly, various ingenious methods have been designed to allow erection of steel ring beams or segmental lining to support the rock close to the face. On other occasions the machines have had to accommodate rock bolting procedures. All these special requirements have led to a proliferation of designs rather than a universal machine, and for good reasons.

The observation has often been made how wasteful of energy it must be

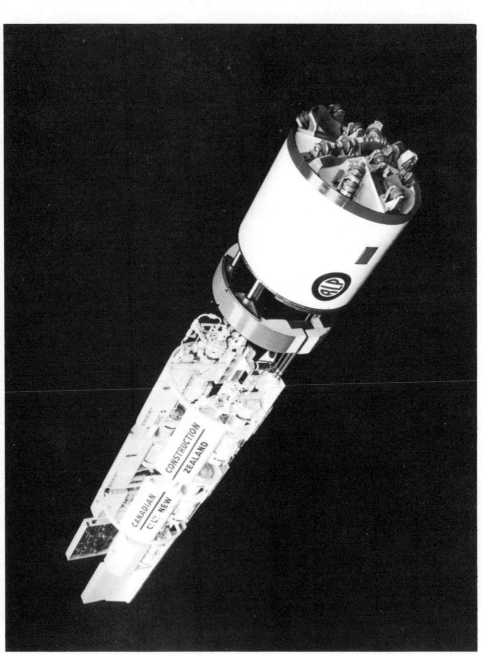

Fig. 7.11 – A versatile machine for use in New Zealand. Shielded full face machine 2.65 m dia. For use in hard and soft ground, utilising expanding anchor ring for thrust reaction in hard ground or lining segments in soft. Cutting head can accept disc or pick cutters (Robert

Fig. 7.12 — A 10,7 m dia. machine which, with its fellows, has achieved unprecedented output in boring hard dolomitic limestone and shale for storm water reservoirs (the famous TARP project) under Chicago (The Robbins Co.).

to grind rock into small pieces for removal. Such comment does less than justice to the work which has been done to optimise the size distribution of TBM spoil by tool design and spacing but these cannot be changed to meet variations in the rock over the area of a large face or as the face advances. Even with today's high energy costs, the power used in excavation is a small proportion of tunnelling costs. But energy costs are rising, and in long tunnels, apart from direct cost, excess power used by the TBM generates much heat, which has to be removed at additional cost.

It is tempting to envisage a TBM designed to cut forwards ahead of the face a deep groove following the perimeter (thus giving the advantage of a smooth cut bore) and to follow by breaking the bulk of the rock core into large (but handleable) pieces by other means. For small tunnels the core splitting might be achieved by drilling a central hole from which mechanical devices would apply pressure to break the remaining annulus of rock. For larger tunnels a pattern of such holes would be necessary. It may be that hydraulic pressure or even small explosive charges could be used to break the rock. At present it would appear that the ever-improving performance of orthodox TBMs precludes the investment required to develop such a machine with no certainty of commercial advantage, but the time may come. An interesting method was recently used to construct a large tunnel for the Paris metro. In very soft rock, a machine akin to a chain saw was used to cut a thin slot ahead of the working face around the upper perimeter of the tunnel. The slot was then filled with concrete, forming a buried arch. The face was excavated within the pre-placed initial support and the process repeated. Such a method would not appear to lend itself to widespread use, and it is unlikely that the rate of progress would make it attractive for long tunnels. Nevertheless, it offers a new safeguard against settlement or collapse in, for instance, certain soft rocks which deteriorate rapidly on exposure to air. The 'chain saws' required are undoubtedly miniature rock tunnelling machines and it is interesting to note that they must incorporate probably unknowingly many of the principles of the original Thompson ladder excavator used in the 1890's, the first machine mentioned in this chapter.

BIBLIOGRAPHY

This is a new and growing subject involving machines of increasing diversity and complexity. The brief bibliography which follows indicates some sources of additional information on current developments.

Donovan, H. J., *Modern tunnelling methods*, Public Works and Municipal Services Congress, London, 1968.
Muirhead, I. R. and Glossop, L. G., 'Hard rock tunnelling machines', *Trans. Instn. Min. Metall.*, 1968, **77A**, 1. *See also* discussion, 118.

Megaw, T. M. and others, 'Mersey Kingsway Tunnel', *Proc. Instn. Civ. Engrs.,* 1972, **51** (Mar). *See also* discussion, 1973, **54** (Mar.).

Pirrie, N. D., 'The use of rock tunnel machines', *ibid*, 1973, **54** (Feb.). *See also* discussion 1973, **54** (Nov.).

Bartlett, J. V. and others, 'The Bentonite tunnelling machine, *ibid*, 1973, **54** (Nov.). *See also* discussion 1974, **56** (Aug.).

Robbins, R. J., 'Mechanised tunnelling, progress and expectations,' *Tunnelling 76, Proc. Int. Symp.,* London, 1976.

Johnson, A. D. and Parkes, D. B., 'The use of roadheading machines in the construction of the Liverpool Link Line', *2nd Australian Conference on Tunnelling,* Melbourne, 1976.

8

Permanent Linings

8.1 NEED FOR LININGS

Permanent linings are required in most tunnels, always in soft ground and frequently in rock. They are required for two purposes: structurally, to contain and support the exposed ground, and operationally, to provide an internal surface appropriate to the function of the tunnel. The sequence of lining operations is varied and often complex so that the terminology is sometimes ambiguous.

The term 'primary lining' in British practice is frequently used to refer to the function of permanent structural support, and 'secondary lining' to subsequent interior treatment. This is quite appropriate to much soft ground tunnelling procedure, but less so in rock tunnelling and would not be generally understood in the U.S.A. In American practice 'ground support' is the term used for the structural supports, which are classified as 'permanent' when specified and incorporated in the design calculations, and as 'temporary' when left to be provided by the contractor as found necessary for safety in construction. *In situ* concrete, or other material, is the 'lining', incorporating the earlier permanent supports. Further secondary finishings for operational or aesthetic reasons may be provided.

This chapter is principally concerned with permanent structural linings. Immediate temporary support requirements are discussed in Chapters 4 and 6. Secondary linings for operational purposes are referred to in Chapter 2, and discussed in some specialised contexts in Volume 2. Both temporary support and secondary lining may be essential aspects of the design and construction of permanent linings, as will appear in context.

8.2 PRIMARY REQUIREMENTS

The primary requirements for permanent structural linings are:

1. To provide necessary structural support
2. To control or eliminate inflow or escape of water
3. To accommodate the operational cross-section

In meeting these requirements the chosen lining system must be capable of safe and economic construction, and be adaptable to possible variations and unforeseen contingencies encountered in the progress of the work.

Adaptability of the lining system may be a very important factor, as the urgent need to change to a different lining even for a short length of difficult ground can cause much delay and disruption to the programme and result in heavy additional cost.

8.2.1 Structural support

When a tunnel is excavated the existing stable equilibrium of the ground is disturbed and a new stress pattern must be established with the aid of supporting structures. In sound homogeneous rock an arching action will develop, and added support may not be necessary, whereas in soft plastic ground something close to hydrostatic pressure is likely to develop, quickly or slowly, and make it necessary to provide support competent to carry the whole overburden pressure. In most tunnels the requirement lies somewhere between these extremes, and the art of tunnel design lies in assessing the real needs at each stage and providing accordingly, with proper margins for the unexpected. Timing of support is of vital importance, to restrain immediately any movement which might develop catastrophically, but to allow strain movements in the surrounding ground, with concomitant stress changes, to establish a new and stable equilibrium. It is a matter partly of calculation from ascertained properties of the ground, but largely of experienced judgement, how to achieve the best final result. The major question is that of foreseeing and controlling the stresses and movements in the surrounding ground as a whole, but there must also be provision against loss of ground by local frittering away, or ravelling, at the exposed surface, or collapse of loose blocks of rock, or erosion by water. These subjects have been discussed in the context of excavation in Chapters 4 and 6 and may be further referred to below when dealing with the various forms of lining.

Design of linings for strength has in practice been largely empirical, based on experience. In cast-iron segmental linings for soft ground tunnels there has almost always been such a substantial margin of strength to suit foundry practice and to stand up to handling and erection procedures that the close analysis of the finished structure was not pursued. Precast concrete segmental linings were developed largely by adaptation from cast-iron.

Much tunnelling in rock is carried out on the basis that the cavity formed will largely be self-supporting, but that as the excavation proceeds conditions will be continually assessed and supports provided where needed. Nevertheless, much valuable work done over the last quarter century has greatly increased detailed understanding of the nature of rock tunnel support, and now allows rational estimates of requirements to be made.

In soft ground, the basis of modern analysis and design is that ground and lining ultimately act together as a composite structure. The soil has both plastic and elastic properties, and the complex stress pattern which ultimately develops depends on the stress history of the components, determined by the sequence and timing of the operations of excavation and support. In addition to the direct hydrostatic pressures on an impermeable lining, possibly modified by leakage, ground water is an important factor in the stress-strain relationships in cohesive soils, involving soil mechanics studies of pore pressures, drainage and consolidation, and other aspects.

In rock, the properties of sample cores are by themselves an inadequate basis for prediction of behaviour. Of overriding importance is the joint structure of the mass, which is much more difficult to ascertain by any exploration in advance.

It is not intended here to present or further discuss the various mathematical formulations which are tools of tunnel design. It may be noted that the structural design process for a tunnel is not comparable with that for a bridge or other surface structure: not merely because the ground imposing the loadings is not fully known in advance, but because of the interactions between ground, construction procedures and structure.

An important aspect of lining design in soft ground is the change of shape of the excavated cavity. A circular hole will usually distort to an ellipse with its major axis horizontal, because of the action of vertical stress resulting from the overburden. A rigid circular lining within this will resist distortion and be subject to bending stresses, whereas a flexible lining will conform to the ellipse but develop passive earth pressure where it displaces the soil outwards. A flexible lining acting compositely with the soil offers a thinner and lighter design than a rigid cylinder which must resist heavy bending moments.

8.2.2 Control of water
In water-bearing ground substantial watertightness of the permanent lining is usually important, but absolute watertightness is very difficult, if not impossible, to achieve and is likely to be very costly. As in so many aspects of tunnel construction the choice of lining and waterproofing methods must be made in the light of costs, balancing initial expenditure against operation and maintenance.

In rail tunnels some leakage may be acceptable provided any water is deflected away from overhead wires and from other electrical equipment into a drainage system. In road tunnels a higher standard may be required, eliminating altogether 'droppers' in the traffic space and preserving clean and dry wall surfaces. In metros the running tunnels are comparable to main line railways but there may be more delicate electrical equipment to safeguard, whereas in the station tunnels a high decorative standard will be sought. In sewer tunnels watertightness is important to the degree that ground water must not carry in silt, or enlarge leaks, or significantly add to the volume of flow, and most particularly that outward leakage must not contaminate the ground and any aquifers.

Pressure tunnels in hydroelectric power systems are a special case. The lining, usually welded steel or *in situ* reinforced concrete, must be completely watertight against high internal pressure, and must also be watertight and mechanically stable against, possibly high, external pressure when emptied for maintenance or other reasons.

Deep subaqueous tunnels may also be subject to high external water pressure and, rather than design the lining to exclude it absolutely, controlled inflow may be accepted and dealt with by drainage and pumping. The pore water in the surrounding ground is thus subject to a pressure gradient and the ground develops stresses to carry the loading.

8.2.3 Cross section

In tunnels generally arching action is the preferred method of carrying ground loads. The tunnel roof is therefore nearly always in the form of an arch, except in most cut-and-cover and many submerged tunnels. The arch may be completed below springing as a horseshoe form or with vertical side walls or as a complete circle or oval, depending on the ground conditions and the function of the tunnel. The circular form offers major structural advantages in ground where loads from all directions are encountered. It is usually operationally best for carrying water or sewage, and it also is the preferred form excavated by a shield or full face machine. In railways, the structure gauge must be accommodated within the circle above rail level and the permanent way and drainage in the invert so that the circular area is less fully utilised than is a horseshoe section. In highway tunnels the roadway and the rectangular traffic space above it only occupy about 50% of the area, although the extra space may be utilised for ventilation and other ducts.

The horseshoe form is the obvious cross section in rock which is largely self-supporting, but where lateral pressures develop, a lining is necessary and the side walls must be securely anchored at the toe, either into sound rock, or by struts across the invert or by a complete invert lining. Particular care may be necessary to ensure that drainage water does not soften or erode clay or soft rock in the invert or at the bases of the side walls.

8.3 PRINCIPAL MATERIALS

The principal materials and construction methods for permanent lining of bored tunnels are:

1. *In situ* concrete

2. Sprayed concrete

3. Preformed segments bolted or flexible

4. Brickwork and masonry

8.4 IN SITU CONCRETE

Concrete placed *in situ* is the most widespread form of permanent lining in rock tunnels. It has the advantage that it can be designed to accommodate any desired shape of cross section. It is ordinarily cast with the use of a travelling shutter well behind the working face, both in time and distance, embodying any immediate permanent supports already in place, and possibly also temporary supports. As far as practicable the lining is designed to function in compression without heavy bending moments and therefore rod reinforcement is largely avoided although it may be needed where loading is uneven and variable.

It is often preferable to complete the concreting of roof and walls before the invert, but sometimes it is thought advantageous to cast the invert first, thereby providing a smooth continuous support for the main shutters. Conditions for concreting are not always favourable to obtaining a consistently high quality, and thicknesses are often such that only low strength need be specified. Mixing of concrete at the surface and placing by pump may be of limited advantage as the distance from the shaft increases. Transport by skip, with appropriate agitation, and transfer to the shutters by a pneumatic placer is of more general application. There is always difficulty in ensuring dense uniform concrete in the crown of the arch and particular care is necessary if voids are to be prevented. In any case special provision for grouting is likely to be required.

In a large tunnel there may be three sets of shutters, each say 10 m in length and so designed that they can be partly dismantled, or folded and moved forward through the two sets in use for re-use 30 m ahead. Fig. 8.1.

Where it is thought important to complete the concrete lining quickly after excavation shutters may be for a much shorter length, as little perhaps as the depth of each advance, possibly 1½ m, but much of the advantage of large scale *in situ* concreting is lost, and use of precast segmental lining might be more appropriate.

8.4.1 Waterproofing

Because of the conditions in which it is placed it is particularly difficult to ensure watertightness in *in situ* concrete tunnel linings. Construction joints can be spanned by waterstops, although they cannot readily be embedded accurately in the concrete and are liable to displacement when a pneumatic placer is used. The problem of the crown has already been mentioned.

A plastic membrane which can be hot air welded is found reliable where rock is largely free from running water. After excavation any substantial flows of water are sealed locally and piped down to drains. Fixing pegs with plastic covered heads are grouted in and the exposed rock generally is coated with sprayed mortar or concrete against which first a plastic 'fleece' may be secured providing a smooth surface for the membrane of plastic sheeting fixed by means of the pegs, edges and any defects being welded. The structural *in situ* concrete

Fig. 8.1 − Travelling shutter for *in situ* reinforced concrete lining.

lining is cast against this membrane. The piped leaks run freely and the 'fleece' remains permeable so that water pressure does not build up before the concrete is complete. They can then be left open, or back grouted and capped off as appropriate to the site and the use of the tunnel.

8.5 SPRAYED CONCRETE AND ROCK BOLTS

Sprayed concrete has become an increasingly widespread technique of ground support, by itself or in combination with such methods as rock bolting, steel arch ribs, and mesh reinforcement. It plays an important part in the so-called New Austrian Tunnelling Method (N.A.T.M.) whose basic principle is to ascertain and control the development of stresses and deflections and their interaction with supports and lining, and thereby to establish within the surrounding rock a load-bearing ring.

Sprayed concrete is applied in thicknesses up to about 75 mm to rock surfaces. Aggregate, up to about 12 mm, and cement are mixed in a gun and sprayed forcefully on to the surface, water, carefully gauged to give a low water/cement ratio, being added, either at the nozzle in the 'dry' process, or earlier at the mixing stage in the 'wet' process. In all cases there is a substantial volume of 'rebound' which can be kept as low as perhaps 10% with well designed equipment and skilled operators but may be as much as 50% in unfavourable conditions. Where desired, reinforcement can be embodied in the finished lining. It is desirable that the rock surface should be clean and free from running water. When sprayed forcefully against freshly exposed rock, at a velocity of the order of 100 m/s, the cement mortar in the mix is driven into fine cracks and fissures and also forms a skin on the surface, on which a layer thoroughly bonded to the rock is built up. This acts to assist in both the purposes of support referred to earlier, by bonding the rock mass into a monolithic whole and by preventing loose surface material from progressive deterioration.

It will be clear that the sprayed concrete as deposited is in no sense to be treated as an independent structural element but as an integral part of a thick rock cylinder. It is indeed considered important that the concrete should be thin enough to be flexible and to conform to changes of shape without starting cracks. Extra bending strength is claimed for sprayed concrete incorporating steel fibres, or possibly alkali-resistant glass fibres.

Rock bolts cannot in themselves constitute a lining in any sense, but are an ancillary means of support which can be particularly effective in conjunction with sprayed concrete. The support function has been discussed in Chapter 6. They contribute to the establishment of the stressed rock cylinder around the tunnel.

8.6 SEGMENTAL LININGS

Circular segmental rings of cast-iron or concrete provide an immediate permanent lining of great strength, provided that when erected they can be brought into close contact with the excavated ground by grouting or otherwise. Their use in tunnels dates from London's Tower Subway (1869) and may have derived from cast-iron 'tubbing' employed in shaft sinking for mines at the end of the 18th century. The Tower Subway pioneered the combination of circular form, Greathead shield, cast-iron segments and use of grout. When compressed air working was added, the Blackwall tunnel (1897) and the Hudson river tunnel (1906) and their successors in London and New York and elsewhere became feasible. Cast-iron lining became the standard for metro tunnels in London and was unchallenged in this field until the 1930's. Precast concrete was then introduced as an alternative on some sections of the Ilford extension of the Central Line, and since then the special merits of cast-iron have had to compete against the lower cost of concrete, and other particular advantages in special uses.

As permanent linings all the segmental types share the basic advantage of providing immediately on erection a strong supporting structure with useful flexibility, but in developing the interaction between lining and ground the timing of grouting operations is relevant. In potential for waterproofing the different types vary and their suitability must be assessed in relation to operating requirements and the nature of the ground. In shape the circular form is almost always adopted, except that egg-shaped sewers have been tunnelled with cast-iron segments. In some special cases junctions and transitions between circular cast-iron tunnels have been formed continuously with C.I. castings of complex geometry.

The principal variants in materials for segmental linings are in the use of grey cast-iron, S.G. Iron, welded steel, or precast concrete and in structure either bolted and grouted rings or flexibly jointed rings. The ordinary form of cast-iron lining with flanged segments bolted together will first be discussed in sufficient detail to allow its advantages and disadvantages to be appreciated; the merits of the variants will then be examined, providing a basis for evaluation for any particular application. Indeed, it is by such a process that the variants have been developed to meet constructional and operational requirements in different uses.

8.6.1 Bolted cast-iron rings

The tunnelling process for bolted C.I. rings is, in outline, that excavation is advanced one ring width at a time, and the new ring is immediately erected by bolting the segments to one another by the cross joint, and bolting them back to the circumferential flange of the previous completed ring. In a typical ring there are six or more flanged segments and a narrow 'key' (Figures 8.2(a) and 8.2(b). The segments are identical except for the two 'top' segments which are slightly curtailed at one end, and have there an oblique end flange to provide a tapered gap for the key; the erection of a ring can be completed from inside the excavation by final entry and bolting up of the key. Grouting up with cement grout to fill the working clearance between the skin of the iron and the ground should follow as quickly as practicable to allow the lining to carry the load from the ground without avoidable settlement.

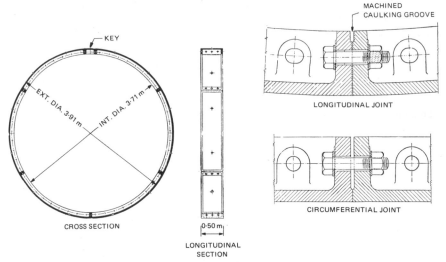

Fig. 8.2(a) — Typical ring of bolted C.I. segments.

Fig. 8.2(b) — Bolted segmental C.I. lining.

8.6.1.1 Cast-iron
Wide use has been made of grey cast-iron of a relatively low grade. It has very adequate compressive strength but relatively low tensile strength and is brittle. Its density is high. When used in circular tunnel rings most of the ground loading is carried as direct compressive stress. Bending moments, and the consequent tensile stresses, are usually minimal in these rings by reason of slight flexibility at the cross joints which allows the shape of ring to accommodate to a slightly elliptical form.

In transport, handling and erection the segments must be capable of standing up to rough handling in difficult conditions, including being dropped. When erected behind a shield the longitudinal thrust from the jacks is liable to be imposed unevenly on the skin of the segments. The proportioning of typical segments has developed accordingly. A factor limiting maximum weight and therefore sizes of segments for small and medium tunnels has been the need at times to be able to lift them into place finally by manpower. In larger tunnels mechanical lift devices can be accommodated, but conditions often remain cramped and access difficult.

Another limitation on design and dimensioning of individual segments lies in casting practice in the foundry. Experience dictates much of the detail in proportioning flange and skin thickness and connecting radii, with strengthening fillets and tapers to prevent shrinkage cracks and ensure dimensional accuracy and stability against distortion.

Dimensional precision, to ensure close fitting joints lending themselves to accurate erection and sealing against water, may be aided by accurate machining of the matching joint surfaces. The cross joints are nearly always machined in modern practice, and the circumferential joints are also frequently machined where the cost can be justified but may be left as cast and provided with packings. It may be noted that where a tunnel has to be built on a curve, whether by design or to correct deviations, tapered packings between successive rings are necessary, unless special tapered rings are specified for the purpose. Fig. 8.3. It further happens that, even with fully machined iron; errors may creep in and become cumulative where silt or other deposits intrude between rings, particularly where the invert has to be built in wet and dirty conditions, and that corrective packings to restore rings to a true plane face cannot be avoided.

8.6.1.2 Corrosion
Grey cast-iron has over a century proved itself to be surprisingly resistant in tunnels to rust and other corrosion. The castings after cleaning up from the moulds are usually hot dipped in a bituminous or similar solution, although any subsequent machining or drilling will obviously expose fresh iron surfaces which must be given appropriate additional protection. It seems that in the sand casting process a thin film of fused sand is embodied in the surface and offers valuable added protection. Alkaline conditions associated with cement grouting

Fig. 8.3 – Complex castings to provide for curves and tapers.

also are helpful for preservation, but cases of acid attack, probably from oxidation of sulphides in the ground, have been recorded.

Corrosive attack on the mild steel bolts in the flanges is also possible, but these can be painted or otherwise protected and are usually sealed by use of grummets against flow of water past the head and nut. Ultimately they are replaceable, although in a finished tunnel, in which ground stresses have stabilised, flange bolts serve little structural purpose.

8.6.1.3 Availability and cost
Availability of C.I. segments as such depends on the existence of suitably equipped iron foundries which can produce adequate supplies at the required dates. If sound and accurately dimensioned castings are to be ensured consistently considerable specialised experience is a great advantage. Conversely, large production runs over a lengthy period allow techniques to be improved and costs to be reduced.

Cost generally is now found to be substantially higher than that for concrete rings of similar size and type, but there may be valuable advantages, in many cases, in construction procedures, watertightness and operational convenience.

8.6.1.4 Waterproofing
As a material, sound cast-iron is itself completely impermeable except in occasional small zones of porosity where 'pinholes' may allow leakage of water at high pressure. These can usually be drilled out and plugged as thought necessary.

To back up the lining, the first defence against water is the grout layer injected through the lining to fill the voids left in the tunnelling process. Supplementary grouting at increased pressure is possible, but in water-bearing ground it is further necessary to waterproof, by caulking or otherwise, the cross joints, the circumferential joints, and the bolt holes and grout holes. In such cases it is usual for the cross joints to be manufactured with machined meeting faces, which leave caulking grooves about 6 mm wide and 25 mm deep in the exposed edges of the assembled joints. The circumferential flanges may be similarly machined, but they may be left unmachined in which case they usually have a much deeper groove, nearly the full flange depth, to accommodate wood or other packing, which can where necessary be cut out and replaced with caulking.

For the most difficult conditions strip lead or lead wool is favoured as the caulking material, one reason being that it can be recaulked if necessary subsequently. For most applications an asbestos-cement composition is found to meet requirements, at a substantially lower cost.

Bolt holes in flanges must also be sealed by fitting washers and grummets at each end. Plastic polythene grummets compressed by tightening of the bolts, squeeze into the neck of the hole and provide a satisfactory seal. Grout holes, through the web of segments, are preferably screw threaded so as to hold the grouting nozzle under pressure and to allow screwed plugs to seal them off.

Caulking and grummeting are costly and labour intensive operations. The substantial quantities in a major cast-iron tunnel may be illustrated by the 1.4 km long first Dartford tunnel (1963), in which joints caulked with lead strip amounted to 90 km and bolts grummeted to 260,000.

Other joint sealing techniques depend on the insertion of some form of plastic strip between segments during erection, but it is extremely difficult to ensure the necessary care and cleanliness in a necessarily wet and dirty tunnel.

8.6.1.5 Operational considerations

Where flanged C.I. rings are built into a tunnel the pattern of ribs may be advantageous in a few cases, as for fixing frequent cable and pipe brackets in a rail tunnel, but it may be necessary to provide a smooth and easily drained invert by means of concrete filling, or a complete smooth bore lining for a sewer. If a secondary lining is in any case necessary the ribbed iron may not be disadvantageous except in respect of the invert.

8.6.2 Spheroidal graphite iron

S.G. cast-iron has nearly the same chemical composition as grey C.I. but the graphite content is of nodular rather than flaky form. The effect is that its tensile strength is much greater and its compressive strength is also somewhat higher while it is less brittle and probably more resistant to corrosion. Its behaviour is more like that of mild steel, but it may be employed for cast segmental linings in exactly the same manner as grey iron. Somewhat thinner and lighter sections may be used, and with a structurally more economical distribution of material, provided that in the casting process distortion during cooling can be kept within acceptable limits.

The lower weight of material to transport and handle into place has obvious advantages in construction; in all the other tunnel lining aspects referred to it is virtually the same as grey C.I. Cost per ton is higher, which is not usually fully offset by the reduced weight, but valuable savings are possible in handling and time of erection.

8.6.3 Welded steel segments

Welded steel has not been widely used for segmental circular linings. It is sometimes employed at positions where abnormal loadings are imposed by adjacent structures or in junctions and other openings in a tunnel, for sake of the extra strength in bending and tension of steel compared with cast iron. Welded steel bolted segmental linings have been used for substantial lengths of tunnel in the U.S.A., and were adopted in preference to cast-iron for the circulating water tunnels at Dungeness nuclear power station, principally to sustain very high thrust loading from the shield during tunnelling.

Waterproofing presents the same problems as with other bolted linings unless welding is found practicable. Corrosion in unfavourable ground demands more attention than does cast-iron. There is no great difference in the corrosion resistance in the ground of the two materials but (1) steel lacks the surface film of fused sand on the castings and (2) if advantage is taken of the strength to use thinner sections the proportionate loss when attacked is greater. More elaborate protective coating methods may therefore be necessary.

8.6.4 Bolted precast concrete
The first major substitution of concrete for cast-iron was, as stated, for the Ilford extension of the London Central Line in 1939. The design and principal dimensions followed very closely the pattern of cast-iron segments. Flanges were substantially thicker, longitudinal stiffening ribs were introduced to carry shield jacking thrust, and the number of bolts in the circle was reduced. See Figs. 8.4(a) and 8.4(b).

As compared with cast-iron, high quality concrete requires greater thickness and must have steel reinforcement where tension may occur. The segments are more liable to suffer damage in handling and in jacking and also after erection because of greater rigidity; cracks may not appear until shown up by leakage later. Cross joints are usually erected with a bituminous packing. Waterproofing is more difficult than with machined cast-iron segments, which are likely to be specified where difficult conditions are expected. Dimensional accuracy and reliability demand a very high standard of manufacture, and this has been progressively improved with experience. Resistance to corrosion has not the long history in use of cast-iron, and in chemically aggressive ground the problems require careful study. Concrete quality and cover over reinforcement need to be controlled accurately, with use of sulphate resisting cement where appropriate.

A range of standardised sizes are available from specialist manufacturers and cost is of the order of one third less than for cast-iron rings. Fig. 8.4(c).

8.6.5 Expanded linings
The development of flexible joined expanding linings was an important departure from flanged bolted linings, whether of cast-iron or concrete, which formed a rigid continuous cylinder and had to be grouted immediately, as one phase of the cycle of operations, to secure the ground. The new technique is particularly suited to stiff clay. The principle is that the ring of segments is assembled directly behind the shield in close contact with accurately trimmed ground, and appropriate compressive hoop stress is applied by wedging or jacking. There is no gap to be grouted and the excavation can be advanced immediately wedging is complete. A further saving of time and cost is the complete elimination of bolts, both in cross joints and circumferential joints. These time savings are favourable to the use of digger shields because excavation is interrupted for a smaller proportion of the cycle.

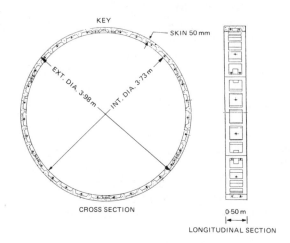

Fig. 8.4(a) – Precast concrete segmental lining. Original London Transport pattern.

Fig. 8.4(b) – Precast concrete segmental lining as used in Toronto subway.

Fig. 8.4(c) – Concrete mould for segmental lining (Charcon Ltd.).

Large scale applications of the principle were in the Potter's Bar railway tunnels (1959) and the Don Seg system used for a 27 km water tunnel across London (1959) and flexible cast-iron and concrete segmental linings designed for the Victoria Line (1968) and subsequent London metro tunnels. The Don Seg system uses 10 identical solid concrete segments in a ring, each tapered longitudinally but alternated in reverse directions. Very accurate casting is necessary. The rings are compressed against the clay by using the shield jacks to shove the segments into alignment against the taper. It provides a smooth bore lining. The Wedge Block system developed from this employs only a single longitudinally tapered key block, jacked in at the crown. In the Victoria Line concrete rings, jacks low on each side were used to stress the rings and the gaps were packed and wedged. Cast-iron rings embodying the same principles were used for the central section of the line, as providing a greater margin of strength and more flexibility in the thinner segment to adapt to uneven loading and distortion. Experiments in the use of S.G. iron made clear its advantages, but material costs for any form of cast-iron can only compete against concrete in special circumstances.

The difficulty of waterproofing any of these flexible systems is such that they are not normally suitable for water-bearing ground. Figs. 8.5(a), (b), (c), (d).

8.6.6 Grouted smooth bore lining
The requirement for a smooth bore for water or sewer tunnels and some others can be met directly by various systems of segmental concrete. Don Seg and Wedge Block have already been referred to, but they are not intended for grouting. Others are designed to be built on a former ring leaving an external space of about 25 mm to be grouted as with flanged and bolted segments. The Mini-tunnel is a special system for driving sewers of about 1 m diameter, a ring of three segments being erected behind a special shield, and grouted in. A concrete segmental lining was designed for Phase II of the Channel Tunnel (1974) which was erected immediately behind the shield and wedged back to the ground by a key segment. Each segment bore on the ground locally by four projecting pads, leaving space for grouting as found appropriate to the strata encountered (see Fig. 10.2(d)).

8.7 BRICKWORK AND MASONRY
Neither brickwork nor masonry is now a normal material for the structural lining of a tunnel. Most early British canal and railway tunnels were brick lined, the bricks often being manufactured on site. The whole 'English method' was based on alternating excavation and timbering with bricklaying and the necessary skills were highly developed; it would not be easy to revive them. Sewer tunnels were usually built in brickwork and hard blue brick was specified for the invert as the material best able to resist erosion by the scouring action of grit.

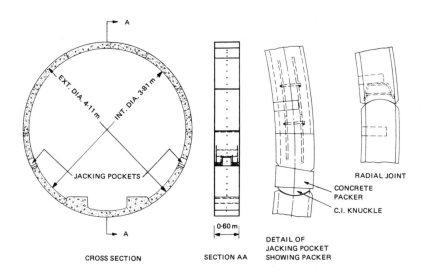

Fig. 8.5(a) — Expanded flexible concrete lining as used on Victoria Line.

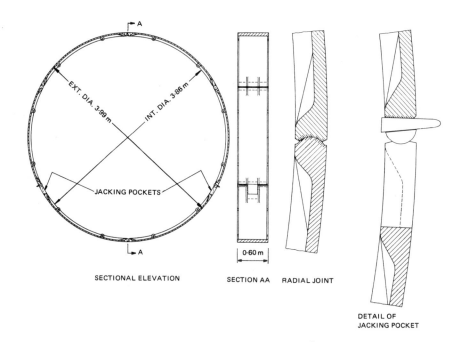

Fig. 8.5(b) — Expanded flexible cast iron lining as used on Victoria Line.

Fig. 8.5(c) – Completion of jacking in cast iron.

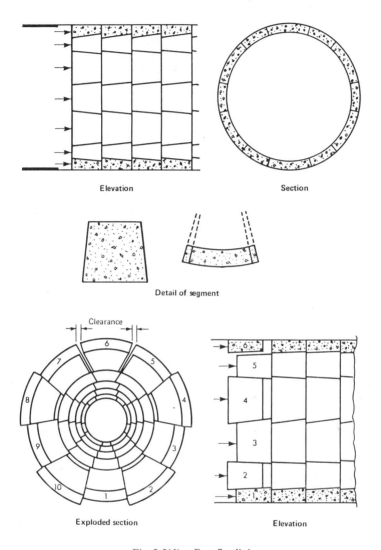

Fig. 8.5(d) – Don Seg lining.

Masonry was less commonly used where local stone thought to be suitable was available.

Problems of repair of these linings in old railway and sewer tunnels in particular may become increasingly important and may range from re-pointing and local replacement of bricks to much more extensive rebuilding, or possibly opening out completely.

BIBLIOGRAPHY
This chapter bibliography is a brief guide to further sources of information on linings and their function and design. As with so many specialised aspects of tunnels, much invaluable material is to be found in descriptions of particular projects, in periodicals and in proceedings of conferences. A general bibliography appears in Volume 2.

Groves, G. L., 'Tunnel linings, with special reference to a new form of reinforced concrete lining', *J. Instn. Civ. Engrs.*, 1943, **20** (Mar.).

Scott, P. A., 'A 75-inch diameter water main in tunnel: a new method of tunnelling in London clay', *Proc. Instn. Civ. Engrs.*, 1952, **1** (Nov.).

Jaeger, C., 'Present trends in design of pressure tunnels and shafts for underground hydro-electric power stations', *ibid*, 1955, **4** (Mar.).

Tattersall, F. and others, 'Investigations into the design of pressure tunnels in London clay', *ibid*, 1955, **4** (July).

Dawson, O., 'Tunnel linings', *Trans. Instn. Civ. Engrs. Ireland*, 1956, **83**.

Morgan, H. D., 'A contribution to the analysis of stress in a circular tunnel', *Geotechnique*, 1961, **11** (Mar.).

Deere, D. U. and others, *Design of tunnel liners and support systems*, U.S. Department of Transportation (NTIS PB 183799), 1969.

Peck, R. B. and others, *Some design considerations in the selection of underground support systems*, U.S. Department of Transportation (NTIS PB 190443), 1969.

Bartlett, J. V. and others, 'Precast concrete tunnel linings for Toronto subway', *J. Constr. Div., Proc. Amer. Soc. Civ. Engrs.*, 1971, **97** (Nov.).

Engineering Foundation (New York) Conferences:
Using shotcrete for underground structural support; South Berwick, Maine, 1973.
Shotcrete for ground support, Easton, Maryland, 1976.
Shotcrete for underground support III, St. Anton am Arlberg, Austria, 1978.

Tough, S. G. and Noskiewicz, T. M., 'Preformed linings in tunnelling practice', *Proceedings, Rapid Excavation and Tunneling Conference*, San Francisco, 1974.

Muir Wood, A. M., 'The circular tunnel in elastic ground', *Geotechnique*, 1975, **25** (Mar.). *See also* discussion, 1976, **26** (Mar.).

Lyons, A. C., 'Some developments in segmental tunnel linings designed in the United Kingdom', *Underground Space*, 1977, **1**, no. 3.

Craig, R. N. and Muir Wood, A. M., 'A review of tunnel lining practice in the United Kingdom', *Supplementary Report 335*, Transport and Road Research Laboratory, Crowthorne, 1978.

9

Survey and Control

9.1 SURVEY NETWORKS

Tunnel Survey, of which setting out is a part, comprises a number of phases and operations.

The initial stage is a topographic survey to provide a contoured map on which possible tunnel alignments can be laid out so that the best may be selected. This provides a network from which the tunnel alignment is set out on the ground and used for construction. The surface network must then be extended underground progressively as that tunnel advances, being used for detailed control of excavation at the face and lining. The underground network has to be repeatedly resurveyed and adjusted if accuracy in construction is to be maintained. There is usually a final operation of accurate survey of the completed tunnel.

The operations of survey and setting out are closely interdependent, particularly so in tunnelling, because lines cannot be carried ahead of excavation and survey stations in a tunnel are liable to be disturbed by ground movement as well as by construction operations.

There is inherently greater potential for precision in surveying than in setting out because the same stations can be surveyed separately and checked and resurveyed as often as necessary, whereas setting out is essentially the operation of fixing a station and marking it once and for all. Hence, apart from the danger of disturbance, there is an inherent limit to precision in setting out.

In tunnelling the whole surface network must be sufficiently established to include and relate both ends of the tunnel before work can commence, but the corresponding underground network can only be built up as excavation progresses and cannot be completed and finally checked until the tunnel breakthrough has been made. Essentially, the underground survey network depends in most cases on extension forwards from a relatively short base — indeed a very short base when access is by a vertical shaft — and extreme precision of angular measurement is therefore necessary.

The requirement of a high degree of accuracy is in conflict with the physical conditions in which the work must be done, particularly as regards the underground part of the survey in which conditions are often necessarily dirty and cramped and work has to be done under pressure of time, in addition to which the network also is usually constrained to a badly structured geometrical layout.

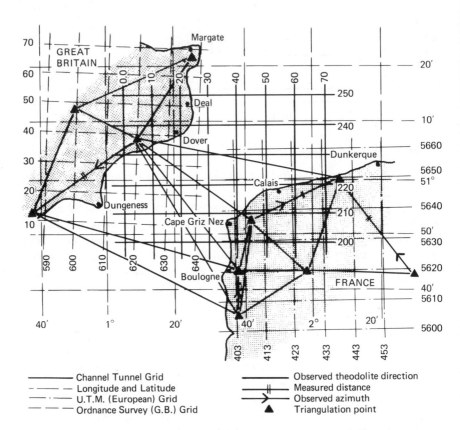

Channel Tunnel Grid
Longitude and Latitude
U.T.M. (European) Grid
Ordnance Survey (G.B.) Grid

Observed theodolite direction
Measured distance
Observed azimuth
Triangulation point

Fig. 9.1 – Channel Tunnel Survey. The figure shows the pattern of triangulation necessary in connecting the British and French survey grids, and in establishing a Channel Tunnel grid for use in the project.

9.1.1 Map Projections

A tunnel survey usually covers a sufficiently limited area for plane geometry to be applicable without reference to earth curvature, and is self contained. Correlation to a national or wider system may then be simply achieved by the incorporation of two or more common points in the network which may be utilised as necessary for transformation of coordinates.

For very long tunnels, such as the Channel tunnel, geodetic considerations arising from curvature of the earth's surface make the survey problems more complex. In that particular example further difficulties arise in the coordination of the differing national and international survey grids and also the long water crossing.

In long tunnels, such as those for water supply, aspects of curvature may be significant in control of levels and gradients, and also in convergence of meridians if true north is relevant to the survey. The essentially linear nature of such tunnels usually avoids the increase in complexity which would result from considerations of double curvature.

9.1.2 Accuracy

The tolerance acceptable in a completed tunnel will vary with its purpose but may be as little as ±40 mm for a metro tunnel in which a precast segmental lining is erected behind the advancing face. In water supply tunnels, obviously, local tolerances may be greater, but in sewer tunnels levels must be closely specified. In all cases, where a tunnel is driven from both ends to meet, accuracy of junction is a prime consideration and should normally be less than 75 mm. Where this cannot be attained with certainty, a long pilot heading may be required to effect a smooth junction.

The required angular precision of the survey lines in the tunnel will obviously depend on the length of drive from the nearest access shaft, which will be relatively short in metro tunnels, but may be several kilometres in water tunnels. For the Channel Tunnel 18 km drives from each side were contemplated. The desired survey accuracy may thus range from 1/20,000 to 1/200,000.

The skeleton of the main topographical survey requires to be of appreciably higher precision than the working lines. Accuracy of 1 in 20,000, which represents an angle of 10 sec. is acceptable for short drives, but for long drives higher accuracy is to be sought. 1 in 200,000 is an ideal figure with a one-second theodolite, but in practice 1 in 60,000 is unlikely to be bettered.

9.2 GROUND SURVEY

The surface survey may be based on triangualtion, traversing, trilateration or any combination. Triangulation is probably best in reasonably open country, but in city streets traversing is much more suitable. Trilateration has been very unusual except perhaps for local detail but modern EDM instruments may have advantages.

In urban areas roof top surveys may be helpful but tall buildings move with change of temperature and in strong winds, and additionally transfer down to ground level and below is difficult to effect accurately.

Detailing may be done manually from the survey lines, or may be provided by aerial photography where control points are identified, for which roof top stations have then considerable merits.

In busy city areas it is usually quite impracticable to survey at street level during normal working hours, and the work must be done in late evening, night and early morning, or at weekends. Night work has also advantages in instrumental accuracy when temperatures are steady, and changes from sunshine to shadow are avoided.

9.2.1 Layout of Survey

Although the prime function of the survey is to link the two ends of the tunnel with an accurate network, it should also be laid out to help in locating and mapping accurately relevant topographical detail.

In open country watercourses, points of reduced cover, and other relevant features will be required. In urban conditions, street frontages, cellars and indications of underground services are among the structures to be surveyed. The layout should be as simple and direct as is compatible with these requirements and with a sound geometrical network.

One important aspect of layout is that stations should be so sited that they can be preserved for re-use, either for checking or for extension of the network or further detailing.

9.2.2 Triangulation

In extensive surveys triangulation has been the most efficient method of providing an accurate network over large areas, because measurement of angles can be effected with precision over long lengths even where direct access between points is difficult, whereas distance measurement has hitherto been much more laborious and often impossible to effect with accuracy.

Electronic Distance Measurement (EDM) has changed the balance of advantage somewhat because direct access between stations is no longer required and network lengths can be measured wherever required.

The fundamental feature of triangulation is the measurement of all angles in a network of triangles and the calculation of all lengths, by methods of plane or spherical trigonometry from a principal base line laid out on the most favourable terrain available and measured with every precaution and refinement.

Base lines are usually laid out on ground as nearly level as possible and to be as long as practicable consistent with their ends being sited where they provide good sight lines to the other survey stations and 'well conditioned' triangles.

In the past they have usually been measured by use of 'Invar' steel bands and the methods remain useful.

The degree of precision necessary in any particular case will depend on the extent of the triangulation to be built up from it and the use to which it is to be put, but a brief outline of the precautions adopted may be helpful.

The base line is set out as an exact straight line in bays of about 30 m and level differences between the ends of each bay are ascertained precisely. The 'Invar' band is suspended as a caternary under known constant tension by use of weights and pulleys. Both ends are read using vernier or microscope as appropriate. Measurements are repeated as often as necessary to ensure the required precision. In the most important geodetic work further precautions and refinements will be necessary.

The alternative of EDM is now available and makes possible checks on length as often as necessary in the triangulation, avoiding the complete dependence on a single base length. Difference of level between the ends must again be ascertained. Offset stations may be established at either end of the base line to facilitate simultaneous reciprocal readings by use of two sets of instruments which can then be exchanged end for end. Air temperatures, wet and dry bulb, and air pressure should be recorded at the beginning and end of each set of measurements to provide appropriate allowances for refraction and frequency modulation.

In either method there may be a need to make corrections for earth's curvature and height above sea level.

9.2.3 Levelling

The survey network is in fact three-dimensional but is separated practically as far as possible into horizontal plane geometry and vertical height.

Levelling is preferably reintegrated with the triangulation or traverse so that all stations are observed. All levelling should be done in closed circuits, which are less laborious when automatic levels of acceptable accuracy are available.

Movement of level points is a particular problem in tunnel work as 'draw down' is likely to affect a considerable area. More especially where a tunnel follows a street line, it may be impossible to arrange for all points to be outside the area of potential settlement.

Subsidence must be considered probable, its magnitude depending on geological factors and construction methods. It may be important to observe its rate of development, for which levelling techniques of considerable precision will be required.

9.2.3.1 Bench Marks

For every project, however small, reference bench marks are essential, well outside the zone of influence of tunnel excavation, and founded in a stratum unlikely to be affected by the tunnelling or by its influence on the water table.

For larger projects, especially if of long duration, the provision of an adequate network of 'base' bench marks is appropriate. They may have to be founded at considerable depth in sound rock, being constructed of reinforced concrete, or a steel rod or pipe keyed into the rock and insulated from shear by a surrounding envelope of coarse sand. At the top will be a level pin of non-corrosive metal with a protective cover.

For a long tunnel a series of such 'base' bench marks will be of great value throughout construction.

They should be precisely levelled in relation to each other initially and at regular intervals, and any one can then be used locally for accurate measurement.

Circuit closures should be attainable within 3 mm over 1 km, the accuracy over longer circuits being proportional to the square root of the number of sights.

9.2.3.2 *Monitoring of Subsidence*
For structures, levelling points should be attached to columns, beams or foundations either as brackets securely bolted on or as pins or bolts firmly grouted in.

For ground movement a substantial block of concrete founded at a depth on a metre or more should carry a reference levelling point near the surface protected by a cover. Kerbs and similar ground level features are unsuitable for precise long term use as being liable to damage and to local disturbance.

9.2.3.3 *Precise Levelling Instruments*
The older types of precise level are capable of high accuracy but are more time consuming and more easily affected by temperature change and vibration from wind and traffic than are modern automatic instruments; in sunny conditions shading by an umbrella may be desirable but perhaps impracticable.

Most instrument manufacturers offer precise automatic levels. A nominal accuracy of 2 mm per km is appropriate for tunnel work.

Precise levelling staves having a body of metal or wood incorporate an Invar calibrated strip and have two reading scales with a fixed difference between them so that readings at difficult points on one scale are automatically checked. For 'change points' in a levelling run a solidly based point is essential. Suitable equipment is available.

All instruments should be checked regularly for damage or maladjustment: levels for collimation in particular, and staves for cleanliness of seating and for correctness of bubble level. An annual check by instrument technicians should be arranged.

9.2.3.4 *Procedure*
Normal good practice in levelling should be followed and for precision work particular attention should be given to a number of points.

Backsights and foresight should be equal and of moderate length, not generally exceeding about 35 m, to avoid substantial refraction effects and to allow scales to be read more quickly and accurately. Of course, when several points other than backsight and foresight are read from one station the sight lengths for these intermediate points may be unequal.

Both scales on the staff should be read and the difference checked within ±0.15 mm. Although two or more staves may be in use to expedite the taking of a series of levels, care should be taken to ensure that the same staff is used on all bench marks and in closing the run so as to eliminate errors of zero positions on the staves.

Where it is impractical to close the circuit in levelling a series of monitoring points the standard deviation of the scale differences (variance from staff constant) for all staff readings may be calculated as a check and should not exceed ±0.07 mm.

Precise levelling demands care and concentration and is time-consuming. Three assistants to the surveyor namely, an assistant to book the readings and two staff men, can contribute to speed and accuracy and security of equipment; if various levels additional to backsights and foresights are required, an extra staff man can prove helpful in speeding up the work.

The procedure for a record of readings should be: backsight on left scale, foresight on left scale, foresight on right scale, backsight on right scale.

Continuous sequence of observations should not exceed four to five hours even in favourable conditions if errors are to be minimised. Ideal observing conditions are on a cool, overcast, calm day and at a time free from traffic and other vibration.

9.2.3.5 *Records of Subsidence*
Frequent monitoring of subsidence by precise levelling is advisable at intervals of time governed by the rate of subsidence. A graph of subsidence against time for each point is the best record, supplemented by longitudinal and cross sections. If an extensive area is involved a contoured plan of subsidence is likely to be useful. The initial pattern of points to be monitored should be planned with such records in view.

9.3 PHOTOGRAMMETRIC SURVEY AND MAPPING

Photogrammetry is the preparation of accurate maps from aerial or other photographs.

It is extremely useful for making the necessary detailed topographic surveys for tunnel works both in urban and rural areas, and, where the works are extensive, is likely to be more economical than equivalent ground survey, which cannot, however, be wholly eliminated as it is essential in the setting out and underground network.

Photogrammetry necessitates the use of elaborate and expensive equipment for photography and for transformation of the photographs to precise scales, and must be carried out by specialist organisations.

9.3.1 Photographic Equipment
The cameras must produce images of low distortion and uniform scale, for which stable focal length and a truly plane film are essential.

The intervals between exposures must be so controlled during flight as to provide ample overlap between successive pictures. 60% overlap in the direction of flight and 40% side lap are usual. An intervalometer is used to assist the navigation the timing being dependent on height, ground speed, and angle covered by the lens. Film sizes up to 300 × 300 mm are available. Stereoscopic pairs of photographs taken from the overlaps allow contour plans or three-dimensional models to be made.

9.3.2 Control

Although normally the camera is nominally vertical, errors are quite inevitable and a ground control network is necessary in order to orient and scale the photographs accurately. It is obviously desirable that the ground control points should be a part of the ground survey with which they must ultimately be integrated. Four or five points should be established so as to be clearly identifiable in the aerial photographs and of known co-ordinates and elevation.

Where modern digital design methods are to be used permanent control points rigorously corrected and precisely identifiable are essential.

Aerial triangulation is sometimes employed but rather for extensive topographic mapping than for tunnel survey. Photo co-ordinates are transferred progressively along overlapping pictures from one controlled base to another. Correction and adjustment of closing errors is likely to be necessary.

9.3.3 Mapping

The fundamental problem in mapping from photographs is the transformation of the image produced on the emulsion to an orthogonal projection on a horizontal plane. When working from a single photograph differences in ground levels introduce uncertainties into the mapping. Nevertheless a controlled mosaic using portions of photographs individually rectified and enlarged to the scale of known ground distances can produce a well scaled plan.

For most purposes requiring accuracy stereometric methods are used by employment of overlapping photography from which three-dimensional co-ordinates can be obtained. Fig. 9.2. There are two basic methods: optical or mechanical projection from glass based diapositives.

Optical projection is by use of lenses, similar to the camera lenses, projecting the image on to special tracing platens, whereas mechanical projection uses rods, pivoting at a point representing the projection centre of the camera to define the light rays. The latter system is more readily adaptable to varying focal length, different photographic formats, varied plotting scales and digitising of co-ordinates.

Where the requirement is simply to update accurate maps already existing, or to fill in topographic detail, simpler plotting instruments can be used.

9.3.4 Accuracy

The accuracy of the finished plan will obviously depend on the photographic equipment, the flying height and techniques and the methods of projection.

Rectified photographs alone are of very limited accuracy. Controlled mosaics are also limited, depending on control density and on elevation differences.

With more refined techniques and accurate plotters positional accuracy of points may be of the order of 0.012% of flying height for the range of 1000–2600 m. Height accuracy of points on the ground is of the order of 0.067%.

Fig. 9.2 – Air Survey for photogrammetry. The two photographs from a line of survey are not successive, an intermediate one being omitted, but even so there is a small overlap. Successive pictures overlap by 60% providing for stereometric plotting.

Terrestrial photogrammetry may be utilised for filling in detail on aerial mapping, for underground work, and for detail of near vertical features. Cameras, using glass plates, are oriented by theodolite. They are available in pairs with parallel focal axes for direct stereoscopic photography. Terrestrial plotters are normally of the mechanical projector type, adapted to the short focal lengths and precisely known orientation.

9.3.5 Topographical Detail

Much of the detail required for planning a project and for acquisition of necessary land can be obtained from aerial survey with a ground control network, but it is likely that ground survey will be necessary for precise delineation of critical features, particularly in urban work. Offsetting by tape from surveyed lines remains a very useful method for such features as building frontages, although direct reading tachometers may be found more expeditious where a substantial volume of work is involved. A small section of a 1/500 plan in an urban area is reproduced (Fig. 9.3) to show the mapping required for a metro system.

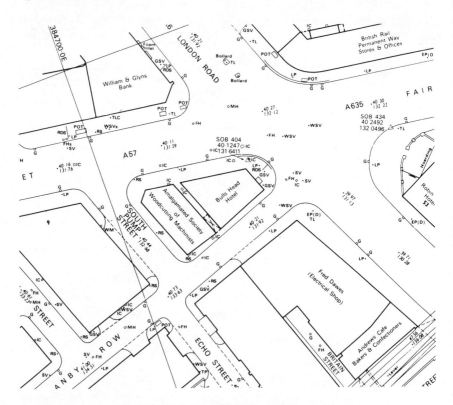

Fig. 9.3 — Mapping required for a metro system.

9.3.6 Automatic Plotting

Where three dimensional co-ordinates of any point are readily obtained computer directed plotters can be used for the automatic production of maps and associated sections.

9.4 BURIED SERVICES AND STRUCTURES

Records of the buried services of Public Utilities are rarely of the necessary precision; minor deviations during construction may be unrecorded, or positions may have been identified in relation to a kerb line and road level which have subsequently been altered. Manhole and valve positions help in location of services, and can usually be identified on aerial surveys, while detecting instruments may be helpful in tracing pipes and cable. Nevertheless, at critical sections, trial pits to expose the services and relate them precisely to the survey usually are necessary.

Few subsurface structures are connected by a reliable survey to an established grid system. Any tunnelling work in their vicinity usually requires a new survey, possibly with trial pits and borings. Even where the interior of a structure is accurately located, the actual thickness of a wall may be greater than supposed because of overbreak, and the lengths of piles may not be known. Other deviations from original plans may remain unrecorded.

Abandoned workings associated with mining or quarrying are rarely adequately recorded, but some help may be obtained from the local records of learned societies or other bodies (see Chapter 3).

It is worth repeating that all underground excavation whether temporary or permanent or overbreak should be recorded in a form which will be available for future reference. Mining regulations generally embody such a requirement.

9.5 SURVEY INSTRUMENTS

Theodolites and levels have undergone considerable design changes in recent years. For the same or higher accuracy they are more compact and simpler in use and are generally better protected against damage and intrusion of moisture and dirt.

Constrained centreing of theodolites, targets, electronic distance meters (E.D.M.'s) and optical plummets has been devised to permit accurate interchange, so as to minimise angular errors arising from errors of centreing over survey points.

9.5.1 Theodolites

For precise underground work on control surveys and deformation monitoring the 'one second' theodolite is most suitable. It reads to one second of arc and with suitable observing procedures the standard deviation of angles may be

±2 secs. for control surveys and less than one second from monitoring pillars at night.

Circle eccentricity is unlikely to be measurable in such modern instruments nor 'run' in the micrometer; they have 'double circle reading' so that opposite sides of the scale are read simultaneously.

For vertical angles most modern theodolites incorporate automatic vertical circle indexing, some with liquid compensators having no moving mechanical parts. This eliminates an annoying source of error where levelling of the vertical circle is omitted. Compensators are claimed to be accurate to one second. Adjustment errors are eliminated by observing in both telescope positions.

For underground survey a theodolite should be equipped with lighting of adjustable intensity for the circle and graticule. Right angle extensions to eyepiece and micrometer will be required for steep sights and also a striding level to ensure greater precision transversely. Other useful equipment includes optical micrometers, illuminated targets and special short range targets, and trivets for mounting the instrument on pillars or wall brackets. A top centreing mark for setting the instrument under a station fixed in the roof may also be requisite.

If setting out only, and not precision survey, is required simpler 10 second or 20 second theodolites may be adequate. Useful features are: additional anticlockwise circle divisions, self reducing tacheometer graticules, automatic vertical circle indexing and, again, a top centreing mark.

For very precise monitoring of horizontal movement there may be a use for 'geodetic' theodolites reading to 0.5 seconds but it is rarely that the one second instrument is not adequate.

9.5.2 Levels

Automatic levels have largely supplemented the tilting type for underground use. Speed, convenience and accuracy are markedly improved. There is no need to illuminate a level bubble and no danger of misreading it when poorly illuminated. Compensators are very reliable but occasional testing is advisable, and it is prudent to check against sticking by light tapping of the instrument.

A graticule without stadia hairs is to be preferred to eliminate misreading in poor light.

Staves can usually be of the reflective type for which lighting by reflection from a miner's cap lamp is adequate at usual ranges. A staff with 'even' ends, whose lengths is an exact number of metres, is of advantage when taking levels in crown and invert of a tunnel, because it need not be inverted for soffit readings.

The risk of misreading scale fractions because of reversal is eliminated, but of course the appropriate correction in whole metres must be made.

Observing techniques with precise levels have been referred to above. A recent automatic precise level has been designed to overcome the necessity for equality of sight lengths.

9.5.3 Lasers
There are two particular uses of lasers in tunnel survey.

That of most general application is to provide a visible guide line for control of excavation at the face. The older systems involved repeated fixing of sight lines using survey stations, in the crown of the tunnel from which plumb bobs were suspended so that survey lines might be projected forward to the face. Having established a point at the face it was necessary to make adjustments for any curves and to fix the axis level, then to determine the desired tunnel perimeter, the whole operation having to be fitted into the tunnel construction cycle.

The laser beam, set up and aligned by conventional theodolite techniques, provides a clearly identifiable line, and a recognisable spot continuously projected on to the tunnel face from an unmanned instrument, with obvious advantages in time saving, convenience and skilled manpower. The useful operational length is limited by natural dispersion in the tunnel atmosphere and of course by any requirement for driving on a curve. Necessary precautions include the use of intermediate screen to cut off the beam if the source is inadvertently deflected and regular checks by a surveyor and readjustment for curves.

A second application is to provide increased range as a carrier for electronic distance measurement.

The usual type in tunnels is the Helium-Neon gas laser. It is of low efficiency (0.1%), but has the advantages of running continuously without elaborate cooling devices, and of retaining spectral purity. The hazards to vision of direct observation are not great because of the low power of the beam; nevertheless in tunnel conditions, where general illumination is often poor and where consequently the pupil of the eye is dilated, laser beams should be sited to minimise the chance of direct impact on the eye of anyone in the tunnel.

9.5.4 Distance Measurement
The calibrated steel band, requiring calculation of corrections for level, temperature, tension and sag remains an indispensible tool for much tunnel survey. Banding is probably the most accurate nethod for lengths up to 100 m or so, and when surveying urban detail may also be the basis for offset measurements.

For large projects requiring precise work banding has given way to the use of electronic distance meters (EDM), which within limits of range measure lengths in a single operation.

There are savings of time and reduced opportunities of error compared with the multiple operations and calculations of corrections in banding. There is also the great convenience of measuring across difficult or inaccessible ground, as across water courses, railways, highways or precipitous ground or direct to elevated survey stations or within tunnels. Where all sides in a triangulation or traverse can be accurately measured precision in adjustment of the network is generally improved.

The instruments are of course much more expensive than steel bands but in an extensive survey there can be a very great saving in the cost and time of field-work. Experience in use of the instruments is necessary and knowledge of instrumental errors. There are in EDM work three principal sources of potential error, namely:

(1) levelling and plumbing of instrument and target over survey stations
(2) 'index', a correction particular to the instruments used
(3) 'cyclic error', which is inherent in the electronic resolution of the measuring frequency.

Regular calibration against an established base length is of great importance.

9.5.5 Recent Developments in Instruments

The recent advances have mainly been in distance measurement. The 'Mekometer' developed by the National Physical Laboratory has an accuracy comparable with that of an Invar band for ranges up to 3 km, the accuracy being; ± 0.2 mm constant $\pm$ length $\times 10^{-6}$.

Electronic tachemometers such as the Zeiss-Oberkochen Reg Elta 14 with an infra red carrier beam or the Aga Geodimeter 710 with a laser carrier beam dispense with scale circles and employ electronically coded angle measurement systems. They allow data to be observed and directly recorded on punched tape for computer processing. Observed or reduced measurements are also displayed. Accuracy in length measurement is about ± 10 mm, and in angular measurement ± 2 secs. A number of manufacturers are now in process of developing and marketing such instruments. They are costly, but on suitable projects are potentially very valuable. Figs. 9.4(a) and 9.4(b).

Conventional theodolites may be equipped with auxiliary EDM's such as the Wild D13 incorporating a slope distance reduction computer or the Kern DM 500, fitting round the telescope and powered by the instrument lighting circuit. Both systems are 'short range' (about 2 km) and use infra red carrier beams. Accuracy in distance is about ± 6 mm.

Long range (up to 30 km) microwave EDM's such as the CA1000 Tellmometer have been greatly reduced in size, and in weight to about 3½ kg with an accuracy of ± 15 mm $\pm$ length $\times 5 \times 10^{-6}$. They have the added advantage of providing radio communication. In tunnels, reflection from solids of the microwaves may preclude their use.

Gyro theodolites have been developed, which can be of particular assistance in carrying underground accurate orientation, (further referred to below). They comprise essentially a theodolite in conjunction with a suspended gyro. Experience in their use, and an understanding of the variables affecting accuracy are necessary if they are to be employed. Base line checks should be incorporated in all observations to minimise the variations that may occur in the spin-up of the gyro and in the so called 'tape constant' as well as possible diurnal variations. The instruments are sensitive to ground vibration which should be eliminated as far as possible during observations.

Fig. 9.4(a) — N.P.L. Mekometer in use in tunnel. Note plumb bob from survey
station above, and support bracket secured to tunnel segments.

Fig. 9.4(b) – Kern Mekometer ME3000 (Kern, per Survey & General Instrument Co. Ltd.).

Canadian Geodetic Survey methods are claimed to achieve bearings with a standard deviation of ±2 secs by observation of oscillations when the instrument is clamped near North.

Even in local survey convergence of meridians may become significant if high precision is sought. The gyro-theodolite identifies true astronomical north for which the convergence at 45° latitude (λ) is about 30 secs per km of E-W distance, and is therefore significant in accurate survey work, and increasingly so, in proportion to tan λ at higher latitudes. At very high latitudes, exceeding about 80° the gyro-theodolite ceases to be useful as its axis is too nearly coincidental with that of the earth.

9.5.6 Tape Recorders

Recording of survey observations can be speeded up by use of miniature portable cassette recorders, which may save the services of a booker. Accuracy should be high because readings are spoken while viewing the scale. Relevant descriptive information is easily added at the same time, and the whole transcription time can be kept within usable limits by means of a microphone switch. The method is of particular value in reading repetitive data in such operations as precise levelling, stadia tacheometry and EDM tacheometry.

9.5.7 Calculators and Computers

The development of pocket and desk calculators has contributed greatly to survey work by providing flexibility in methods and allowing every sort of numerical calculation to be done quickly and accurately in the field and allowing immediate checks on complex observations.

Computers with their capacity for handling and analysing vast volumes of data make possible much more accurate adjustment of survey networks and can be programmed to provide without delay all necessary information for setting out and optimising curves within a tunnel.

9.6 SETTING OUT AND CONTROL

In short tunnels the centre line or an offset line may sometimes be established on the surface, but in general the starting points for tunnelling, whether through adits or from shafts, cannot be aligned directly but must be connected through a coordinate grid established in the survey. From permanent stations of the network a reference base line is established at each working site and this base line is then used to transfer bearings and distances into the tunnel workings.

The stations of the reference base line should be substantial and stable, sited where not liable to disturbance by excavation, or by traffic. It is not always possible to ensure absolute stability, in which case frequent checking from the survey network will be necessary.

If the tunnel is driven from an adit or from the portal survey lines can be extended into the tunnel and underground survey stations can be established either in the roof of the tunnel using plumb bobs to sight on and for centreing the theodolite or on brackets at the sides, or more rarely in the tunnel invert, where interference from traffic and from spillage is probable.

9.6.1 Shaft plumbing

If work is initiated from a vertical shaft the problem of transferring alignment accurately from surface to underground becomes difficult especially with a narrow and deep shaft. The simplest method is that of co-planing in which two wires carrying heavy suspended weights are hung down the shaft. They are set in exact alignment in the desired direction. Underground, a theodolite is set up and brought into exact alignment with the wires and used to fix permanent marks on the alignment. The positions of the wires are measured from the surface survey and their coordinates established, from which the whole coordinate system can be continued underground. The accuracy of the transfer, particularly as regards bearings, is restricted by the shortness of the base length between wires and by the difficulty of ensuring that the wires are at rest. It is essential for the surveyors to have unobstructed possession of the shaft for a considerable time. The method is obviously very direct, and can be used quite quickly for starting off a heading from the bottom of a shaft, but when the alignment must be extended for a long tunnel drive, the utmost care and refinement are necessary if bearings are to be maintained within a few seconds.

Another system of shaft plumbing is the 'Weisbach Method'. In this again two plumb wires are used, but, instead of seeking exact alignment between wires, surface station and underground station, closely approximate alignment only is required, with accurate measurement of the small angles and of the distances. Advantages of the system are that both surface and underground theodolite stations can be securely established in advance and that measurements can be repeated as often as thought appropriate and averaged. They can be checked at any time even with slightly different plumb wire positions.

Figure 9.5 shows the layout for the Weisbach method. A is the theodolite station and B & C the plumb wires. The distance, AB, should be as short as practicable and preferably not greater than twice the distance between wires. The angle BAC should in no case exceed about 10 mins but it is better if it can be made as small as 30 secs.

Angles XAB, BAC are measured with the theodolite and distances AB, BC are taped. The angle BCA of the very flat triangle is very small and can be calculated by the sine rule, with the simplification that the angle and its sine are proportional, so that:

$$\text{Angle BCA} = \frac{\text{AB}}{\text{BC}} \times \text{Angle BAC}$$

The operations are repeated underground.

The points BC are then incorporated just as are any other stations.

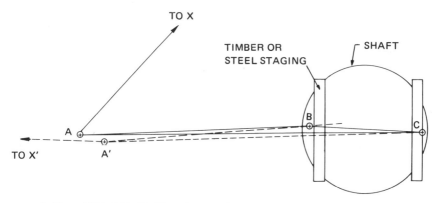

A, A'   THEODOLITE STATIONS ON SURFACE AND IN TUNNEL
X, X'   NEXT STATION IN SURVEY NETWORK
B, C   PLUMB WIRES HANGING DOWN SHAFT

Fig. 9.5 — Shaft Plumbing, Weisbach method.

Of all the main survey operations it is probably shaft plumbing that is essentially least precise, and it should therefore be carried out with extreme care and repeated as an independent check.

9.6.1.1 *Gyro-theodolite*

It has already been observed that deep narrow shafts increase the difficulties of bearing transfer to underground work. The use of gyro-theodolites can therefore be advantageous, certainly at depth—particularly at depths exceeding 50 m. Accuracy of 20 secs. is readily achieved and can be improved by repeated observations, but it is essential that the instrument should be checked against a standard line before and after each set of observations.

9.6.2 Underground Survey

The essence of tunnel setting out is to provide accurate information at the working face of position and direction. The survey underground becomes an open-ended traverse in which disturbance of stations is always to be feared: it must therefore be the subject of repeated re-survey and correction as necessary.

The stations established should be simple and robust. They are exposed to particularly arduous service in drill and blast operations. For security and ease of use they are preferably fixed in the upper part of the tunnel.

In rock tunnels temporary stations may be secured to timber or steel supports, but these are likely to move under load progressively and it is preferable if possible to drill up into the rock soffit and insert a suitable plug from which a plumb line can be hung. The rock is not immune from movements and resurvey will be necessary. Where the station is being used directly to guide tunnelling it may be equipped with a graduated scale and movable cursor so that it can be adjusted exactly to give a predetermined line.

Where segmental lining to the tunnel is erected directly behind the advancing face survey stations may be established by a hacksaw cut into a metallic flange into which a cord can be hammered, or by drilling into concrete and plugging a small hole. Stations of this type are directly affected by the tendency of such linings to 'squat' and they must therefore be resurveyed at intervals until stability is ensured in about 3-6 months.

In tunnels of large cross section it may be necessary to fix wall plates secured either by rock bolting or by bolting or plugging to a segmental lining. Such brackets facilitate erection of instruments and of special targets such as those used with EDM equipment. If correctly sited they enable the surveyor to make his observations without obstructing other activities. They may incorporate facilities for constrained centreing if required, and if adequate protection is possible.

9.6.2.1 *Permanent Stations*

In some cases permanent survey stations are required within the finished tunnel as for example in metro systems with very small clearances. In an unlined tunnel, or one with segmental lining immediately erected, the principal construction stations may suffice, particularly if they are in the soffit and near the centre line. Where the finished lining is *in situ* concrete a brass plug and identifying plate can be cast in and surveyed after movements of the concrete have finished.

Secondary stations for such purposes as rail track alignment may also be required. They are readily established from the permanent stations.

9.6.3 Control of Tunnel Drive

There are, broadly, three aspects of survey work within the tunnel with considerable overlap between them as the face advances.

First, the initial survey for setting out, which must keep pace with the advancing excavation, is often executed in difficult conditions. Lengths of sight lines will be limited by the tunnel atmosphere and by the tunnel geometry and the needs of face control. Stations and level marks may be required at intervals as close as 15 m or may be possible at 150 m. Almost always there are risks of movement and damage which may be mitigated by careful referencing of points.

The second phase is that of the primary control survey, necessary to strengthen and check the initial survey. Initial stations can be used, or new ones established to provide a better layout of the principal lines. Work should be done under the most favourable conditions practicable with minimum air currents, clear air, and uniformity of temperature to minimise horizontal and vertical refraction.

This survey must keep pace with the tunnel advance and ensure that the initial survey is not extended for more than 3 or 4 stations without check from the primary control. Much depends on the stability of the stations, but regular resurvey is always necessary if accuracy of bearing is to be maintained.

The third aspect is that of face control to ensure that excavation is regulated within the required limits. For hand tunnelling or drill and blast work control of line at the face is still frequently exercised by visual sighting of pairs of string lines, with similar methods for level. Laser lines are now being adopted widely as they provide continuous visual indication of line and level and, although they too must be subject to regular checking and adjustment, they release the surveyor for less routine tasks.

Where a shield or full face machine is employed, additional survey checks are necessary to ensure not only that the shield is on line but also that its aspect is correct. There are three measurements to be verified:

(1) 'Lead' − the horizontal angle of the face of the shield, measured as the distance by which one side of the shield leads the other in relation to 'square marks' set out across the tunnel at right angles to the axis of advance, which may of course be on a curve.

(2) 'Look-up' or 'overhang' − the vertical angle of the face of the shield, measured as the distance by which the invert leads, or lags behind, the crown. It may be measured from a plumb line registering on a circular scale.

(3) 'Roll' − the rotation of the shield about the axis of the tunnel, measured by spirit level or plumb bob.

Where circular segmental linings are being built, whether or not with a shield, the leading ring needs to be surveyed for the same three measurements and in addition for shape as a true circle, or other specified cross section, and for the plane of the face. Unless these are controlled within close limits assembly of segments becomes progressively more difficult and the shape can be seriously distorted.

Increasing mechanisation of operations at the face makes access for survey lines and measurements more restricted and suitable sight lines hard to secure. This is more particularly the case with tunnel boring machines, yet their faster advance demands stricter control if large deviations are to be avoided. Laser beams projected to a screen directly visible to the machine operator can display to him visually the exact position of the machine. With added instrumentation it can also indicate lead, look-up and roll.

Errors of position cannot be corrected abruptly and the machine must be steered to bring it back on course when a deviation is observed. Predictors have been devised and fitted to indicate continuously a point a few metres ahead towards which the shield should be aimed so as to provide the optimum correction. In their simplest form these can be little more than two graticules through which the beam passes, fixed to the machine and separated as widely as practicable; the distance of the beam off centre on each graticule indicates errors of line and direction.

More elaborate devices may be necessary where machines are operating continuously and the laser beam can be split and carried round a more complicated light path to indicate the appropriate steering. It is worth noting that there are dangers of unwanted refraction in such light paths, caused by heating from motors and other equipment.

9.6.3.1 *Correction of Errors*

Careful and frequent checking at the face, or continuous control when a machine is in use, should prevent gross errors, but tunnels do go off line and corrective measures become necessary. Where the tunnel is initially unlined, with intermittent support only, local enlargement to clear tight spots is usually possible, but where the final lining is erected close behind the face special measures are necessary. With a continuous cast-iron or concrete segmental lining some adjustment is usually possible from one ring to the next by suitable packing or by use of special taper rings, (provided primarily for constructing curves), but it sometimes becomes necessary to make a fresh start with an independent ring and subsequently to dismantle and rebuild the badly aligned length.

9.6.4 Final Survey and Adjustment

Survey of the completed tunnel is usually necessary to check adherence to critical design requirements. This must be particularly exact in metro tunnels where clearances between rolling stock and lining must be maintained and where the track is laid to precise curves. The survey is to measure actual cross sections at appropriate intervals, which may be closely spaced. Each cross section is examined in relation to the specified centre line and clearances to identify any critical points requiring adjustment. It is usually possible to accommodate minor encroachments on the specified clearances by some adjustment of the track centre line and it is this modified centre line that is known as the 'wriggle diagram'. Specified limits of curvature and gradient must be maintained, but tangent points can be moved and small changes in curvature or gradient accepted. After development of the wriggle diagram there may remain tight points requiring cutting away or rebuilding, which can be a formidable problem in bad ground.

Various survey methods have been developed to speed up and simplify the survey as compared with the use of theodolite and level at every critical point.

They include:

Photogrammetry in which stereoscopic photography from precisely defined bases in the tunnel is used to locate in 3 dimensions any identifiable spot on the tunnel walls or lining. There are difficulties in ensuring suitable lighting and in uninterrupted access.

Graphical. Details of cross sections are prepared with the aid of a 'sunflower' device set up in precise relationship to the control survey. This is most suited to relatively small tunnels.

Geometric. In lined tunnels the specified geometry can be checked by a suitably designed template preferably in conjunction with EDM, the data being processed directly by computer.

9.6.4.1 *Adjustments*

Adjustment of Underground Surveys may be appropriate where there is redundancy within the network, or an external check such as a link to the surface survey through an intermediate shaft or adit, and ultimately when drives from opposite directions meet.

Internal redundancy of the underground network may be used most simply, and in many cases satisfactorily, to adjust coordinates by Bowditch's method, but the method of least squares is to be preferred if the correction is other than nominal and if there is access to a computer for the calculations.

Surface ties showing up an accumulated error in the underground survey may again be similarly used to recalculate and adjust its coordinates. The question then arises whether to adjust the tunnel excavation and lining to the corrected alignment, or to modify the design alignment to accommodate the tunnel as actually constructed. This is essentially the same problem as in the preparation of the 'wriggle diagram' and the choice can only be made after full consideration of the consequences for construction and future use.

BIBLIOGRAPHY

The list which follows refers first to the general field of tunnel survey, after which are noted references to some specialised aspects.

Peele, R. (ed.), *Mining Engineer's Handbook* (Section 18), J. Wiley, 3rd edn., 1941.

Jenkins, R. B. M., *Curve Surveying,* Cleaver-Hume, 1960.

Hurst, G., 'Survey and setting-out', Chapter 3 in C. A. Pequignot (ed.) *Tunnels and Tunnelling,* Hutchinson, 1963.

Wasserman, W., 'Underground survey procedures', *New Zealand Surveyor,* 1967 (Mar.).

Chrzanowski, A. and others, 'Underground survey measurements, research for progress', *Canadian Mining and Metallurgical Bulletin,* 1967 (June).

Clark, D., *Plane and Geodetic Surveying for Engineers,* Constable, 1972.

Peterson, E. W. and Frobenius, P., 'Tunnel Survey and tunneling machine control', *J. Surv. Map Divn., Proc. Amer. Soc. Civ. Engrs.,* 1973, **99** (Sept.).

Specialised references

Cooke, L. H., 'Underground orientation by exact and approximate alignments of plumb wires in one shaft', *Trans. Instn. Min. Metal.,* 1925, **34**, 391.

Shepherd, J. S., 'Precise azimuths from steep sights', *Bull. Instn. Min. Metal.,* No. 554, 1953 (Jan.).

Thomas, T. L., 'The correlation of local grid to national grid co-ordinates',
  RICS Journal, 1954 (Dec.).

Hallert, B., *Photogrammetry*, McGraw-Hill, 1960.

Thompson, M. M. (ed.), *Manual of Photogrammetry*, Amer. Soc. Photogrammetry, 3rd edn., 1966.

Davies, O. V., 'Lasers and distance measurement', *Surv. Rev.,* 1966 (Jan. and
  Apr.).

Thomas, T. L., 'The precision indicator of the Meridian, theory and application', *Proc. 3rd S. Afric. Nat. Surv. Conf.,* 1967.

Price, W. F., 'Lasers and laser safety', *Surv. Rev.,* 1974 (July).

Thomas T. L. and Asquith, D., 'The suspended gyroscope', *Chart. Surv., Land
  Hydrogr. Min. Q.,* 1975, **2**, no. 3 and 1976, **3**, no. 3.

10
The Channel Tunnel and Seikan Tunnel

The Channel Tunnel and Seikan Tunnel are subaqueous tunnels of so special a character as to deserve separate description and discussion.

Projects for the Channel Tunnel have a long history, stretching back to the beginning of the 19th century, but may at last be approaching realisation, although tunnelling has twice been started in earnest, only to be frustrated by political decisions, not by engineering obstacles.

The Seikan Tunnel is a comparable project to connect the main Japanese island of Honshu with the northern island of Hokkaido, passing under the Tsugaru Strait. It has been under construction now for over 10 years, but early completion of tunnelling is a reasonable hope.

The special feature of these tunnels is that they are very long crossings under the open sea, and they are therefore particularly vulnerable to the hazard of inundation at high pressure from a boundless reservoir, through undetected fissures or buried channels. Shorter undersea tunnels already built are those in the Chesapeake Bay bridge/tunnel crossing and the Japanese Kanmon tunnels. Other undersea tunnels contemplated are one between Denmark and Sweden, one under the Straits of Messina and one under the Straits of Gibraltar. The latter two are very ambitious major projects requiring novel technology; they have not been worked out in any such practical detail as have the tunnels here under discussion.

For the Channel Tunnel various options still remain open, but a railway tunnel has always seemed the most acceptable in terms of engineering and finance, and as causing no obstruction to shipping. For the Seikan Tunnel no alternatives to rail have appeared practicable, and the project under construction is for very high speed railway operation, combined with use by slower local services. The great advantage of rail as against highway is that ventilation requirements are manageable, and that the traffic is fully organised and controlled.

10.1 CHANNEL TUNNEL

Ideas for a fixed link across the 35 km wide channel between England and France, whether tunnel, bridge, causeway or some hybrid scheme, date back to the beginning of the 19th century. Many of the schemes were fantastic, others were too far ahead of current technology in their demands, and all called for heavy capital expenditure without absolute assurance of practicability or ultimate profitability. Railway development in both countries stimulated the promotion of schemes, and until the middle of the 20th century all but the most unrealistic proposals were for a rail tunnel.

Since then the growth of road transport and advances in technology have stimulated proposals for highway tunnels and bridges usually in combination with a rail crossing. The rail schemes have continued to be favoured as demanding smaller capital outlay and providing more certain returns.

10.1.1 Bridge and other projects

Bridge. Many bridge projects have been advanced but even if within proved engineering capacity they have generally been considered to present too great a hazard of collisions with shipping, both during construction and in service. The straits carry a greater volume of international shipping than any comparable waterway, with the added complexity of a great number of ferries cutting across the main channel passage. The establishment of a system of control, restricting shipping to defined safe lanes, is not likely to be quick or easy, particularly as the not infrequent conditions of storm or fog must be provided for. Some agreed rules are already in effect, and more precise control could no doubt be progressively effected. At best the dangers of faulty navigation and ships out of control would continue. The Chesapeake Bay bridge/tunnel crossing exemplifies some of the hazards to such bridges, even in enclosed waters under national control.

Additional disadvantages in service of a highway bridge are the exposure of vehicles to severe gales, and the cost and difficulty of satisfactory structural maintenance in such exposed and corrosive marine conditions.

Capital cost has usually appeared to be much higher than for a rail tunnel, but there would be advantages in independent traffic flow avoiding road/rail transfer delays. As compared with a tunnel the absence of any ventilation problem may be noted.

Highway tunnel. On considering the alternative of a highway tunnel as compared with a rail tunnel, a number of factors are very unfavourable to a roadway. Adequate ventilation of a highway tunnel to dilute and remove the noxious exhaust gases from internal combustion engines is a problem which increases unmanageably in a long tunnel carrying heavy traffic (see Volume 2). Artificial islands in the waterway might be an engineering possibility but would be very costly in construction and would be hazardous to shipping, perhaps also creating the risk of inundation of the tunnel. In such a long tunnel the hazards from vehicle breakdown and from inexperienced and largely untrained car drivers would be substantial. There would be no normal facilities for stopping ot relaxing over an enclosed distance exceeding 40 km, and the claustrophobic conditions might affect some drivers to a dangerous degree. The hazards arising from collision and fire are obviously much greater than with rail transport.

Bridge/tunnel. Schemes for composite bridge/tunnel construction relate primarily to highway use for which they are attractive in that:

1. they allow clear shipping lanes wider than any bridge span, and with no height limitation;
2. tunnel lengths are much shorter and offer some possibility of ventilation adequate for highway traffic.

They are unsuitable for railway operation because of the restriction of gradients to about 1 in 100: to emerge from a depth of as little as 20 m below water to a height of 50 m, plus a structure depth of 10 m, a length of 8000 m would be necessary, constituting a major barrier to shipping. Even for a highway gradient of 1 in 25 the corresponding length is 2000 m, but it could geometrically be laid out as a helix of 650 m diameter. Another obstacle to a railway bridge is the difficulty of accepting rail loads on a long, and necessarily flexible, suspension span.

Submerged tunnel. Schemes for prefabricated unit submerged tunnels have been proposed many times in the history of the project, but have never yet found favour in the ultimate comparison with a bored tunnel. The latest bridge/tunnel schemes incorporate such methods. Novel technology is needed, as briefly described in Volume 2.

10.1.2 Geology

The geology of the crossing at the favoured site for a bored tunnel is relatively straightforward. The presence of similar chalk cliffs on both sides of the straits suggested continuity beneath the sea, and this has been confirmed by numerous borings and surveys. The most favourable tunnelling stratum is a 65–80 m thick band of 'grey chalk', the Lower Chalk or Cenomanian, which is a chalk marl with substantial clay content contributing to plasticity and low permeability. It is easily excavated and self-supporting at a tunnel face for the necessary time. The pilot tunnels of 1882 remain sound. The Middle and Upper Chalk are whiter and harder but extensively fissured, and therefore water bearing. The Lower (grey) Chalk rests directly on the Gault clay, because the Upper Greensand is missing here. The Gault, again, is underlain by the Lower Greensand, typically water-bearing and highly permeable. In this area, all the strata dip fairly uniformly towards the north east, and therefore, in the absence of discontinuity, a tunnel can be planned to lie almost wholly within the very favourable stratum of the Lower Chalk, by aligning it towards the north east as it deepens and towards the south west as it rises to the surface.

Such a route has been adopted by all the most favoured proposals from the 1870's onwards, always with the proviso that more geological information was needed to determine precisely the best alignment and more especially to confirm the continuity of the stratum and the absence of fissures or buried valleys in the sea bed.

10.1.3 History to 1981

The first realistic proposal for a twin rail tunnel was advanced in 1856 by Thomé de Gamond and led to a series of projects and promotions.

Work on shafts and exploratory pilot tunnels was actually started on the French side at Sangatte in 1878 and on the English side near Dover in 1882, but military objections on the English side brought work to a standstill. Attempts to revive the project were rejected in England by Parliament in 1890, by the Committee of Imperial Defence in 1914, by Parliament again, by 7 votes, in 1930, always on fears of its potential for invasion. In 1957, there was an important joint initiative by the then Channel Tunnel Co., the Suez Canal Co., the French Société Concessionaire and the American Technical Studies Inc., who formed the Channel Tunnel Study Group. They organised and financed a comprehensive study covering traffic, geology, civil engineering and financial and legal aspects. They considered both rail and road crossings by bored tunnel, submerged tunnel, bridge and combined bridge/tunnel and reported strongly in favour of twin bored railway tunnels as appearing geologically feasible and being cheapest in construction cost and providing the quickest return. Following this, the two Governments concerned set up a working party of officials in November 1961 to report on this bored rail tunnel proposal, but also on a bridge proposal of a rival group. Their report in September 1963 again favoured strongly the tunnel proposal on grounds of feasibility, cost and economic return, with a proviso about further geological and other site investigations.

In 1964, the Governments announced their intention to proceed with the project. The Channel Tunnel Study Group were asked to organise further site investigations, which were carried out in 1964/1965 and included 73 marine boreholes, supplemented by geophysical profiling to provide fuller detail of the morphology and stratigraphy of the area, particularly on the proposed line of the bored tunnel. Data on winds, waves, tides and currents and transport of sediment were obtained, more particularly to assist in study of a submerged tunnel. A bored tunnel route within the Lower Chalk was proposed, conforming to a maximum gradient of 1%, a minimum gradient (for drainage) of 0.08% (1 in 1250), and a minimum radius of 4200 m.

In 1966, the Prime Ministers of the United Kingdom and France announced a decision to proceed 'subject to finding a solution for the construction work on mutually acceptable terms'. Three groups, in which financial interests had a major part, submitted proposals, but none was found acceptable. A new combined group was formed, which made revised proposals which were accepted early in 1972. This new Group organised two companies: yet another British Channel Tunnel Company, and the Société Francais du Tunnel sous la Manche.

Late in 1972 the British and French Governments concluded with the companies parallel agreements covering:

Phase I: for studies to be carried out immediately and completed by mid-1973.

Phase II: outline arrangements for shaft sinking and experimental tunnel boring up to 1975.

Phase III: for the major construction operations up to 1980, together with complex financial provisions in which the Governments undertook to guarantee up to 90% of the capital to be borrowed by the Group for the costs of construction.

In 1971-72 a further 17 marine boreholes and 8 land boreholes in the Folkestone area were sunk in coordination with another comprehensive geophysical survey of the route using much improved equipment. This allowed particular attention to be given to zones of weathering in the chalk. This geophysical work was very successful and gave greater confidence in the continuity between boreholes. No major structural fault zones were detected on the route and it was concluded that conditions were favourable to tunnelling; there was still no absolute certainty that no fissures or other discontinuities had been missed. The alignment of the tunnel was adjusted so as to pass the coast under the Shakespeare cliff rather than under Dover harbour, providing a working site well clear of the former heavily built up urban area. Fig. 10.1.

The Phase I programme was duly completed, with the tunnel design developed and brought up to date and with new and more detailed forecasts of traffic and revenue. A revised scheme was found necessary for the eventual sharing of receipts. A British Government White Paper, which sets out in considerable detail the case for the tunnel scheme, was endorsed by Parliament in November 1973, followed immediately by the initialling of a Treaty between the United Kingdom and France.

Phase II then started with the signature of Agreement No. 2. On the engineering side it included construction of access works on both sides and the driving of trial lengths of the permanent service tunnel, −2 km at the English coast and 1½ km at the French coast. It also included comprehensive and detailed studies for, and design of, the tunnels, the terminals, and the railway works and equipment and rolling stock, and also geodetic surveys to link the national grids. Thus, by May 1975 plans were to be brought up to the stage where contracts could be placed for the whole project, to comprise Phase III and to be covered by Agreement No. 3.

All was brought to a stop early in 1975 at a time when Phase II work was progressing satisfactorily and machine driving of the English service tunnel was just starting. The British Government decided not to proceed with ratification of the Treaty. Economies in spending were thought necessary, doubts were cast on the forecast rates of growth of traffic and particular emphasis was laid on the

Fig. 10.1 — Channel Tunnel — English working site. Shakespeare Cliff and Dover Harbour appear in the background. An access tunnel leads down to the ramp from above the cliff, and the working access tunnel descends under the cliff just to the right of the railway

greatly increased estimates of cost for the rail link to London. As had been the case nearly a century earlier, a very promising start with the engineering was literally submerged as a consequence of political and financial doubts and hesitations. The dependence of major projects on politics and finance may be unavoidable, but it certainly is very frustrating to engineers, particularly when work in progress is brought abruptly to a halt.

Not unexpectedly, renewed interest has been shown by those concerned, including an EEC Committee, in the subject of a cross Channel link. British and French railways have studied jointly a possible single rail track tunnel as being the least demanding on economic resources. In 1980, this and other schemes were submitted for consideration by the Transport Committee of the House of Commons. The proposals ranged from the single track bored tunnel to a high level road and rail bridge and included a comprehensive, and costly, scheme combining a railway in submerged tunnel with a highway part in tunnel and part on bridge, and with artificial islands.

The Parliamentary Committee in March 1981, reported in favour of a single track bored rail tunnel and service tunnel, as in the 1980 'economy' plan proposed by the railways and described below, but with a larger tunnel diameter which could at a later date be utilised to accommodate all ferry traffic, as in the 1975 plan.

10.1.4 Rail tunnel planning

It is worth examining the plans adopted for the 1973 scheme together with those for the minimal 1980 British Rail scheme, as exemplifying the principles discussed elsewhere in the book. Fig. 10.2(a).

In broad terms the 1973 plan was for a comprehensive rail ferry service combined with very high speed passenger trains between London and Paris and Brussels. The 1980 'economy' plan leaves the heavy vehicle ferry business to shipping and caters only for passengers, passenger cars, and normal railway freight including containers. Very high speed is no longer planned, and the initial proposal is that a single tunnel (plus a service tunnel) should take traffic alternately in each direction. The implications are explained below in more detail.

Alignment. The proposed alignments were determined by the geology as described above and by railway operational requirements. It was considered that the undersea tunnelling should be as near the base of the Lower Chalk as possible, avoiding by at least 10 m cover any weathered rock which had been identified in strata communicating with the sea bed.

The original scheme was intended to accommodate frequent long and heavy trains at speeds up to 200 km/hour, but in the revised scheme a normal working speed of 120 km/hour is contemplated with a possible increase to 160 km/hour.

Maximum gradient was to be about 1% and minimum for reasons of drainage 0.1%. Minimum horizontal radius is specified as 4200 m, originally determined

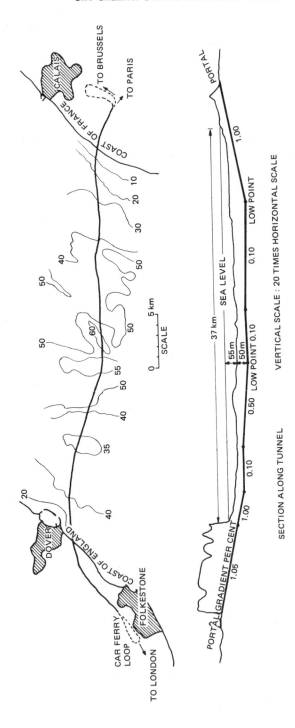

Fig. 10.2(a) – Channel Tunnel – plan and section showing alignment of 1973 scheme.

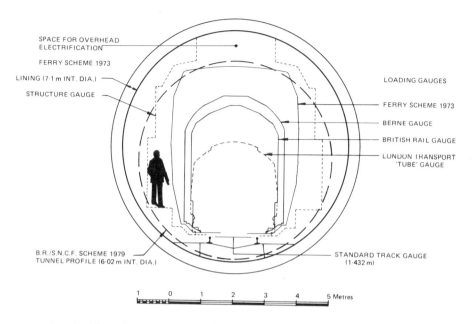

Fig. 10.2(b) — 7.1 m dia. circular lining accommodating standard loading gauges and proposed (1973) gauge together with 6.02 m circle proposed for 1980 scheme.

in relation to a design speed of 200 km/hour and with rail cant of 50 mm. The radius is retained but maximum cant is reduced to 40 mm.

The major problem of gradient is on the English side where the topography, with high coastal cliffs, fixed the rail level at portal as about +42 m, while the requirement for rock cover where the tunnel passes under the coast line imposes a rail level of −40 m. At a gradient of 1% the necessary length of descent is 8 km, which emphasises the importance to capital cost of adopting the steepest acceptable gradient. In fact, after careful study of train loads in relation to available locomotives, it was found possible originally to steepen the gradient to 1.03% and thus shorten the tunnel length by about ¼ km, and in the current proposals to steepen the gradient further to 1.11% with further substantial economy in construction cost.

On the French side, where the portal is on lower ground, it was found best to tunnel the descent under land, through the water bearing Middle and Upper Chalk, and to deal with the water by pumping and waterproofing.

The overall length between portals was established as 50 km, now reduced to 49.4 km.

Cross section. Special considerations applied to the selection of an appropriate cross section for the tunnel. It was very far from being comparable to an ordinary rail tunnel because it was intended also to function as a vehicle ferry, which would accommodate the largest of normal road transport vehicles—currently 40 tonne lorries with a maximum height of 4 m. This required the height within the tunnel above rail level to be 5.18 m after allowing for: wagon deck height 0.94, vehicle 4.00, clearance 0.10, wagon roof structure 0.14, to which must be added space for overhead line equipment. In comparison, the Berne loading gauge height of the Union Internationale des Chemins de Fer is 4.28 m with a proposed future increase to 4.65 m for new lines; the British gauge is smaller in height and width. Fig. 10.2(b).

For a circular tunnel this abnormal height of 5.18 m determined the diameter for a single track to be 7.1 m, with the use of special stock to carry heavy goods vehicles. It made possible the use of double decker wagons for cars, and the carriage of twice as many cars in a train of standard length.

In the current scheme the Berne UIC gauge has been adopted allowing all but abnormal loads to be carried within a tunnel diameter of 6.02 m, which effects a substantial saving in tunnelling volume and cost.

A pair of single-track running tunnels was preferred to a double-track tunnel as it minimises the risk of collision and dangers from derailments. There appeared to be no substantial difference in construction cost between twin tunnels and one double-track tunnel, in relation to which the comments in Chapter 4 on problems of scale may be referred to.

Studies have shown that a single one-track tunnel as the link between surface lines can be operated with a three-hour cycle, in which up to ten trains with a journey time of 35 minutes pass in one direction and clear the tunnel during a period of 1½ hours, and are succeeded by a similar flow in the reverse direction. Sixty trains a day in each direction can thus be handled, leaving a six-hour maintenance period.

In both schemes an additional service tunnel, of 4.5 m diameter, is to be driven. In operation, it gives access to the running tunnels for maintenance, and acts as a fresh air supply duct, and is also available for emergencies. During construction, it would be driven ahead of the main tunnel, functioning as a pilot, to prove the ground and make possible any necessary ground treatment. Fig. 10.2(c).

Loading loops.   Another consequence of the abnormal loading gauge of the ferry trains was that they could not be used on track with normal structure gauge limits on either side of the Channel, and therefore that special terminal areas as close as possible to the portals became necessary for the loading and unloading of the ferry trains. Continuous loops of track were provided to handle the traffic without reversing the trains. Such elaborate provisions are unnecessary in the smaller scheme; some sidings would be required near the portals, and a simpler road/rail interchange wherever convenient to serve local traffic.

High speed rail links.   Normal rail traffic—passenger, goods and container trains —could, of course, use the tunnel without difficulty. The connection to London

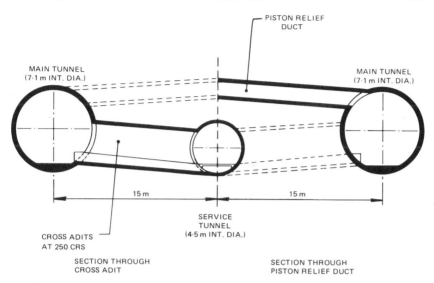

Fig. 10.2(c) – The figure shows the cross sectional arrangement of the running tunnels, service tunnel, cross adits and piston relief ducts adopted for the 1973 scheme. The 1980 proposal is for a single running tunnel of smaller diameter, but with a similar service tunnel and cross adits at 500 m centres.

is not built to the Berne gauge and could not handle the full volume of traffic anticipated, nor the proposed high speed intercity trains envisaged. Substantial new works were therefore contemplated, virtually duplicating much of the existing track and including new terminal facilities in London. It would also have involved further tunnelling, some orthodox hill tunnels and some to avoid urban congestion.

These extensive works have been abandoned in the current proposals, except for limited improvements of the existing track, and probably not giving the Berne gauge clearances.

Excavation. Machine tunnelling with a full face excavator was decided on as the best system for rapid and efficient excavation; the chalk could be relied on in general to stand unsupported for at least twenty-four hours, by which time the lining should be in place. Spoil disposal would probably be by rail, the surplus going to fill disused gravel pits; much material was required as fill in preparation of the terminal loading areas. Proposals for pumping out surplus chalk as a slurry into the sea bed received serious consideration and seemed likely to be advantageous. It would not be detrimental environmentally as the chalk would be rapidly and widely dispersed by swift and varying currents, and chalk in suspension is, in any case, a naturally occurring constituent in the straits.

Lining. A structural lining is essential to the safety in operation of such a tunnel. The headings of 1882 had stood up very well with minimal support and much exposed chalk, but the serious consequences of any fall of rock, with the added risk of falls attributable to vibration and drying out and the presence of local irregularities in the strata, could not be accepted in a running tunnel.

Temporary support with steel arch ribs, followed by an *in situ* concrete lining was considered, but it did not seem possible to ensure that the two separated major construction operations, each subject to unforeseeable delays, could be coordinated satisfactorily to avoid disruptions in the whole rapid construction programme. *In situ* concrete also was less readily adapted to the provision of openings for numerous cross adits.

Precast segmental expanded linings were, therefore, chosen, generally of concrete, but with the alternative of S.G. cast iron in any apparently unstable ground. For the Phase II length of the service tunnel on the French side cast iron rings were preferred in the special circumstances of timetable, availability and overall economy.

Much thought and study has gone into the design of the concrete rings, because even a small saving in manufacture, handling and erection is multiplied up to a very large economy in so long and uniform a tunnel. Finality had not been reached on the details of design in 1975, but new methods of calculation had been evolved, and tests have been made in the short lengths of service tunnel completed on the stress and deformations in ground and lining. These studies have allowed a substantial saving to be effected in the current scheme, whereby the thickness for the service tunnel segments has been reduced by about 0.1 m with corresponding savings in the running tunnel. Fig. 10.2(d).

Ventilation and aerodynamics. With electric traction the problem of fresh air supply to passengers does not usually call for any special provision, but in the Channel Tunnel the great length of tunnel without shafts and the high peak frequency of trains meant that many thousands of passengers might be in the tunnel and that the air at midway would not be readily replaced. The service tunnel was, therefore, utilised as a fresh air supply duct supplying the average requirement, while there were supplementary fans to supply peak and emergency requirements direct through the running tunnels. These fans might also be used in smoke control in case of fire.

The aerodynamic problems of rail tunnels are discussed in Volume 2. The particular problems of the Channel Tunnel were the long single tunnels, high speed working, and proportion of loading gauge to clear area. To provide relief from the pressure surges ahead of trains and to reduce aerodynamic drag, cross adits were to be constructed between the two running tunnels at 250 m spacing. They were separate from the cross passages connecting running tunnel and service tunnel because this gave a better environment for men and equipment in the service tunnel and left it available as the air supply duct.

With a lower operating speed in the current scheme, and with smaller

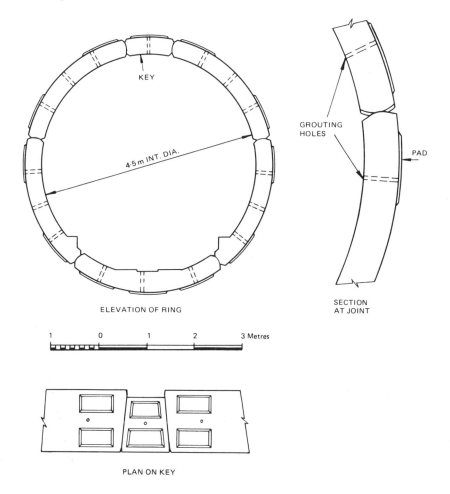

ELEVATION OF RING

SECTION
AT JOINT

PLAN ON KEY

Fig. 10.2(d) – The diagram shows the flexible jointed lining, expanded by means of a wedge segment in the crown, and having raised pads on the outer face to ensure grouting space.

frontal area and weight of trains, the heat output is reduced and the aerodynamic problems are less severe. Cross adits between running tunnel and service tunnel are to be provided at a spacing of 500 m to serve for access and for ventilation and relief of aerodynamic surges.

10.2 SEIKAN TUNNEL

The Seikan tunnel in Japan provides an interesting comparison with the Channel tunnel. It also is an undersea railway tunnel, connecting the main Japanese island of Honshu to the northern island of Hokkaido by crossing under the Tsugaru strait where it is 23 km wide. The tunnel is designed to carry the high speed Shinkansen trains as well as local services on a narrow gauge (1.097 m) line. The decision to build appears to have been broadly political and strategic rather than narrowly economic. Dependence on ferry services as a link between the islands has been seen as inadequate, especially since the tragic loss of 1414 lives in the sinking of five ferries in a typhoon in 1954. In addition to replacing existing ferries by a much faster and more reliable service it is intended to make more attractive expansion from the overcrowded industrial areas into the more sparsely populated northern island. A large proportion of Honshu's area is mountainous and cannot provide for increased population.

10.2.1 Planning

Investigations and surveys were started in 1946 and in 1964 a possible site had been chosen and a start was made on the ground.

The western end of the Tsugaru strait was preferred as being shallower and less liable to seismic disturbances than the eastern end. It has proved possible to select a line on which the maximum depth of channel is 140 m compared with 260 m at the eastern end. Rock cover of 100 m has been specified on the basis of experience in undersea coal mines, and the tunnel at its deepest is therefore over 240 m below water level, corresponding to a hydrostatic pressure of over 24 bar.

The original plan had been for a tunnel 36 km long, carrying narrow gauge train services only, with a gradient of 2%, but in 1971 the decision was taken to provide also for high speed (Shinkansen) trains running at 210 km/hr. The ruling gradient was then reduced to 1.2% and the minimum radius set at 6500 m. The combination of this gradient with the great depth makes the tunnelled length 53.85 km, exceeding the proposed Channel tunnel by 4 km and far longer than any other such tunnel. The undersea length is 23.3 km and the approach lengths are respectively 13.55 km and 17.0 km for the Honshu (south) and Hokkaido (north) sides.

The question whether to have a double-track tunnel or twin tunnels was the subject of much consideration, and the final decision in favour of the larger double-track tunnel, 9.6 m wide, was strongly influenced by two factors:

1. the excavated volume, working to Shinkansen standard sections is about 25% less than for twin tunnels;
2. the undersea section requires extensive and elaborate grouting of fissured and faulted rock, and it was considered to be safer and more efficient to concentrate ground treatment on one tunnel.

Information is lacking on the operational ventilation and aerodynamic problems in the two-way tunnel, but it must be supposed that the experience gained in Shinkansen lines is an adequate guide. This applies also to the other problems to which so much study has been applied in the Channel tunnel design, such as evacuation of passengers from a breakdown and fire and emergency precautions generally.

In addition to the large running tunnel there are two subsidiary tunnels, namely:

1. a deep level drainage tunnel about 3.6 m diameter, initially driven as a pilot tunnel and serving also during construction for access, exploration, drainage and ventilation;
2. a service tunnel about 4 m diameter parallel to the running tunnel at a distance of 30 m, and driven in advance of it, also used initially for exploration, ground treatment, access, transportation and ventilation, and ultimately for services, maintenance, ventilation and emergencies.

The two subsidiary tunnels merge in the mid-tunnel section of 5 km. Fig. 10.3 shows plan and section of the crossing and a cross section of the three tunnels.

The geological structure is of Miocene strata, through which the tunnel passes, overlying at greater depth palaeozoic and granitic rocks. A wide variety of beds occur, many of volcanic origin. In the south half there is a predominance of andesites and basalts which are associated with much fissuring and therefore require extensive grouting to seal off inflow of water. In the north half there are volcanic tuffs, andesites, breccia, shale, siltstone, sandstone. Most of the rock is competent, but some of the mudstones swell following excavation. Across the line of the tunnel under the strait there are known to be nine principal faults with brecciated zones. In the middle third of the strait lie the most recent 'Kuromatsumi' strata of weak mudstones.

In designing the tunnel and its lining the principle adopted to deal with the very heavy water pressure is to grout as tightly as possible a cut-off ring of rock clear outside the tunnel and to drain off continuously from behind the tunnel lining any residual water seeping through. The loads resulting from water pressure and rock pressure are then carried by redistribution of stresses in the rock. The immediate support of the tunnel excavation is normally provided by arch ribs and sprayed concrete, followed up at the appropriate time by an *in situ* concrete ring up to 900 mm thick. In lengths where the ground is bad a circular section is adopted with 300 mm steel pipes reinforced and filled with mortar as ribs at 0.7 m centres.

The normal linings for the drainage pilot and the service tunnel also comprise steel ribs and sprayed concrete up to 200 mm thick. For the former no additional *in situ* concrete is thought necessary.

10.2.2 Surveys
Progressively more detailed topographical and geological surveys were made over the period 1946–1966. Coast lines were surveyed in 1946–1949, followed from

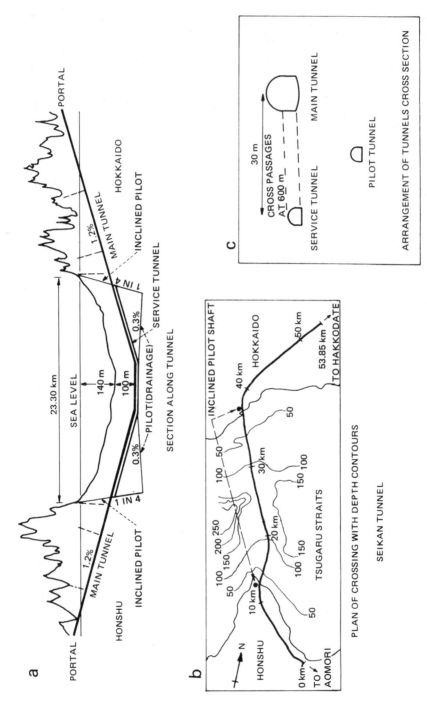

Fig. 10.3 — Seikan Tunnel. (a) section; (b) plan; (c) cross section.

1953-1961 by aerial surveys of the two peninsulas to be connected, the mapping in the last year being on scales of 1/2500 and 1/10 000, followed in 1963 by 1/500 detail surveys, and linking surveys across the straits in 1965, 1966, 1967.

Acoustic soundings to establish sea bed contours with a 2 m interval were carried out in 1954.

The geology was studied similarly over the same period with borings on land from 1946-1955 and 1961-1965 and on the sea bottom in 1956 and from 1960-1966. Seismic profiles were obtained about the same periods and sonic and magnetic traverses of the sea bottom were made in 1959, 1961 and 1962. Tidal observations were also recorded.

This preliminary work was carried out under the Japanese National Railways until the Japanese Railway Construction Public Corporation (JRCC) was established in 1964 to take responsibility for construction of this and other major railway projects.

10.2.3 Construction

Exploratory construction started in 1964 with the sinking of a 1210 m inclined shaft at a gradient of 1 in 4 on Hokkaido over a period of 3 years. After construction of various service chambers at the shaft bottom, driving of the drainage pilot tunnel seawards began on a rising gradient of 0.3%. A similar shaft was sunk on the Honshu side from 1966 to 1970 and the pilot also started. At the end of 1968 the Hokkaido service tunnel was started seawards from halfway down the shaft followed in early 1971 by the Honshu service tunnel. The work up to 1970 had been considered exploratory but the decision that the line should be constructed was then taken and the project was authorised, to Shinkansen standards, the following year. The work was divided into nine lengths: four under land in Honshu, two of 13.0 and 14.7 km under the strait, and three under land in Hokkaido, contracts being let for all except the drainage pilot, where work continues to be by the JRCC itself. The service tunnel construction was transferred from the JRCC to contractors in 1972. The land approaches are major tunnels in their own right, but cannot be further described here.

In driving the pilots and service tunnels, full face machines were tried with some success for substantial lengths, but frequent variations in the ground and difficulties of access to the face, together with problems of steering, particularly in soft ground, resulted in a decision to discontinue their use and adopt drill and blast methods throughout. The fear of undue disturbance of surrounding rock by blasting was somewhat relieved by comparison of elastic wave measurements showing the loosened rock when blasted to extend 1.2 m to 1.4 m compared with 0.6 m to 1.0 m when machine excavated.

The service tunnels have been used to open up and serve a number of faces in the main tunnels by driving adits at ½ to 1 km intervals.

The problems of excavation and construction are formidable enough because of the length and depth of the tunnel, but above all the major hazard is inundation from the sea through faults and fissures. The full hydrostatic water pressure has been experienced and, as is the characteristic of subaqueous tunnels in contrast to mountain tunnels, there is no hope of relieving it by drainage of the reservoir. The strategy of construction has been to explore the structure of the ground as thoroughly as possible by means of the drainage and service tunnels functioning as pilots and by exploratory drilling ahead of these tunnels. Drilled lengths of up to 800 m have been attained, and equipment with a claimed range of 2000 m has been acquired. As soon as fissures are located extensive grouting at pressures up to 80 kgf/cm² (three times the hydrostatic head) has been done, principally based on a specially developed combination of very finely ground blast furnace cement with waterglass, using the appropriate water-cement ratio to achieve the required setting time.

Despite these and other precautions the tunnels have been flooded on several occasions, the worst being in 1976 when the Hokkaido service tunnel struck a fault about 4.6 km out from the shore. It was not in fact one of the major faults. Inflow rose in a few hours to a rate of 70 m³/min but stabilised at 30 m³/min after 1½ days. For this time the inflow exceeded the pumping capacity but it was found possible to direct the water into the main tunnel, whose storage capacity proved adequate, and thus to avoid flooding the pumping plant in the low-level drainage tunnel. Additional pumps were installed, cut-off gates and bulkheads constructed and grouting carried out so that the service tunnel was recovered to within 70 m of the face. From here a by-pass was driven through the fault at right angles. These operations took eight months.

This technique of diverting the service tunnel so as to get a shorter and safer crossing of a fault is obviously not one that can be repeated for the main tunnel. Advance grouting of the whole zone will have to be intensive and every move at the main face will have to be most carefully monitored.

The pattern and cycle of excavation of the main tunnels has varied according to the ground conditions encountered. In the best ground the procedure followed has been advance of the arch, excavating and supporting the upper half, followed by excavation and lining below axis. Where this is not practicable a bottom pilot heading has first been excavated ahead, from which ground treatment can be effected as necessary, followed by excavation of the upper half and fixing of the arch ribs and then by invert excavation and construction. In weaker ground, bottom side headings have first been taken out to allow the concrete side walls to be built up to axis; excavation and fixing of arch ribs has followed and finally excavation of the dumpling and concreting of the invert.

In the worst ground a circular form has been adopted, side headings at axis being excavated and filled followed by the excavation and fixing of reinforced steel pipes as ribs for the upper arch, pipe struts at axis, and finally excavation of dumpling and circular invert, and fixing of ribs in the invert. Final permanent lining has been left for six months to allow rock stresses to develop, but heavy deflections have been experienced.

Removal of spoil has been by mine cars along the tunnels to hoppers and crushers and then by conveyor up the inclined shafts to surface tips. The handling capacity is hardly adequate for the number of faces being worked and the problem is bound to increase as the distances lengthen.

Pumping during construction is a major item. Capacity at each end has had to be increased to over 100 m³/min after the flooding experienced. The average has been 26 m³/min on the fissured Honshu side and 7 m³/min on the Hokkaido side.

Ventilation has been important not only for fresh air supply but because of heat and humidity. Water has been encountered at temperatures of 20°-30°C and there is a substantial addition of heat from machine operation and the setting of cement. A circulation has been established utilising the whole cross section of the tunnels and connecting passages as follows: inclined shaft → pilot tunnel → connecting vertical shaft → service tunnel → main tunnel → vertical shaft. With this the temperature in the tunnels has been held to 25°C.

Early in 1980 the stage reached in construction on the main contracts, which total 27.70 km between shafts, was that the excavation of the main tunnel was nearly 80% of the distance across between shafts, leaving less than 6 km to be excavated. For the pilot tunnel the gap was about 3 km. The problems remaining are formidable but there is great determination to complete construction successfully. Probing ahead, extensive grouting and cautious advance through fault zones and other difficult ground are obviously the essentials in meeting the hazards of the geological disruptions and of unlimited water at high pressure.

10.3 COMPARISON

There are many points of interest in comparing the two major undersea tunnels. The Seikan tunnel is under construction and fast becoming a reality, while the Channel tunnel having been designed in considerable detail and brought to the point of actual construction in 1975 is still in abeyance. It may be revived but not necessarily to meet the same demands.

The Channel tunnel is the senior project having been the subject of serious proposals and progressively more detailed investigation and survey for well over one hundred years. The Seikan tunnel took some twenty years from the initiation of the concept in 1946 to start of work on the ground, and another five years to the authorisation of the full scheme and placing of construction contracts in 1971.

The political and strategic aspects have throughout been a major handicap to the engineering concepts in the Channel, because two independent nations have had to be in accord simultaneously on the scheme and its financing, and to agree on the division of responsibilities, with legal and administrative arrangements for construction and operation. There has been no clear national interest in either country overriding narrower sectional interests. The railway interest has been the most dominant in favour, but the shipping interests have naturally been less than enthusiastic, and development of air travel has drawn off an important element of passenger demand. Despite these and other diverse commercial aspects it is probable that the enterprise would have been launched about 1930 if military thinking had not continued its earlier opposition to the supposed hazard of invasion. In the 1973 project all these conflicting interests appeared to have been resolved, the special interest of road transport being the subject of elaborate provision, but the whole was found unacceptably costly in a time of economic difficulty. A wide range of schemes are again being actively discussed and evaluated, and again the initially favoured proposal is for a bored rail tunnel.

The contrast of the Seikan tunnel is startling—a single national government, deeply concerned to link the separate major islands of the kingdom was also concerned to eliminate the hazards and delays of shipping. The multiple competing routes between England and different continental ports have no parallel; there is one ferry route between Aomori and Hakkodate. The scheme formed part of the great national effort to provide rail links of a high standard throughout all parts of the mountainous islands so that when the tunnel project was finally authorised in 1970, it was upgraded and substantially enlarged to form part of the major system.

The Channel tunnel would link the United Kingdom, with a population of 55 million, to the European continent, whose EEC population exceeds 200 million, as compared with the Seikan link between the 70 million population of the main island of Honshu and the 5 million of Hokkaido, whose only very large city is Sapporo with a population of about 1½ million. To complete the connection to Tokyo, the Shinkansen line, at present under construction to Morioka 500 km north of Tokyo, must be extended by another 550 km, or a new line of greater length must be built up the west coast from Niigata. The comparable need for a new high speed line over 100 km long between London and Folkestone and improvements, or possibly a new line of 300 km, from Sangatte to Paris provides an interesting parallel to the Shinkansen proposal, emphasised by the fact that the existing Folkestone to London line cannot accept the full Berne loading gauge although the rail gauge is unchanged.

The forecast of passengers to be carried through the Channel tunnel in 1980 was 9 million by rail only, plus 6 million accompanied by about 2 million passenger cars; freight was estimated at 5 million tons, leaving 9 million tons carried by sea. In Japan, the current annual traffic across the Tsugaru strait by sea between Aomori and Hakkodate is 5 million passengers, mostly on railway ferries, and 15 million tons of goods, less than half on railway ferries; passenger cars are not separately described. There are also air services between the two islands. It is to be expected that much of the freight would continue to be carried by sea, but it seems unlikely that a frequent passenger ferry service would be maintained.

The topography of the two straits differs in that the Tsugaru sea bed reaches more than twice the depth of the Channel, while the 100 m chalk cliffs of Dover make a more abrupt change from land to sea than in Japan.

The geology shows marked and important differences influencing every aspect of the tunnel construction. In the Channel it has been found possible to locate with some precision a stratum of grey chalk and to align the tunnel to remain within it for all of its length except at the portals. It is fairly homogeneous, and believed to be free from significant faulting, so that excavation by a full face machine followed by erection of segmental lining could be specified. While no tunnel of such length can hope to avoid some unpredictable ground conditions, any anomalies should be over limited lengths and should be found in advance by probing ahead.

In the Seikan tunnel the line runs through many different and disturbed strata, intersected by at least nine significant faults under the sea. The ground ranges from soft and swelling siltstones and volcanic ash in various forms through sedimentary rocks to igneous intrusions and lavas of geologically recent date (Miocene). The faults are marked by shattered belts of rock allowing fissures to develop connecting with the sea bed and therefore threatening inundation. Machine boring techniques have been found insufficiently adaptable to the variations in ground, and the familiar and well tried techniques of drill and blast have therefore been adopted with sequences of heading excavation, enlargement and support, continuously adapted to the conditions disclosed by exploration ahead. The lining likewise is adapted to the ground.

On the railway engineering aspects the first comparisons are perhaps gradient and curves. There is a significant difference between the 1.03% or 1.11% of the Channel tunnel and the 1.2% of the Seikan tunnel; adoption of the former for a rise of 250 m would lengthen the Seikan approach by 3.4 km. Conversely, if the rise of 82 m near Dover were taken at 1.2% it would be reduced in length by 1.3 km. The Channel tunnel gradient was related to the operation of very long and heavy vehicle ferry trains rather than to through running of fast trains or to lighter trains of mixed freight.

The Channel curve limit of 4200 m related to a speed of 200 km/hr compared with the Seikan curve of 6500 m which has been adopted as the latest Shinkansen standard for 260 km/hr, the first, Tokaido, line being built to 2500 m and the next, Sanyo, line to 4000 m.

The choice of twin tunnels for the Channel was determined by operating advantages in respect of safety, ventilation and aerodynamics in which context the ferrying of very large road vehicles imposes special requirements; twin tunnels would also be preferred constructionally. For Seikan it is clear that the dominant consideration was the complexity of tunnelling in a difficult and dangerous ground. A wide zone outside the tunnel lining has to be grouted with meticulous care to ensure that the ground itself is substantially watertight and structurally sound. To repeat these operations for a duplicate tunnel a short distance away has obviously been found unattractive, especially when the excavation may disturb the equilibrium already attained round the first bore. Nevertheless, the decision to cut the larger hole in this difficult rock can only have been taken after much thought.

The drainage systems adopted also differ. Low level drainage tunnels leading down from mid-channel to pumping shafts near the coasts were considered for the Channel but rejected in favour of discharging seepage through a sequence of pumps and sumps, using the service tunnel. The tunnel profile under the Channel is not of V form but a flattened W. Although the tunnel will not be fully caulked, to avoid build-up of pressure, large volumes of water are not expected in the finished tunnel, nor during construction. At Seikan the situation is quite different. Even apart from inundations large volumes of water have to be drained and pumped out during construction and there is no question of an ultimately watertight tunnel, because pressures must not be allowed to build up. It has been essential to the whole construction strategy to construct the low-level drainage pilot tunnel ahead of the other work which can normally be drained by gravity to the bottoms of the inclined working shafts. The normal pumping requirement during construction has been about 26 m^3/min at the south and 7 m^3/min at the north shaft. The ultimate pumping requirement in operation may well be of this order.

Ventilation of the Channel tunnel has been referred to and is further discussed in Volume 2, but comparable information on the Seikan tunnel is not known. The moderately high temperatures experienced during construction suggest that some system of heat extraction, possibly by fresh air supply, will be essential to prevent a build-up of heat even if passengers are protected by air conditioning during normal operation. Problems of accident and fire and the evacuation of passengers have no doubt been fully considered.

BIBLIOGRAPHY
There is an extensive range of publications on the Channel Tunnel covering various aspects of its history. This selection is intended to be particularly relevent to current aspects. More comprehensive references are cited in the general bibliography in Volume 2.

Channel Tunnel
Economic Advisory Council, Channel Tunnel Committee, *Report, Cmnd. 3513*, HMSO, 1930.

Slater, H. and Barnett, C., *The Channel Tunnel*, Wingate, 1958.

Bruckshaw, J. M. and others, 'The work of the Channel Tunnel Study Group 1958-60', *Proc. Instn. Civ. Engrs.*, 1961, **18** (Feb.). *See also* discussion, 1962, **21** (Mar.).

Ministry of Transport, *Proposals for a fixed Channel Link, Cmnd. 2137*, HMSO, 1963.

Pequignot, C. A., *Chunnel*, CR Books, 1965.

Grange, A. and Muir Wood, A. M., 'The site investigations for a Channel Tunnel, 1964-65', *Proc. Instn. Civ. Engrs.*, 1970, **45** (Jan.). *See also* discussion 1970, **47** (Dec.).

Department of the Environment, *The Channel Tunnel Project, Cmnd. 5256*, HMSO, 1973.

Department of the Environment, *The Channel Tunnel, Cmnd. 5430*, HMSO, 1973.

Haining, P., *Eurotunnel, an illustrated history of the Channel Tunnel scheme*, New English Library, 1973.

Gould, H. B. and others, 'The design of the Channel Tunnel', *Struct. Engr.*, 1975, **53** (Feb.). *See also* discussion, 1975, **53** (Dec.).

Morgan, J. M. and others, *The tunnelling system for the British section of the Channel Tunnel phase II works, Laboratory Report 734*, Transport and Road Research Laboratory, Crowthorne, 1977.

House of Commons, Second Report from the Transport Committee, Session 1980-81, *The Channel Link, Report and Minutes, (HoC 155 – I, II & III)*, HMSO, 1981.

Seikan Tunnel

Sources of material are limited to papers from conferences and periodicals.

Tanaka, T., 'Seikan undersea tunnel', *Civil Engineering in Japan*, 1970.

Hama, K., 'The Seikan undersea tunnel', *Japanese Railway Engineering*, 1972 (Jan.).

Mochida, Y., 'Long horizontal boring', *Permanent Way*, 1973, **14** (Apr.).

Shinohara, H. and Akita, H., 'Grouting in pilot tunnel heading', *Permanent Way*, 1973, **14** (Apr.).

Hayward, D., 'Tale of a tunnel, on the survival story of sub-sea Seikan', *New Civil Engineer*, 1977 (19 May).

Matsuo S. and Endo, K., 'Seikan undersea tunnel', *Civil Engineering in Japan*, 1977.

Fujita, M., 'Seikan undersea tunnel', *International Tunnel Symposium*, Tokyo, 1978.

Mochida, Y., 'Excavation of expansive ground formation for the Seikan undersea tunnel project', *Tunnelling '79, 2nd International Symposium*, London, 1979.

Mochida, Y. and Kikuchi, T., 'Exploration undertaken as a safety measure in the construction of the Seikan tunnel, *The Safety of Underground Works, International Symposium, Brussels*, 1980.

'Seikan Undersea Tunnel', *The Present Status of Tunnelling Activities in Japan, Part 1*, Japan Tunnelling Association, Tokyo, 1980, 60-69.

Index